Biotechnology
Science for the New Millennium

Instructor's Guide
Text and Laboratory Manual

Ellyn Daugherty, MST
San Mateo Biotechnology Career Pathway

Paradigm PUBLISHING

Contents

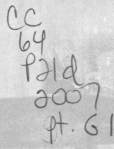

© 2007 by Paradigm Publishing, Inc. 875 Montreal Way, St. Paul, MN 55102; phone: 800-535-6865; e-mail: educate@emcp.com; Web site: www.emcp.com

Printed in the United States of America

3   4   5   6   7   8   9   10

Part

1

Establishing a
Biotechnology Program

Section

1

Careers, Training Needs, and Available Resources

This instructor's guide (IG) presents the essentials for planning and implementing a biotechnology program. The strategies and course planning and teaching tools create a framework from which to build a program that meets the needs of your student population and industry partners.

The instructor's guide consists of four parts: Part 1 addresses how to plan a biotechnology program, Part 2 offers guidelines and resources for planning various types of courses, Part 3 focuses on assessment, and Part 4 provides a set of resources you may want to copy and distribute to students, including a glossary of terms from the lab manual, tutorials on creating charts and graphs in Excel, guidelines for writing effective conclusions to experiments, and hints for conducting effective Internet searches.

Within Part 1 are sections focused on the following topics.

- Section 1 presents the industry trends that compel us to teach biotechnology in high schools and community and technical colleges. It gives an overview of how the *Biotechnology: Science for the New Millennium* curriculum prepares students for the workforce and for higher levels of science instruction.
- Section 2 describes the key issues in setting up and running a biotechnology program. These include creating a vision for your program, mobilizing resources, developing a course syllabus, and using the curriculum to meet your program objectives.

Part 2 consists of sections dealing with the following topics.

- Section 1 provides suggested syllabi/scope and sequence models for typical course structures.
- Section 2 describes the features of the text, lab manual, and Encore CD and offers suggestions about how to use them most effectively. A lab equipment list details the instruments and materials needed for completing all of the lab experiments.
- Section 3 presents the structure and elements of lesson plans for the text and lab manual. Sample lesson plans are provided.

Part 3 details the importance of authentic assessment in a biotechnology training program and presents tools and strategies for evaluating your students' skill and concept development. Another important form of assessment is feedback from customers, and this part of the IG includes a document instructors can use to suggest product improvements and to query the author about specific points or potential issues.

Section 2 of Part 3 provides answers to the text *Section Review* questions and the text and lab manual *Thinking Like a Biotechnician* questions.

Part 4 includes the following materials, which may be photocopied and distributed to students:

- Laboratory Manual Glossary
- Laboratory Safety Guidelines
- Review of Metric Measurements
- Tutorial on Using Microsoft Excel® to Create Graphs
- Tutorial on Using Microsoft Excel® to Create Data Tables
- Guidelines for Writing Effective Conclusions to Experiments

Science Careers for the 21st Century

You have heard of the Industrial Age and the Information Age. Some say we are now at the beginning of "The Age of Biotechnology." Advances in the science and industry of biotechnology are creating exciting and meaningful career opportunities that will last well into the next century. *Biotechnology: Science for the New Millennium*, a comprehensive biotechnology text and lab manual curriculum, is designed to prepare teenagers and adults to launch a career in the wide-open, rewarding field of biotechnology.

Biotechnology has become one of the fastest-growing industries in the nation. Employment in the biotech field increased nationwide by almost 50 percent between 1997 and 2002 (*Careers in Biotechnology, 2nd Edition*). As companies move from research and development to the manufacturing of pharmaceuticals, industrial, and agricultural products, an increase in job opportunities will continue with a particularly high demand for entry-level, certificated biomanufacturing technicians.

The biotechnology industry includes a diverse assortment of applications based on the use of living things or their parts to improve the human condition, understand scientific phenomena, or create a product. Many biotechnology products are proteins used for medicinal therapeutics or diagnostics. Some of these are harvested from nature, while some are made by genetic engineering (recombinant proteins). Most agricultural and horticultural products are the result of biotechnology. Some industrial products are made through biotechnology, such as stain-fighting enzymes in detergents and molecules that make tissue softer. Other biotechnology products include the instruments and reagents that are used in scientific research, manufacturing, and diagnostics.

A Growing Industry Demand for Biotechnologists

As the industry grows, the opportunities for employees seem limitless. A variety of workers with varied levels of education, training, and experience are required (see Figure 1). Common to all biotech employees, though, is a basic understanding of the science and economics of the industry. Of course, as in any industry, the more education and experience a potential employee has, the greater the employment and advancement options. The majority of laboratory positions in research and development (R&D) require a four-year college degree, for example, a Bachelor of Science degree in biochemistry, molecular biology, genetics, or biology.

In the area of product manufacturing, technicians with more experience are preferred. In fact, currently there is a shortage of lab technicians in the United States. The Bureau of Labor Statistics (BLS) forecasts an increase in the need for biology technicians due to "the growing number of agricultural and medicinal products developed from using biotechnology techniques," with fastest employment growth occurring in the drug manufacturing industry and research and testing firms (The Bureau of Labor Statistics, 2003). At several large biotech companies, the majority of posted jobs are for laboratory technicians. Many technical and community colleges have developed one- and two-year training programs, including internships, to address this need.

The shortage of trained technicians may limit the growth of the biotechnology industry throughout the United States and in other countries. After making an investment of hundreds of millions of dollars, biotech-

Certificates, Degrees, Experience Needed for Biotechnology Careers

Post Doctorate ◄──► Scientist

Doctorate ◄──► Scientist

Master's Degree ◄──► Research Associate

Bachelor's Degree ◄──► Research Associate

One- or Two-Year Certificate ◄──► **Biotechnician**

High School Diploma ◄──► Lab Assistant

Figure 1. Motivated individuals can qualify for rewarding positions in biotechnology with as little as one or two years of training and experience.

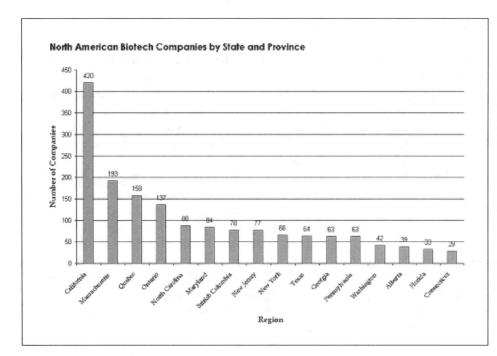

North American Biotech Companies by State and Province

Figure 2. According to the Biotechnology Industry Organization, by 2004 there were 1,473 biotechnology companies throughout the United States, with over 198,000 employees. Source: Ernst & Young LLP, *America's Biotechnology Report: Resurgence, 2004.* Reprinted from Biotechnology Industry Organization, Biotechnology Industry Facts, www.bio.org/speeches/pubs/er/statistics.asp

Graphic courtesy of the Biotechnology Industry Organization.

nology companies must still hire trained individuals to operate and manage these tightly regulated facilities. Currently, and in the foreseeable future, there is an acute shortage of skilled employees in research/development and manufacturing. In fact, companies such as Genentech, Genencor, Cell Genesys, Gilead Sciences, Novartis, and Amgen are not only hiring, but making deals with educational facilities and their students to get them to focus their education and training for entry into biomanufacturing. The jobs that are being created are quite specialized and thus are relatively high paying. Students who accept these positions are likely to enjoy great job satisfaction.

Need for Biotechnician Training Programs

Virtually every state in the U.S. has some kind of biotechnology industry (see Figure 2). The Biotechnology Industry Organization Web site (www.bio.org/members/) lists biotechnology companies and facilities state by state. Most states have a biotechnology industry support organization that is anxious to work with high schools and technical and community colleges to prepare the workforce needed to attract new biotechnology business to their area (visit www2.bio.org/members/biostateaffiliates.asp). *Biotechnology: Science for the New Millennium* prepares students to make sound educational and career choices in preparation to fill the workforce needs.

Curriculum Overview

Biotechnology: Science for the New Millennium is a standards-based curriculum that acts as a platform from which *any* teacher can prepare *any* student for further education or the workplace. The power of the curriculum is that it meets so many student and teacher objectives. With input from industry partners and science educators, the *Biotechnology: Science for the New Millennium* curriculum is designed to be used with students of every academic level, teaching the introductory math and chemistry needed to perform standard biotechnology laboratory operating procedures. The underlying philosophy of the material is that students should have the opportunity to master skills and concepts—and that this mastery might not materialize the first time students encounter new applications and content, but through repeated use of the technology. Once a concept or skill is mastered, students proceed to the next skill development.

Since biotechnologists may work in a variety of settings, training programs should begin with a comprehensive course that surveys the basic skills and concepts used in any entry-level position. The *Biotechnology: Science for the New Millennium* curriculum (text and lab manual) begins with a large unit of standard lab operating procedures including documenting laboratory experiments, following oral and written instructions, conducting volume and mass measurements, using standard safety practices, collecting and analyzing data, preparing solutions and media, using sterile technique, preparing cell cultures, isolating and analyzing DNA and proteins, and performing electrophoresis. Following the unit of standard lab operating procedures are three units focused on recombinant protein manufacturing, agricultural and pharmaceutical biotechnology, and diagnostic biotechnology, respectively. From these units, instructors at colleges and high schools can pick and choose the scope and sequence of topics and activities and the depth to which they should be taught. This allows a school to develop a unique program that meets the needs of a community's industry and workers.

For schools with certificate programs, the *Biotechnology: Science for the New Millennium* curriculum provides a platform from which to access specialty courses. Following a first course of introductory biotechnology, a program may offer courses unique to the local industry. Some programs may provide courses of particular interest to an instructor or to a certain student population. For example, in regions with an abundance of protein biomanufacturing companies, the succeeding courses might focus on mammalian tissue culture,

fermentation, or protein purification courses. Some schools may offer marine biotechnology, agricultural biotech, bioinstrumentation, forensics, or biodefense following an initial introductory biotechnology course.

The *Biotechnology: Science for the New Millennium* curriculum has been written with the goal of providing the utmost flexibility. Your school may design a one-year course or a multiple-year pathway. Your program may require specific math, biology, and chemistry courses as prerequisites or it may teach the timely math and science concepts as students need them in order to learn new technical skills. You may focus on laboratory skills development or focus on the scientific concepts. There are many ways to teach biotech, but the goal is to give your students as many options as possible for a future in biotechnology. In the next section, strategies are outlined for designing and implementing a biotechnology program that meets the needs of your particular setting.

Section

2

Identifying and Implementing Program Resources

Starting any kind of new educational program is a challenge, but launching a program that includes a strong emphasis on laboratory skills in a relatively new scientific discipline, such as biotechnology, is a huge undertaking. Many teachers are excited about setting up programs but are apprehensive because they may not have been in a lab for a long time and may not have had any real laboratory research experience in college or in industry. One of the best things about teaching biotechnology using the *Biotechnology: Science for the New Millennium* curriculum is that it will refresh and improve your laboratory research skills.

Because biotechnology is a new academic subject in many regions, you may need to actually create a class, course, or program. This section gives guidelines on how to start a program at your high school or college using *Biotechnology: Science for the New Millennium* as the basis for the curriculum. It includes strategies for accessing resources, creating a vision of a program that meets the needs of the community, and implementing a plan of action.

Securing the moral, technical, and financial support to plan and launch a biotech program requires that a teacher act in a manner similar to that of the CEO of a company. Like a CEO, a biotechnology teacher has to pull together the resources to create and put into action a vision, much like a business plan, for the program, including goals and objectives. The first strategy is to recruit people who can help you.

Organizing an Advisory Committee

One effective strategy for starting a biotech program is to set up an advisory committee. Bring together members of the education and business communities who are likely to have an interest in your program. Scientists, businessmen and women, educators, parents, and students bring a plethora of resources that may be harnessed in developing and implementing a program plan.

Depending on your school site, you might consider for your advisory committee supportive people representing the following groups:

Educators:	One or more biology, chemistry, English, or economics/business instructors
Students:	One or more students currently attending the school targeted for the program
School Site Administrators:	Principal and/or Assistant Principal, Counselor
School District or Corporate Administrators	Superintendent; Corporate President or Vice President, CEO, COO, or CSO
Industry:	Several representatives from biotechnology companies, research labs, or medical facilities, including lab technicians, research associates, scientists, human resource managers, corporate administrators
Business Community:	Rotary International, Chamber of Commerce, Lions Club, etc.
Community/Government:	Police, forensic scientists, U.S. Fish and Wildlife, Workforce Development, Career and Tech Ed, etc.
Parents/Parent Groups:	PTA/PTO/Boosters

Creating a Program Plan

Developing a comprehensive biotechnology program plan, course of study, curriculum, and a laboratory of authentic, technical equipment and supplies may take several years and the commitment, effort, and support of several people. An advisory committee speeds up the process

There are several things for the advisory committee to consider when designing a biotechnology program. By answering the following eight questions, the committee can formulate a vision of the program and a plan for its implementation.

- Who is the target student population?
- What are the industrial and educational targets for the student population?
- What are the overall goals and specific objectives given the program targets?
- What types of courses will meet the goals and objectives of the program?
- How will the curriculum be used to meet the objectives?
- What type of facility is needed to deliver the curriculum?
- What type of support is needed to implement the curriculum?
- What is the timeline for implementation of the program plan?

Target Student Population

Virtually any student can have a positive biotechnology experience, one that provides skill and concept development along with career exploration. To participate in an entry-level program supported by the *Biotechnology: Science for the New Millennium* curriculum, students need to possess basic English literacy at approximately the 10th grade reading level, math that includes simple arithmetic operations and calculator operation, and some entry-level computer literacy including word-processing and Web navigation.

More important than prior scientific knowledge, biotechnology students must possess a good work ethic, an attention to detail, the willingness to learn and benefit from training, and good communication and interpersonal skills.

When designing a biotechnology program plan, the question of which students will be recruited and served must be considered. Should the program be targeted toward honors students, who mostly plan to go to four-year colleges and into professional programs? Should the program recruit and give special attention to low-level or high-risk students, who mostly are not destined to matriculate to college? Or, should the program recruit and focus on the mid-range student, the middle 50% of the student population, who may or may not be considering a college experience? Finally, should the program encourage participation from any or all students of any and all academic levels and try to meet the needs of a very diverse student population?

The advisory committee should consider the needs of students, the school site, the community, and the local biotechnology industry when determining the target student population. Is there a student population that may benefit from such a program? Are there programs at local colleges that might articulate with the program and provide an educational target for the program's graduates? Is there local industry that needs and wants program graduates? Are there college or industry requirements that students may be able to meet while in the biotechnology program?

Once a target student population is determined, consider how students will be recruited and supported in the program. How will students learn about the biotech program and the opportunities it will afford? How will students be accepted or enrolled in the program? What support services will be available to biotechnology students? Will there be financial aid, guidance and counseling, and/or tutoring?

How many students are desired or needed in the program? How many students and how many teachers per class? What will the student-to-instructor ratio be? What factors will impact the number of students that can participate in the biotech program? How often will students be able to start the program? What will happen if a student has to temporarily leave the program?

Industrial and Educational Targets for the Student Population

Targets for employment or externships (workplace experiences) in biotechnology include companies that develop or manufacture pharmaceuticals (medicines), industrial products, biotechnology instrumentation, or agricultural products. Targets may also include companies, academic facilities, or government agencies that conduct research, perform testing, or provide other services. Some potential employers or externship sites for your students may be found in:

1. Corporate/industry labs
   - Pharmaceuticals R&D, manufacturing, quality control (QC)
   - Industrial R&D, manufacturing, QC
   - Instrumentation R&D, manufacturing, QC
   - Greenhouses
2. Government funded agencies/labs
   - US Fish & Wildlife Service
   - County/city forensics
   - Research facilities such as the National Institutes of Health (NIH), Salk, Scripps
   - Department of Energy (DOE)
   - State Division of Forestry
3. Academic laboratories
   - University/college labs
   - Medical schools
   - Dental schools
4. Medical facilities
   - Hospitals
   - Clinical labs
   - Pharmacies

Depending on a program's curriculum and scope and sequence of courses, as well as industry needs, program graduates may be prepared to enter the biotechnology industry directly as biotechnicians, biomanufacturing technicians, quality control technicians, or lab technicians, or they may require additional or higher-level training and education.

Currently, there is no nationally recognized certification program for biotechnicians, and depending on the high school, career, or community college program and industry needs, students may be prepared to go directly into the workforce. Working with local industry, educational institutions may develop certificate or diploma programs that are recognized by the partner companies. These may include:
- AA/AS Biotechnology
- AA/AS Biology, Chemistry
- BA/BS Biochemistry, Biotechnology.
- Biotechnician Certificate or Diploma program
- Biotechnology Career Pathway Program Certificate
- Biotechnician Externship Certificate of Completion

When programs are developed by an advisory committee as part of a comprehensive biotechnology program plan, local industry and educational institutions become partners in the program and are more likely to assist biotech student program graduates in finding appropriate employment and educational targets.

Throughout the *Biotechnology: Science for the New Millennium* curriculum, students explore the local and national workforce needs and employment opportunities using the Internet and Web-based projects. Where available, students may have workplace experiences such as field trips, career projects, job-shadows, and internships or externships. Classroom visits by human resources personnel or employment agencies also shed light on employment targets for your students. A discussion of how and when to use these activities is presented in the lesson plans in the *Course Planner* (and also on the Instructor's side of the Biotechnology IRC).

Overall Goals and Specific Objectives

Once the student population, industry sites, and educational programs for a biotechnology program have been identified, the next step is to write specific goals and objectives. Since each program has a unique set of students, industry partners, and educational facilities, the goals and objectives for a program will be unique to a program site.

Goals for the biotechnology program may be rather general, but they should convey the intent of the program developers. Depending on the program, they may be as global as those in the following list:

Goals for the San Mateo Biotechnology Career Pathway
- To better prepare biotechnology students for matriculation into higher education
- To better prepare biotechnology students for industry placement

- To provide biotechnology students with the resources necessary to make good educational and career choices
- To increase scientific literacy in biotechnology students

On the other hand, the objectives for a biotechnology program are much more specific and have measurable outcomes. For example:

Objectives for the San Mateo Biotechnology Career Pathway
- To enroll 50 new students (enough to fill two classes) each academic year into the Pathway program
- To prepare students for entry-level technician positions in research and manufacturing departments within biotechnology companies that focus on producing pharmaceuticals, industrial products, agricultural products, and instrumentation
- To place at least 50 percent of the program's students into laboratory externships at local industry or academic sites via the San Mateo County Regional Occupational Program (ROP)
- To award at least 25 Certificates of Completion to student graduates of the San Mateo Biotechnology Career Pathway program each year
- To matriculate each program graduate into an educational or workplace program that meets the graduate's academic and career goals

Goals and objectives or outcomes guide the program developers in designing specific courses and curricula to meet the needs of the targeted students, industry partners, and the educational institutions.

Types of Courses

The course framework of a school's biotechnology program may take many shapes. The number and length of courses, the sequence of courses, and the courses' content are some of the first issues that must be resolved when planning a biotech program. Options include:
- One semester, one-year, or multiple-year programs
- Concept-based (lecture/discussion) versus process-based (skill development) programs, or a combination of the two
- Academic emphasis of the courses: core science, elective, technical preparation (Tech-Prep), academy, or honors
- Programs articulated with colleges, universities, and/or industry

The student, educational, and industry targets that have been identified, as well as the goals and objectives of a program, must be considered when developing a proposal for the framework of courses that compose a

biotech program. Geographic regions with an abundance of biotechnology industry and higher education sites may have different program goals and objectives than an area with few or no biotechnology facilities. Thus the type of courses offered in a program vary. Aligning course offerings with the needs of the community plays a large role in the success of the program.

Some schools may choose to have a single biotech class as a science elective or honors course. A one-semester or one-year course in biotech may be concept (lecture) based or process (laboratory skill development) based, or a combination of the two (this approach typically requires a full year). Increasing student interest in science and technology, readying students for the rigors of university science classes, or preparing students for entry into biotechnology certificate programs may be one or more of the goals of a single-course program. The length of these courses often restricts them to concept-based survey courses or a theme-based curriculum.

Other schools may establish multi-year programs such as a biotechnology academy or a biotech tech-prep pathway. Multi-year programs allow more time for skill development and career exploration. Instructors have more freedom to spend additional instructional time on workforce development. Students have time to develop skill sets that expand their educational and employment options.

There is no one right or wrong way to design a pathway model or plan. An optimal plan is a model that meets the needs of the population it is serving. One example of a program framework is the San Mateo Biotechnology Career Pathway (SMBCP), shown in Figure 3. The type and arrangement of courses in the pathway is a result of trying to meet the objectives outlined above in *Objectives for the San Mateo Biotechnology Career Pathway*.

An important question when planning your program is, "Will any of the courses have prerequisite courses or experiences?" There are definite advantages to requiring some biology, chemistry, or math courses before students enter a program. Students come in at a higher level and may progress faster through the biotech program. On the other hand, students may have different experiences in the prerequisite courses. Some of them may be good experiences and some may be discouraging. How many students will shy away from biotech because of a negative experience in a prerequisite course?

Having no prerequisites prior to the biotech program requires that some basic biology, chemistry, and math skills be taught within the program. This takes up valuable instructional time but ensures that all students have a minimum proficiency and a positive experience.

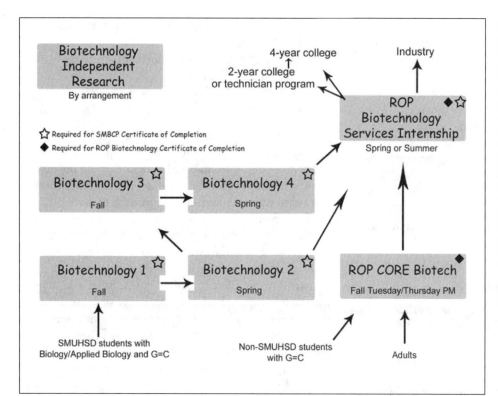

Figure 3. The SMBCP prepares adults and teenagers for entry-level research and manufacturing positions in an assortment of local biotechnology companies. After completing the program, students can enter the workforce directly; move into certificate programs at local community, technical, or career colleges; or enter degree programs at four-year universities. Biotechnology 1 focuses on the development of basic lab skills and understanding the biotech industry as a whole. Biotech 2, 3, and 4 focus on recombinant protein production, agricultural and pharmaceutical biotechnology, and diagnostic biotechnology, respectively. The prerequisite for program admittance is a lab-based biological science class.

Facility Requirements

The ideal biotechnology education facility differs from a typical chemistry or biology classroom or laboratory. This disparity is even greater when the biotechnology facility must function to train students to enter the workforce environment.

Although almost any room can be converted or used, several things are important when designing or modifying a facility to function as a biotech lab room/training facility. Like technicians, students will be expected to work independently and must be able to move freely around the lab in order to access supplies and equipment. Adequate aisles, several large sinks, many refrigerators and freezers, and multiple numbers of certain items, such as hoods, ovens, etc., are necessary for proficiency training. Abundant counter space is required for the large number of small appliances used and for students to set up and run experiments. Adequate storage space is important. Small storage rooms where chemicals or supplies are sequestered make it difficult to access items in a reasonable amount of time and should be avoided.

Plan for the following items when designing or remodeling a room for biotech:

- Physical space for the total estimated number of classes using the facility/time period, the number of students/class, the number of lab groups/lab stations, the amount of equipment and expendable supplies necessary to train the number of students/lab groups
- Sufficient tabletops or countertop space with plenty of electrical outlets and an adequate number of circuits.
- Easy access to water and the placement of sinks adjacent to where lab work is conducted. Sinks at lab stations are not necessary or preferred. Sinks located away from lab stations decrease the hazard of electrical shock and the risk of water damage to instruments.
- Gas lines (methane) to laminar flow hoods and chemical flow hoods. Gas lines are not necessary or desired at individual lab stations.
- Resin-top lab tables where fire or caustic chemicals are used.
- Easy-to-access glass, plastics, chemical, and equipment storage. Lab stations, perimeter counters, and other lab tables should be designed with an abundance of drawers and cabinets for lab station equipment. Stockrooms should be of sufficient size that large numbers of students may move through them safely and quickly.
- Easy and frequent access to computers, printers, and other technology.

Because of the large investment in capital equipment and delicate instruments, consider the feasibility of having a "designated" biotechnology facility. Also, discourage the sharing of the biotechnology laboratory training facility with other non-biotechnology teachers, classes, and students. It is fairly obvious that many items used in the biotech program could be targets for theft or misuse. Only trained staff and students should have access to the facility.

When planning the biotechnology facility and program implementation, be reasonable in your expectations and timeline. The investment in time, money, and people resources likely will be substantial, and it may take program developers many months, even years, to have all the facets of the program in place. Successful programs may be started even if all aspects of the program plan are not initially in place. The planning team can determine which features are required for inauguration of the program.

Types of Support Required

Since every biotechnology program is unique, the support required for each is slightly different. The program planners and advisory committee should determine the kind of support needed to reach the program goals and objectives.

The kinds of support needed to start and sustain a program might fall into the following six areas:

1. Raising funds/long-term funding/finances/ budgeting
2. Setting-up and maintaining facilities/equipment/supplies/materials
3. Setting-up and maintaining computers/technology
4. Curriculum development and implementation
5. Establishing workplace experiences/externships/job-shadows/field trips/speakers' visits
6. Professional development/teacher training/ release time

It is important to identify the type of resources available to support a biotechnology program. By developing a list of organizations and individuals that are possible sources of support for the six areas, the planning team can begin to strategize how to approach each.

A schematic of support groups and their possible role in your pathway may help you visualize the resources available and how they work together (see Figure 4).

As with any new innovative program, especially one that requires significant capital expenditures and annual expendable supply budgets, developers of biotech programs must secure short- and long-term funding in order to establish and maintain a state-of-the-art curriculum. But how is funding secured to start and operate a new biotechnology education program?

Fund-raising and annual operating budgets are important items to flesh out during the program planning stage since setting up a facility may cost many tens or hundreds of thousands of dollars to build and possibly an equal amount to stock with equipment and supplies. In addition, replenishing plastics, chemicals, and biologics may cost several thousands of dollars per year.

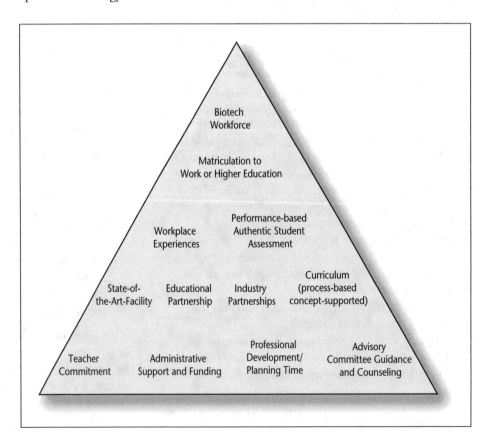

Figure 4. Biotechnology Program Support Pyramid. This diagram shows some of the key factors needed to support one kind of biotechnology technical preparation program.

Often, school sites use tuition or school funding as the base for their annual budgets. Schools may have bond measures or state funds for building or remodeling, but, at some time in every program's tenure, funds must be secured from other sources within or outside of the institution.

It is important and very valuable for one or more members of the planning team to become proficient grant writers. Grant writing has a "snowball effect" and once you are awarded one grant, others seem much easier to write and submit. Some sources of grants and funding include:

The School Site
> Department budget, staff development funds, School to Work funds, academy funding, PTA or PTO, Booster Club, principal's budget, school improvement funds

School District
> Tech-Prep grants, School to Work funds, Eisenhower funds, distributive education funding, grant writer/grant-writing, GATE funding, special programs funding

County/State/Federal
> Regional Occupational Program (ROP), Workforce Development, Tech-Prep, School to Work funds, Carl Perkins funds, Specialized Secondary Program funds, National Science Foundation, National Institutes of Health, U.S. Department of Energy, U.S. Department of Defense, U.S. Department of Labor

Private Foundations /Philanthropy
> GrantsNet, Grantsalert.com, www.eschoolnews.com/erc/funding/, private foundations such as Philanthropic Ventures, Peninsula Community Foundation, or organizations such as the Lions Club

Industry (Foundations/Charitable Donations Committees)
> Oracle, Applied Biosystems, Bayer Biotech, Invitrogen, Amgen, Genzyme, Wyeth, Hewlett-Packard, etc.

Professional Development

Instructors in new biotechnology programs need support in many ways but they particularly need ongoing professional development and good, old-fashioned, moral support. Professional development is necessary because many teachers who serve as biotechnology instructors do not have recent training in biotechnology. Even for instructors coming out of industry, it is likely that their recent work was specialized in one area of biotech research or manufacturing.

Many opportunities for biotechnology training and professional development exist. Program planners should determine methods of supporting instructors that include release time, substitute teachers, and funding to attend workshops, conferences, and meetings. The lists below give some examples of conferences and meetings that provide biotechnology education workshop opportunities. It is, however, only a snapshot of the extensive list of options for biotechnology professional development.

Biotechnology Education Conferences/Workshops

National and State
> Bio-Link; Biotechnology Industry Association (BIO); Biotechnology Institute Teacher Leader Program, National Biology Teacher Association (NABT); National Science Teachers Association (NSTA); Career College Association; State Science Teacher Associations (i.e. CSTA, CAST, FAST, VAST, TSTA, etc); Canadian Biotechnology Education Resource Centre

At both national and state meetings, teacher presentations and exhibitor workshops such as those by VWR/Sargent Welch, Carolina Biological, Fotodyne, Edvotek, Ward's, and BioRad provide a multitude of biotechnology training opportunities.

Regional, County, and Local
> Regional NSTA conferences; Bio-Link Regional Centers; Bay Area Biotechnology Education Consortium (BABEC), The Science Education Partnership, Fred Hutchinson Cancer Research Center; Dolan DNA Learning Center; Carnegie Institute of Washingtion; Fralin Biotechnology Center; Maryland Biotech Institute; The New Hampshire Biotechnology Education and Training (NHBET) Center, BioTeach, Massachusetts Biotechnology Education Foundation; Salk Institute; Scripps; Gene Connection, Santa Clara County Biotechnology Education Partnership (SCCBEP); EBBEP

Community College/University
> The Center for Engineering Plants for Resistance Against Pathogens at UC Davis, University of Maryland Biotechnology Institute; *Base Pair* Summer Teacher Training, University of Mississippi Medial Center, etc.

On the Web

www.bio-link.org; www.accessexcellence.org; www.biospace.org; www.labvelocity.com; www.nal.usda.gov/bic/Education_res/; www.public.asu.edu/~langland/lesson-index.html, Vendor Web sites and/or workshops

I have never met a biotechnology teacher who was not outstanding. It is just the nature of the task that teachers who are not enthusiastic, dedicated, professional, and effective are weeded out. Most biotechnology teachers can meet the challenges of creating a new biotechnology program at their school site if they are given a reasonable amount of support (as outlined above). Administrators should look at additional ways to eliminate the number of obstacles that teachers have to overcome to implement and run a program.

The likelihood of success for a program will increase by ensuring that teachers have:

- A designated classroom that they are allowed to manage (to decrease loss and damage and allow sufficient preparation time)
- A realistic number of course preps (a reasonable number of different courses so that their energy can be focused on curriculum implementation and industry partnerships)
- A reasonable number of students (to allow for authentic assessment of student skill development and proficiencies)
- A reasonable budget (so that materials are not a limiting factor to process-based instruction)
- Assistance from counseling, clerical, and administrative staffs
- A realistic timeline and set of expectations for program plan implementation

Timeline for Implementing a Program

The number of resources and the amount of support available are the major factors that influence how quickly a program can be implemented. An example of a program implementation timeline is shown in Figure 5 to give you an idea of where to start. Notice that most of the eight important issues are addressed in the timeline. Best wishes in planning your biotechnology program.

February 1994	1. Create a biotechnology Advisory Committee (San Mateo Biotechnology Career Pathway Development Committee) with educators, administrators, students, industry, college, county, and district representatives to develop a preliminary pathway plan. 2. Develop the course objectives, scope, sequence, and standards for the *Biotechnology1* course. 3. Conduct articulation meetings with Skyline College, Applied Biosystems, and ROP to get feedback on the scope and sequence of the proposed *Biotechnology 1, 2, and 3* courses. 4. Hold curriculum integration meeting to plan integrated activities with members of the English, Math, and Social Science Departments. 5. Attend CTAP (FWL) assessment meeting. 6. Meet with industry partners to discuss possible assistance in purchasing equipment necessary for the *Biotechnology 1, 2, and 3* courses. **on-going**
Early March 1994	1. District Science Curriculum Council, Management and Principals Group, Instruction Council, and School Board adopt the *Biotechnology 1* course. 2. Hold articulation meetings with Applied Biosystems to outline parameters of a Teacher Intern position to act as a liaison between biotech industries, community colleges and the San Mateo Biotechnology Career Pathway. 3. Meet with San Mateo Biotechnology Career Pathway Advisory Committee. 2/2/95
Late March 1994	1. Teachers and counselors advise students and disseminate flyers about *Biotechnology 1* and the pathway development to freshman, sophomores, and juniors. 2. Students from the Berkeley Biotechnology Education program visit campus and share their enthusiasm and biotech experiences with our target students.
April 1994	1. Order equipment, supplies, and materials necessary for the *Biotechnology 1* course. **on-going**
May 1994	1. Begin to make additional connections with biotechnology companies throughout San Mateo County. **on-going**
June - August 1994	1. Teacher Intern establishes job-shadowing, mentor, and internship positions for student pathway participants, as well as explores funding possibilities and additional equipment acquisition. Possibilities for summer student internships are explored. 2. Conduct curriculum integration meetings with continued planning of integrated activities by members of the English, Math, and Social Science departments.
Sept. 1994 and Jan. 1995	1. The first semester of *Biotechnology 1* is taught in September of 1994 with two sections of 25 students. Students hear guest speakers from industry and the Skyline Community College Biotechnican program. Students take field trips to biotechnology companies to view the variety of positions available and conduct research on a biotechnology career, including a visit to an employee for an onsite interview. Another 50 students enroll in the Spring semester *Biotechnology 1* course. Students begin assembling a (CTAP) portfolio. **on-going** 2. ROP conducts a vocational course, *Biotechnology Services*, on the San Mateo campus beginning in the Spring semester of 1995. The course will have significant work-place experiences including an unpaid, laboratory internship.
Sept. 1994 through August 1995	1. Develop the course objectives, scope, sequence, and standards for the *Biotechnology 2 and 3* courses. 2. Biotechnology teacher acts as the facilitator of the career pathway, using two periods/day. **on-going**
September 1995	1. *Biotechnology 2 and 3* are taught for the first time.
Beyond 1995	San Mateo Biotechnology Career Pathway graduates have the option to enter either: 1. Newly evaluated entry-level jobs at local biotechnology companies. 2. A two-year technical program at Foothill College, City College of San Francisco, Skyline College, or their equal, with advanced placement. 3. A four-year college majoring in Biotechnology, Molecular Biology, Biology, Biochemistry, etc.

Figure 5. Timeline for The San Mateo Biotechnology Career Pathway

Part

2

Planning a
Biotechnology Course

Section

1

Suggested Scope and Sequence/Course Syllabi

When it comes to planning the scope and sequence of curricular topics and activities for a biotechnology course or program, the saying "So much biotech, so little time!" certainly applies. The *Biotechnology: Science for the New Millennium* curriculum was developed to be versatile, providing conceptual material and laboratory skill development curricula that will work well in a variety of school and course settings.

I believe that a biotechnology program is an opportunity to teach science in a way that develops science literacy, research skills, and career awareness for virtually every student. This guiding principle has shaped my program vision and the course curriculum. I wrote the curriculum with the goal that:

- Students learn the skills and gain the confidence and self-directedness that are necessary for independent research and higher-level science courses.
- Students see meaning and application in their math, biology, and chemistry classes.
- Students learn the science and business of biotech so that they are better prepared to make decisions about their futures and the issues impacting society.

The *Biotechnology: Science for the New Millennium* curriculum begins with a focus on standard lab operating procedures (SLOP) in Chapters 1-5, including record-keeping, following oral and written instructions, using scientific methodology, practicing safety, conducting measurement, preparing solutions and media, using sterile technique, culturing cells, isolating DNA and proteins, and performing analyses and electrophoresis. Three units focused on recombinant protein manufacturing (Chapters 6-9), agricultural and pharmaceutical biotechnology (Chapters 10-12), and diagnostic biotechnology (Chapters 13-14) follow the unit on standard lab operating procedures.

Product Components

The text and laboratory manual are the primary courseware for students. Additional product components include the following:

1. Encore Multimedia CD packaged with the text and the lab manual
   - Multimedia presentations of key lab skills and procedures; many presentations incorporate videos of step-by-step demonstrations
   - Quizzes in two modes: practice and scores-reported
   - Full glossary that is also available chapter by chapter
   - Image bank of major illustrations from the text
   - Crossword puzzles

2. Laboratory Notebook with scientific grid pages, numbered
3. Instructor's Resources (CD-ROM, printed Instructor's Guide, and Course Planner/Lesson Plans)
   - Includes course planning tools, teaching hints, model answers, and evaluation guides
   - Instructor materials are also available at the book's Internet Resource Center (IRC)
4. Test Generator and Item Bank
   - Create your own tests from a bank of 50 items per textbook chapter
   - Use any combination of multiple-choice, matching, and short-answer items
   - Deliver tests on print, LAN, or WAN platforms
5. Internet Resource Center:
   - Student resources include study aids, Web links to helpful biotechnology resources, and self-quizzes with results reported to teachers
   - Instructor resources include teaching aids, syllabus suggestions, tests and assessments, answer keys, and Web links
6. Class Connections (WebCT and Blackboard): Includes course syllabi, assignments, Web links, chapter quizzes, and tests

Alternative Course Models

When planning a program's scope and sequence of topics and activities, the instructor or development team must pick and choose which skills and topics to cover. It may be difficult to cover all of the material available in the *Biotechnology: Science for the New Millennium* curriculum. With 14 chapters, 100-plus activities and extensions in the book, and nearly 100 lab activities in the laboratory manual to choose from, instructors should select the lessons and activities that meet the program goals. This allows a school to develop a unique curriculum that works well within its program model and that meets the needs of a community's industries and workers.

The *Biotechnology: Science for the New Millennium* text and lab manual are each designed to be used as a stand-alone instructional tool for a concepts course, a lab skills course, or as partners in a comprehensive program. Some recommended course titles and instructional time blocks are presented below. Your student population, facility and staff availability, and school site and program needs will help you determine the best one for your situation.

Possible Course Title	Grading Period/Credits	Instructional Blocks
Survey of Biotechnology Topics	1 semester, 3 credits	3 hours lecture-discussion per week for 16-18 weeks
Introduction to Biotechnology	1 semester, 4–5 credits	3 hours lecture-discussion plus 3 hours of lab per week for 16-18 weeks
Principles of Biotechnology I and II	1 year (2 semesters), 3 credits per semester	2 hours lecture/discussion per week and one 3-hour lab weekly for 32-36 weeks
Biotechnology Laboratory Fundamentals	1 semester, 3-4 credits	3-4 hours of lab per week for 16-18 weeks

Reviewing the program courses and targets is the first step in planning a curricular scope and sequence. Look at the model below and determine how many class hours are available for direct instruction and skill development. Note that a term may equal a semester, a quarter, or even a full year, depending on how broadly or deeply you want to teach the content. Then you may want to design the scope and sequence of topics from scratch or you may use or adapt one of the models that follow, which include:

- a four-term lab-skill development course supported by conceptual development; terms may be quarters, semesters, or years
- a two-semester, lab-based, concepts-supported course plan using the text and lab manual; the plan also is adaptable to one-semester courses
- a one-semester concepts course plan using the text
- a one-semester lab skills course plan using the lab manual

Four-Term Concepts and Laboratory Skills Program Model

Biotechnology 1 (Term 1): Standard Laboratory Operating Procedures	
Concepts/Lectures/Readings/Chapters	**Process/Laboratory Work (Activities)**
Biotechnology Past and Present Chapters 1, 2, and 3	Setting Up a Legal Scientific Notebook (Lab 1a) Safety in the Biotech Laboratory (Lab 1b) Scientific Methodology Laboratory (Lab 1c) Internet/WWW Research, Microsoft Word, Excel, PowerPoint (Lab 1c) Model Organism Growth (Lab 2b) Bioethics and Decision-Making (one/text chapter) Using the Microscope to Study Cells (Labs 2c-2d) Solution and Dilution Preparation (Labs 3a-3h)
DNA and Protein Structure/Function Chapters 4 and 5	Media Preparation (Lab 4c) Sterile Technique/Cell Culture (Labs 4f-4g) DNA Isolation and Indicator Analysis (Lab 4h) DNA Gel Electrophoresis Analysis (Labs 4i-4j) DNA Synthesis and Lambda PCR (Lab 13e) Protein Structure and Function Studies (Labs 5a-5c) Protein Indicator Analysis (Lab 5d) Protein Electrophoresis (PAGE) (Labs 5e-5f)

Biotechnology 2 (Term 2): Introduction to Recombinant DNA and Protein Production	
Concepts/Lectures/Readings/Chapters	**Process/Laboratory Work (Activities)**
Assay Development Chapters 6 and 7	Amylase Assay Development (Labs 6b-6c) Spectrophotometer/Molecular ID (Labs 7a-7b) Preparing Protein Buffers (Labs 7c-7d) Protein Concentration Assays (Labs 7e-7i)
Recombinant DNA Technology/Transformation/Genetic Engineering Chapter 8	Recombinant Plasmid/Cloning Vectors/Restriction Enzyme Mapping (Labs 8a-8b) Cell Competency/Bacterial Transformation/Selecting Transformants (Labs 6e and 8c) Cell Culture, Growth, and Monitoring (Labs 8d-8e) Plasmid Preps (Labs 8f-8g)
Scale-Up, Manufacturing, Marketing Chapter 9	Harvesting Protein/Protein Product Purification/Protein Testing (Labs 9a-9e) Product Pipelines/Product Studies (Biotech Live)

Biotechnology 3 (Term 3): Agricultural and Pharmaceutical Biotechnology	
Concepts/Lectures/Readings/Chapters	**Process/Laboratory Work (Activities)**
Studying Plant Reproduction Chapters 10 and 11	Plant Growth Labs (Labs 10a-10c) Breeding Plants (Labs 10d-10e) Asexual Reproduction Labs (Labs 11a-11b)
Manipulating/Studying Plants Chapter 11	Plant Tissue Culture/Plant Hormones (Lab 11c) Isolation/Study of Plant DNA (Labs 11d-11f) DNA Concentration/Purity Assays (Labs 11g-11h) GMOs/Plant Transformation/Arabidopsis PCR (Biotech Live and Bioethics)
Discovering New Medicines Chapters 6 and 12	Anti-microbial Plant Substances (Lab 6d) Extracting Compounds from Plants (Labs 6f-6h) Chemical Synthesis/Testing (Labs 12c-12e)

Biotechnology 4 (Term 4): Advanced Biotechnology Techniques and Diagnostics	
Concepts/Lectures/Readings/Chapters	**Process/Laboratory Work (Activities)**
Genomics/DNA Studies Chapters 13 and 14	In Vitro DNA Synthesis Reactions, DNA PAGE/Southern Blotting (Labs 13a-13d) Lambda PCR/Alu PCR and Bioinformatics
Proteomics/Protein Studies Chapters 5 and 14	DNA Fingerprinting and Forensics (Labs 13e-13g) Genomics/Microarrays (Biotech Live) Protein Extractions from Animal Tissue (Lab 5g) ELISA Technology (Lab 14a) Western Blots (Lab 14b)

Syllabus for a Two-Semester Concepts-Supported Lab Skills Course

Course/Credit Hours: 32 weeks; 5-6 hours of lab and lecture/discussion meetings per week
Activities may require adjustment to meet the time limitations of a particular course.

Week	Lab(s)	Lab Lesson Focus	Text Section Support and Lecture Discussion Focus	Key Lab Skill Objectives
1	1a 1b	Scientific Notebook Laboratory Safety	1.1 Defining Biotechnology 1.2 Biotechnology Products 1.3 Selecting Potential Products	• Start and maintain a legal scientific notebook • Learn emergency procedures and the location of safety hazards and emergency equipment
2	1c	Cheese Production	1.4 Scientific Methodology 1.5 Biotech Careers 1.6 Bioethics	• Conduct a controlled experiment; analyze and report data
3	2b 2c	Model Organisms Microscopy	2.1 Organisms and Their Parts 2.2 Cellular Organization	• Grow, maintain, and monitor bacteria and fungi • Learn microscope use for prepared and wet mount slides
4	2d 2e	Microscopic Measurement Properties of Carbohydrates	2.2 Cellular Organization 2.3 Molecules of Cells	• Learn to estimate the size of microscopic specimens • Study the structure and characteristics of different carbohydrates
5	3a 3b	Pipeting Micropipeting	3.1 Measuring Volumes	• Demonstrate skill using pipets and pipet pumps • Demonstrate skill using micropipets

continued

6	3c 3e	Mass Measurement Mass/Volume Solutions	3.2 Making Solutions 3.3 Mass/Volume Solutions	• Demonstrate skill using balances • Prepare various mass/volume solutions
7	3f 3g	Percent Mass/ Volume Solutions Molar Solutions	3.4 Percent Mass/ Volume Solutions 3.5 Molar Solutions	• Prepare various percent mass/volume solutions • Prepare various molar solutions
8	3h 4a 4b	Dilutions DNA Isolation Solutions DNA Spooling	3.6 Dilutions 4.1 DNA Structure and Function	• Prepare dilutions of solutions • Prepare buffers and reagents for DNA isolation • Conduct alcohol precipitation of pure DNA sample
9	4e 4f	Media Prep Sterile Technique	4.2 Sources of DNA	• Prepare LB agar and LB broth • Pour sterile LB agar Petri plates
10	4g 4h	Bacteria Cell Culture Bacteria DNA Extraction	4.2 Sources of DNA 4.3 Isolating and Manipulating DNA	• Streak isolated colonies and start broth cultures • Isolate genomic DNA from bacteria
11	4i 4j	Agarose Gel Prep Agarose Gel Electrophoresis	2.4 The "New" Biotechnology 4.4 Gel Electrophoresis	• Prepare an agarose gel • Load, run, stain, and analyze DNA on a gel
12	13e	Lambda PCR	13.1 Making DNA	• Perform a PCR reaction
13	13f 13g	Human DNA Extraction Alu PCR Genotyping	13.3 Polymerase Chain Reaction 13.4 Applications of PCR Technology	• Isolate DNA from cheek cells for PCR • Use PCR to test DNA for a specific genotype
14	5a 5b	Antibody Function Enzyme Function	5.1 Structure and Function of Proteins 5.3 Enzymes: Protein Catalysts	• Simulate antibody-antigen testing • Test enzyme activity at different concentrations
15	5f	PAGE	5.4 Studying Proteins	• Prepare protein samples and load, run, stain and characterize proteins on a PAGE gel
16	5g	Identifying Proteins	5.5 Applications of Protein Analysis	• Prepare animal muscle tissue samples and run gels to study differences in protein composition
17	6b 6c	Starch and Sugar Assays Amylase Assay	6.1 Sources of Potential Products 6.2 The Use of Assays	• Conduct aldose and starch indicator tests • Test saliva for alpha-amylase activity
18	14a	ELISA	14.3 Advanced Protein Studies	• Conduct a qualitative ELISA (antibody assay)
19	6d	Testing Plant Substances	6.3 Products from Nature 6.4 Plant Proteins as Products	• Extract compounds from plants and test the extracts' antimicrobial activity on the growth of E. coli
20	6e 7a	Searching for Native Amylase Using the Spectrophotometer	6.5 Producing Recombinant DNA Protein Products 7.1 Using the Spectrophotometer	• Predict where amylase-producing bacteria might be found in nature and attempt to isolate colonies • Learn how to operate a spectrophotometer and how light corresponds to colors of the visible spectrum
21	7b 7c	Using the Spec to Study Molecules Measuring pH	7.1 Using the Spectrophotometer 7.2 Introduction to pH	• Use a VIS-spec to determine the absorption spectra and lambdamax for three colored solutions • Learn to use pH paper and a pH meter

continued

22	7d 7e	Making Buffers Demonstrating Buffer Efficacy	7.3 Buffers	• Prepare a buffer to use in making a protein solution • Prepare buffers and test their ability to resist changes in pH
23	7f 7g	Spec Amylase Study Determining Amylase Concentration	7.4 Determining Protein Concentration	• Determine the absorbance spectrum for amylase • Bradford reagent to learn lambdamax • Use a best-fit standard curve to determine the concentrations of unknown amylase solutions
24	7i 8b	Using the UV Spec to Study Proteins Restriction Digestion of pAmylase	7.4 Determining Protein Concentration 8.1 Overview of Genetic Engineering	• Use a UV-VIS spec to determine the lambdamax for a sample of colorless protein Conduct a restriction digestion of the pAmylase to confirm prior to transformation of E. coli cells
25	8c	Transformation	8.2 Transforming Cells	• Transfer plasmids into E. coli and select transformants
26	8e	Scaling-up Transformed Cells	8.3 After Transformation 8.4 Fermentation, Manufacturing, and GMP	• Select colonies and scale them up from a selection plate to selection broth media
27	9a 9b	Harvesting Amylase Dialysis of Protein Buffers	9.1 Harvesting a Protein Product 9.2 Using Chromatography to Study and Separate Molecules	• Separate transformed cells from broth and test the broth for amylase activity Use dialysis tubing to conduct a buffer exchange prior to column chromatography
28	9c	Using Ion-Exchange Chromatography	9.3 Column Chromatography	• Separate lysozyme from albumin on an ion-exchange column
29	9d	Ion-Exchange Purification of Amylase	9.4 Product Quality Control 9.5 Marketing and Sales	• Use an ion-exchange column to determine the overall charge of amylase at pH7.2 and isolate amylase from a broth culture
30	12a 12b	Using the UV Spec to Study Caffeine Using MSDS to Recognize Compounds	12.1 Drug Discovery	• Use the UV spectrophotometer to characterize a colorless organic compound, caffeine • Access MSDS data to learn the characteristics of compounds
31	12c	Synthesis of Aspirin	12.2 Creating Pharmaceuticals by Combinatorial Chemistry	• Synthesize acetylsalicylic acid through combinatorial chemistry
32	12d	Melting Point Determinations for Quality Control	12.3 Creating Pharmaceuticals by Peptide and DNA synthesis 12.4 Creating Pharmaceuticals by Protein Engineering	• Conduct melting point determinations to confirm acetylsalicylic acid production

Syllabus for a One-Semester Concepts-Based Survey Course

Course/Credit Hours: 16 weeks, three 1-hour class lecture-discussion meetings/week; total of 48 class meetings

The corresponding section of the text should be assigned as reading either before or after the class meeting, as determined by the instructor.

Week	Chapter Section	Lesson Objective	Key Concepts in Lecture/Discussion/Lesson
1	1.1 1.2	Defining Biotechnology Biotechnology Products	• Biotechnology definition/description/domains • Examples of products and companies • Genetically engineered products
	1.3	Selecting Potential Products	• Product Development Plan • Research and Development, manufacturing • Testing/clinical trials, regulation
	1.5	Biotech Careers	• Types of Jobs/Careers • Educational Requirements
2 (extends into week 3)	1.6	Bioethics	• Morals and ethics • Values Clarification Model for Decision-making
	2.1 2.2	Organisms and their Parts Cellular Organization	• Levels of biological organization • Prokaryotic versus eukaryotic cells • Model organisms and product manufacture • Cell structure and role in biotech,
	2.3	Molecules of Cells (2 class meetings)	• Survey of carbohydrates, lipids, proteins, and nucleic acids
3	2.4	The New Biotechnology	• Central Dogma of Biology • Recombinant DNA • Synthesis of genetically engineered products
	4.1	DNA Structure and Function	• Double helix of nucleotide chains • Nitrogenous bases and base pairing • Semi-conservative replication • Protein synthesis
4	4.2 4.3	Sources of DNA Isolating DNA	• Prokaryotic, eukaryotic, viral DNA • Gene expression • Media prep, bacterial cell culture, sterile technique • Vectors and rDNA technology • Transformation
	4.4	Studying DNA using Gel Electrophoresis	• How a gel box separates molecules • Agarose gel electrophoresis • Data from agarose gels
	5.1	Protein Structure Protein Function Protein functions	• Importance of antibodies and enzymes

continued

5	5.2	Protein Production	• Protein synthesis • Transcription, Translation
	5.3	Enzymes	• Enzyme activity
	5.4 5.5	Studying Proteins	• Applications of Protein Analysis • Polyacrylamide gel electrophoresis • Protein Indicators • Data from PAGE gels
6	6.1 6.2	Sources of Products Product Assays	• Products from nature • Comprehensive Product Development Plan • Assays and their applications
	6.3	Searching for New Products	• Herbal remedies, Rainforest products • Active ingredients • Antibiotics and antiseptics
	6.4 6.5	Plant Products Producing rDNA Products	• Plant protein products • Recombinant DNA Products
7 (extends into week 8)	8.1	Steps in Genetic Engineering (2 class meetings)	• Locating "genes of interest" • Restriction enzymes and recombinant DNA • Cloning and manufacturing
	8.2	Transforming Cells (2 class meetings)	• Transformation, transduction, and transfection • Making rDNA, endonucleases, and RFLPs • Performing a transformation, selection of transformants
8	8.3	After Transformation	• Scale-up of transformants • Products Assays
	8.4	Fermentation, Manufacturing, and GMP	• Kinds of fermentation • Growing cultures, bacterial and mammalian cell culture • cGMP
9	9.1	Harvesting Protein Product	• Protein recovery from cell culture • Introducti on to column chromatography
	9.4	Product Quality Control (2 class meetings)	• Quality Control, Quality Assurance, QC/QA testing • Clinical Testing
10	9.5	Marketing and Sales	• Factors that affect sales • Proprietary/Patent Rights
	10.1	Plant Propagation	• Sexual versus asexual reproduction (cloning) • Meiosis and sex cell formation • Pollination and fertilization
	10.2 10.3	Plant Anatomy	• Plant Growth and Structure • Plant cells, tissues, and organs • Meristematic tissue • Isolating Plant DNA • Mitosis and growth • Seed germination

continued

11	10.4 10.5	Plant Breeding	• Alternation of generations
			• Genotypes and phenotypes
			• Selective breeding and Punnett squares
		Statistical Analysis	• Averages, 10% rule, standard deviation, and Chi square analysis
	11.1 11.2	Cloning Plants Tissue Culture	• Asexual plant propagation, plant tissue culture
			• Plant hormones
			• Starting and maintaining cultures
	11.3	Biotech in Agriculture and Horticulture	• Selective breeding, inbreeding, genetic testing
			• Genetically modified crops
			• Hydroponics
			• Plant-based Pharmaceuticals
12	11.4 11.5	Plant Genetic Engineering	• Isolating and characterizing plant DNA
			• Modifying plant DNA, *Agrobacterim*, and Ti plasmid
			• *Arabidopsis* as a "model" organism
	12.1 12.2	Drug Discovery Combinatorial Chemistry	• Medical biotechnology, drug development, drug discovery
			• Organic synthesis, combinatorial chemistry, parallel synthesis, screening
	12.3	Peptide and DNA synthesis	• Peptide synthesizers
			• DNA synthesizers
13	12.4	Protein/Antibody Engineering	• Antibody specificity
			• Flow cytometry, vaccines
	13.1	DNA Synthesis	• DNA synthesis in vivo
			• Chromosomes and homologous pairs
			• DNA replication and DNA polymerase
			• In vitro DNA synthesis
	13.2	DNA Synthesis Products/Application	• DNA probes, primers
			• Southern blots
			• Microarrays
14	13.3	Polymerase Chain Reaction (PCR)	• Performing and analyzing a PCR reaction
			• Thermal cyclers
			• PCR optimization
	13.4	Applications of PCR	• DNA fingerprinting, criminalistics, and more
			• VNTRs
			• Forensics
	14.1	DNA Sequencing	• Reasons to sequence
			• Dideoxynucleotide sequencing
			• Sequencing results and "BLAST"
			• Human Genome Project
15 (extends into week 16)	14.2	Genomics	• Genomics and bioinformatics
			• Other genome projects
			• RNA and genomics
	14.3	Protein Studies	• Proteomics
			• X-ray crystallography, mass spectrometry, NMR,
			• ELISA, Western blots
	14.4	Other Applications of Biotechnology	(2 class meetings) Pharmacogenetics, personalized medicine Environmental Biotechnology Biodefense/Bioterrorism
16		Course Final	

Syllabus for One-Semester Lab-Based Survey Course

Course/Credit Hours: 16 weeks, 3 hours of lab meetings/week (either one 3-hour meeting or three 1-hour meetings); total of 48 hours of lab time

Each lab activity should be assigned as a reading assignment prior to the class meeting. Activities may require adjustment to meet the time limitations of a particular course.

Week	Lab(s)	Lab Lesson Focus	Key Objective in Lab Lesson
1	1a 1b	Scientific Notebook Laboratory Safety	Start and maintain a legal scientific notebook Learn emergency procedures and the location of safety hazards and emergency equipment
2	1c	Cheese Production	Conduct a controlled experiment and analyze data
3	2c	Microscopy	Learn microscope use for prepared and wet mount slides
4	3a 3b 3c	Pipeting Micropipetting Mass Measurement	Demonstrate skill using pipets and pipet pumps Demonstrate skill using micropipets Demonstrate skill using balances
5	3e 3f 3g	Mass/Volume Solutions Percent Mass/Volume Molarity Solutions	Prepare mass/volume solutions Prepare percent mass/volume solutions Prepare molar solutions
6	3h 4e 4f	Dilutions Media Prep Sterile Technique	Prepare dilutions of solutions Prepare LB agar and LB broth Pour sterile LB agar Petri plates
7	4g 4b 4h	Bacteria Cell Culture DNA Spooling Bacteria DNA Extraction	Streak isolated colonies and start broth cultures Perform alcohol precipitation of DNA Isolate genomic DNA from bacteria
8	4i 4j	Agarose Gel Preparation Agarose Electrophoresis	Prepare an agarose gel Load, run, stain and analyze DNA on a gel
9	13f 13g	Human DNA Extraction Alu PCR Genotyping	Isolate DNA from cheek cells for PCR Use PCR to test DNA for a specific genotype.
10	5a 5b	Antibody Function Enzyme Function	Simulate antibody-antigen testing Test enzyme activity at different concentrations
11	5f	PAGE	Prepare protein samples and load, run, stain and analyze proteins on a PAGE gel
12	6b 6c	Starch and Sugar Assays Amylase Assay	Conduct aldose and starch indicator tests Test saliva for alpha-amylase activity
13	14a	ELISA	Conduct a qualitative ELISA (antibody assay)
14	7f 7g	Spectrophotometry Concentration Assay	Determine lambdamax for amylase-Bradford Use the spec to determine protein concentrations
15	8b	Restriction Mapping	Conduct a restriction digestion of the pAmylase
16	8c	Transformation	Transfer plasmids into E. coli and select transformants

Section 2

Using the Textbook, Lab Manual, and Encore CD

The *Biotechnology: Science for the New Millennium* textbook and lab manual are each designed to be used as a standalone instructional tool for a survey course or as partners in a comprehensive program.

Features of the Textbook

For instructors who need to deliver a survey course on biotechnology, the text offers a thorough review of concepts and how industry implements those ideas and technologies to create products the market demands. Following the chapters are a complete Glossary of terms and a comprehensive Index.

Chapter Elements

Each chapter is divided into discrete, numbered sections to help students focus on one topic at a time.

Biotech Careers

A wealth of opportunities are available to students in the science or business of biotechnology. To give students a better idea of career opportunities, each chapter profiles a biotechnology employee. Job descriptions give students a feeling of what it is like to work in a specific field. They also give relevancy, showing how what is learned in a chapter is used by real workers. Highlighted careers include positions in research, manufacturing, regulation, diagnostics, instrumentation, administration, sales, marketing, human resources, and computer technology.

Learning Outcomes

Learning outcomes at the beginning of each chapter specify the concepts and skills that each student will master while studying the chapter. Students should use the outcomes when they begin and end a chapter to preview what is coming and to check what they have learned.

Definitions of Key Terms

To be able to effectively communicate in the laboratory, students must master the language of biotechnology. When an important term is presented for the first time, its definition is given in the page margin. The syllabic pronunciation of each term is also shown.

Biotech Online Activities

Biotech Online activities are short (15-30 minute) Web-based activities designed to pique student interest and expand on the concepts taught in the chapter sections. One or more *Biotech Online* activities per section is common. These activities can easily be completed outside of class and encourage learners to explore deeper into areas of biotechnology interest.

Section Review Questions

At the end of each section of a chapter, three to four knowledge-based questions challenge students to share what they have learned. Answers to the *Section Review* questions are provided in the *Instructor's Guide* and in the *Course Planner* lesson plans.

Chapter Review

Each chapter concludes with a set of six sections of review content and activities.

Speaking Biotech

The first section in the *Chapter Review* is an alphabetical list of the key terms with references to pages in the text where the terms are first presented and defined.

Concepts Summary

The *Concepts Summary* at the end of each chapter provides the student with a quick review of key biotechnology principles covered in the chapter. By reading the summary before reading a chapter, students are primed for what they are about to study. Reviewing these concept statements at the end of a chapter reinforces learning.

Lab Practices Summary

The *Lab Practices Summary* presents the essential process development and skills that will be learned in the laboratory manual chapters. It is presented in the text chapter reviews as a preview of how students can apply the text concepts to their laboratory work.

Thinking Like a Biotechnician

This set of ten questions presents problems or situations a lab technician typically faces on the job. The first few are knowledge-based questions that encourage students to share what they have learned in the chapter. The remaining questions are higher-level synthesis and application questions that challenge a student to solve problems by applying the concepts they have learned. Answers to the *Thinking Like a Biotechnician* questions are presented in *Part 3: Assessment* of the *Instructor's Guide* and in the *Course Planner* lesson plans.

Biotech Live Activities

Two to five *Biotech Live* Activities at the end of each chapter allow students an opportunity to stretch themselves and study a topic in more depth. Although most can be considered hour-long activities, some require several days or weeks to complete. Many but not all of the *Biotech Live* activities require Web-based research.

Bioethics

As employees in the biotechnology industry or as consumers, students will need to make decisions or take positions on bioethical issues. A Values Clarification Model for studying ethical issues in science and formulating personal positions is presented in Chapter 1. At the end of each chapter, a bioethical issue surrounding a topic covered in the chapter is presented. Students are asked to study the issue and formulate a position based on their knowledge and personal values.

Features of the Laboratory Manual

Chapters of the lab manual correlate with the order and content of the text. The focus is on experiments and activities that help students apply the text concepts and develop the skills they need to work as technicians in the biotechnology industry.

Chapter Prelude

Each chapter of the laboratory manual opens with an engaging prelude or scenario that sets the stage for the skill development to follow. Skill objectives for the lab activities are outlined to alert students to the new techniques and instruments they will use.

Laboratory Activities

Some activities in the lab manual are open-ended, inquiry-based experiences, but the majority of activities focus on specific laboratory skill development and skill mastery. Each lab activity is presented in a way that puts the responsibility for the process on the students. After a *Background* review, one or more *Purpose* questions or statements outline the objectives of the laboratory activity. A *Materials* list details the equipment and materials students need to gather before they begin working. Short, easy-to-follow *Procedures* follow. Students are expected to collect quantitative data and present it in data tables, wherever possible, and to produce a graph to show results in a visual format. Leading questions (*Data Analysis/Conclusion*) ask students to report their findings following the "results with evidence and explanation/possible errors/practical applications" (REE, PE, PA) method presented in Chapter 1 of the text.

Thinking Like a Biotechnician

At the end of each laboratory activity, two to four higher-level synthesis and application questions challenge students to solve laboratory problems by applying the skills and concepts they have learned. Answers to the *Thinking Like a Biotechnician* questions are offered in Part 3 of the *Instructor's Guide*.

Features of the Biotechnology Encore CD

Designed as a companion CD for the *Biotechnology: Science for the New Millennium* text and lab manual, the Encore program includes valuable new content and additional learning resources to help every student achieve success in the course. The CD includes the following elements:

- Lab Tutorials (25 multimedia presentations teaching key lab skills)
- Glossary and Image Bank (all of the key terms from the text chapters plus related full-color illustrations)
- Flash Cards (interactive flash cards of the key terms)
- Crossword Puzzles (an interactive puzzle for each chapter)
- Quizzes and Tests (15-item quiz for each chapter plus a book-level test)

Hardware and Software Requirements

The Encore CD is programmed to operate in both Windows® and Mac OS environments.

Windows Requirements

Minimum:
64 MB of RAM
16-bit sound card and speakers
Internet connection and Web browser
65,000-color video display (High Color/16-bit)
Windows 98, Windows Me, Windows NT, Windows 2000, or Windows XP

Recommended:
96 MB or more of RAM
56 Kbps or better modem, Internet connection, and Web browser
Full-duplex sound card and speakers
65,000-color (High Color/16-bit) or better video display
Windows 2000 or Windows XP

Mac Requirements

Minimum:
64 MB of RAM
16-bit sound card and speakers
Internet connection and Web browser
Mac OS 10.1 or greater
65,000-color video display (High Color-16-bit)

Recommended:
64 MB of RAM
56 Kbps or better modem, Internet connection, and Web browser
Full-duplex sound card and speakers
Mac OS 10.1 or greater
65,000-color video display (High Color-16-bit)

Lab Tutorial Topics

1. **Reading a Pipet**
   10-, 5-, 2-, and 1-mL pipets
2. **Using a Pipet**
   Choosing the right pipet, using pipet pumps, taking up and dispensing volumes
3. **Introduction to Micropipeting**
   Parts of a micropipet, first and second stops, taking up and dispensing volumes, putting on and ejecting tips
4. **P-10 and P-20 Micropipets**
5. **P-100 and P-200 Micropipets**
6. **P-1000 Micropipets**
7. **Choosing and Using a Balance**
8. **Introduction to Solution Preparation**
   Solution, solute, solvent, aqueous, concentration

9. **Preparing Mass/Volume Solutions**
10. **Preparing % Mass/Volume Solutions**
11. **Preparing Molar Solutions**
12. **Preparing Dilutions**
13. **Introduction to Media Preparation**
    Media, agar vs. broth, mixing, and sterilizing
14. **LB Agar and LB Broth Preparation**
15. **Introduction to Sterile Technique**
16. **Pouring Agar Plates for Cell Culture**
    Disinfecting, labeling plates, flaming bottle, how to melt and pour
17. **Streaking for Isolated Colonies**
18. **Starting a Broth Culture**
19. **Introduction to Gel Electrophoresis**
    Parts, agarose electrophoresis vs. PAGE
20. **Preparing Agarose Gels**
21. **Pouring Agarose Gels**
22. **Running Agarose Gels**
23. **Polyacrylamide Gel Electrophoresis (PAGE)**
24. **Visualizing Agarose Gels**
25. **Visualizing PAGE Gels**

Laboratory Materials List by Product Description

The following list details the equipment and materials needed to complete the lab activities in the *Biotechnology Laboratory Manual*. Since suppliers and products are routinely replaced or modified, it is recommended that an instructor use the most current version of the laboratory materials list available at the Sargent-Welch Web site at www.sargentwelch.com/biotech. You can choose from five versions of the materials list, depending on your needs:

1. Master List of Materials by Lab Number
2. Materials List by Product Description (with Product Numbers)
3. Recommended Materials List based on a $50,000 Budget
4. Recommended Materials List based on a $100,000 Budget
5. Recommended Materials List based on a $200,000 Budget

POP	Rec Qty	Unit	Description	Section
1	5	CS	1.7 mL Reaction Tube Rack, five assorted colors, 5/PK, 5PK/CS	Lab Station Essentials, 3b, 4j, 5d, 5f, 5g, 6c, 6d, 6g, 7g, 7h, 7i, 8a, 8b, 8c, 8e, 8f, 8g, 9a, 9b, 9d, 9e, 10c, 11f, 11g, 11i, 11k, 13a, 13f, 14a, 14b
2	1	EA	1° Anti-Actin Antibody , Developed in Rabbit	14b
3	1	PK	10 KD Microcentrifuge Filter Tubes, 100/PK	9b, 14b
4	16	EA	100xR, Oil, Upright Compound Microscope Objective 43300-530, -532	Additional Laboratory Essentials
5	1		10X PCR BUFFER	11k, 13e
6	1	PK	1-mm grid graph paper, 100/PK	2d
7	1	EA	2° Goat Anti-Rabbit IgG Antibody - Alkaline Phosphatase	14b
8	1	CS	24-Well Microtiter Plate, 50/CS	6c, 8e, 9a, 9b
9	1	EA	25mm MgCl2	11k
10	1	EA	5-Bromo-4-Chloro-3-IND (X-Gluc), 10 mg	11j
11	1	CS	95% Ethanol, 4L, 2/CS	4b, 4h, 5f, 5g, 6g, 8f, 8g, 9e, 11d, 11f, 11j, 11k, 12c, 12e
12	1	PK	96-well Micro-titer Plate, 50/PK	6h, 14a
13	1	EA	Acetaldehyde, 100mL	4c
14	1	EA	Acetic Acid, Glacial, 2.5L	4c, 5f, 5g, 6g, 8g, 9e
15	1	EA	Acetic Anhydride, 500 mL	12c

continued

POP	Rec Qty	Unit	Description	Section
16	1	EA	Acetone, 4L	6g
17	1		Agar for Agrobacterium	11j
18	4	EA	Agarose, 100 g	4i, 4j, 8a, 8b, 8f, 8g, 11f, 11k, 13e, 13g
19			Agrobacterium tumefaciens	11j
20		EA	Air Stone	11e
21	1	PK	Alka Seltzer, Foil Wrapped Tablets, pkg/36	7c
22	2	EA	alpha-Amylase, from B. subtilis, 100 g	5e, 6c, 7d, 7f, 7g, 7h, 7i, 9d, 9e
23	8	EA	Aluminum Foil, Heavy, 25 ft	11c, 11e, 11j, 11k, 13d, 14b
24	1	EA	Ammonia, Household Solution 7-10%, 500mL	7c
25	1	EA	Ampicillin, 25 g	6d, 8c, 8e, 9a
26	1	EA	AmpliTaq Gold DNA Polymerase	11k
27	3	EA	AmpliTaq DNA Polymerase	13e
28	2	EA	Anti-algal, Copper Sulfate Squares, 2/PK	10d
29	1	EA	ANTI-PIG IGG conjugated with HRP	14a
30			Applied Biosystems PCR Kit	11k
31			Arabidopsis thaliana seeds	11k
32			Arabidopsis thaliana seeds, wild type	11j
33	1	EA	Aspergillus sp, plate culture	2b, 2c
34	1	CS	Autoclave Tape, 48/CS	Additional Laboratory Essentials
35	1	PK	B and J Column Reservoir and Frit, 50/PK	9c, 9d
36	1		B and J Column Reservoir closures (top and bottom)	9c, 9d
37	4	EA	Balance, Ohaus Electronic Milligram Pan , 0.001 g	3c, 3d, 3e, 3f, 3g, 3h, 4a, 4e, 4i, 5a, 5b, 5d, 5e, 5f, 5g, 6b, 6c, 6d, 6e, 6g, 6h, 7d, 7e, 7f, 7g, 7h, 7i, 8a, 8b, 8c, 8d, 8e, 8f, 8g, 9a, 9b, 9c, 9d, 9e, 10b, 11c, 11d, 11e, 11f, 11i, 11j, 11k, 12c, 12e, 13b, 13c, 13d, 13e, 13f, 13g, 14a, 14b
38	2	EA	Balance, Ohaus, Adventurer, Analytical, 65 g X 0.1 mg	3c, 3d, 3e, 3f, 3g, 3h, 4a, 5e, 5f, 5g, 6b, 6c, 6e, 7d, 7e, 7f, 7g, 7h, 7i, 8f, 8g, 9c, 9d, 9e, 11i, 11j, 12a, 13b, 13c, 13d, 14a, 14b
39	1	EA	BamH I enzyme, 2500 U, with 10X reaction buffer	8b, 8f, 8g
40	1	EA	BAP, 6-benzylaminopurine	11j
41	1	EA	BCIP(X-Phosphate)/NBT COLOR 1.25/2.5 mL	13d, 14b
42	2	CS	Beaker, 100 mL, 12/PK, 4 PK/CS	2a, 6c, 6d, 7d, 7e, 7f, 7g, 7h, 7i, 8f, 8g, 11f, 11i
43	1	CS	Beaker, 100 mL, plastic tripour, 100/CS	Additional Laboratory Essentials

continued

POP	Rec Qty	Unit	Description	Section
44	1	CS	Beaker, 1000 mL, 6/PK, 4 PK/CS	11j, 11k, 13b, 13c
45	2	PK	Beaker, 2000 mL, 4/PK	9b, 11d
46	2	CS	Beaker, 250 mL, 12/PK, 4 PK/CS	2a, 3f, 4c, 4e, 6b, 8c, 8d, 8e, 8f, 8g, 11a, 11c, 11d, 12c, 14a, 14b
47	1	CS	Beaker, 400 mL, 12/PK, 4 PK/CS	4e, 6e, 8c, 9a, 13a
48	1	CS	Beaker, 400 mL, plastic tripour, 100/CS	Additional Laboratory Essentials
49	2	CS	Beaker, 50 mL, 12/PK, 4 PK/CS	4b, 4h, 4i, 5b, 11f, 13d, 14b
50	3	CS	Beaker, 600 mL, 6/PK, 6 PK/CS	4i
51	4	EA	Beaker, Plastic, 1L with handle, grad	11e
53	1	EA	Benedict's Solution, 4L, Qualitative	2a, 6b, 6c, 8e, 9a, 9b
54	1	EA	Bicine, Ultrol Grade 100 g	14b
55	1	EA	BIODOC-IT System M-26 115V	4d, 4j, 5f, 5g, 6g, 8a, 8b, 8f, 8g, 9e, 11f, 11k, 13e, 13g
56	2	EA	Biotin-tagged Alkaline Phosphatase	13d
57	1	EA	Biotin-tagged Primer 150μL at 1.5 pmol/μL	13a
58	1	EA	BIS-TRIS, Ultrol Grade 100 g	14b
59	1	EA	Bleach solution	2b, 8f, 8g, 10c, 10d, 11a, 11d, 11j, 11k
60	1	EA	Blotted Nylon Membrane	13d
61	1	EA	Boric Acid, 500 g	5e, 5f, 5g, 6g, 9e, 13b, 13c, 14b
62	1	CS	Bottles, polycarbonate, autoclavable, 1000 mL, 12/PK, 4 PK/CS	Additional Laboratory Essentials
63	1	CS	Bottles, polycarbonate, autoclavable, 500 mL, 12/PK, 6 PK/CS	Additional Laboratory Essentials
64	1	EA	Bovine Actin, 100 μg	14b
65	1	EA	Bradford Reagent, AMRESCO	7f, 7g, 9c, 9d
66	1	PK	Brand, UV-Cuvettes, Plastic Disposable, 100/PK	7h, 7i, 8f, 8g, 11f, 11g, 11i, 12a
67	1	EA	Bromophenol Blue, Crystals, 5 g	5f, 5g, 6g, 9e, 14b
68	1		Broth for Agrobacterium	11j
69	1	PK	Brush Natural 1.3 cm, 10/PK	Additional Laboratory Essentials
70	1	PK	Brush Natural 4.1 cm, 10/PK	Additional Laboratory Essentials
71	1	EA	BSA Bovine Serum Albumin, 100 g	5d, 9c, 14b
72	1	EA	Bulk, Water Mat Material, for 18 mats	10d
73	1	EA	Caffeine, 500 g	12a
74	1	EA	Calcium Chloride, 500 g	6c, 7d, 7f, 7g, 7h, 7i, 8c
75	1	EA	Calcium Nitrate, 4-Hydrate, 500 g	5a, 11e
76	1	EA	Camera Microscope Package	2c, 2d
77	1	EA	Capillary Tubes, 100 mm, open-ended, 100/vial	12d

continued

POP	Rec Qty	Unit	Description	Section
78	1	EA	Carbenicillin, 5 g	11j
79	4	EA	Carboy with Spigot, 10L	Additional Laboratory Essentials
80	1	EA	Carboy with Spigot, 20L	Additional Laboratory Essentials
81	4	EA	Carboy with Spigot, 5L	13d
82	1	EA	Cartridge Kit, Harvey DI	Additional Laboratory Essentials
83	1	EA	Cellulase, 25 g	5b, 5e
84	1	EA	Cellulose,100 g	2e
85	2	EA	Centrifuge, 6 place, Table Top for 15 mL tubes	4h, 5g, 6g, 8c, 9a
86	4	PK	Cheesecloth, 3 ft X 15 ft	6g
87	1	EA	Chelex Resin Beads	13f
88	1	EA	Chemical Set, Plant Nutrition	11e
89	1	EA	Chlorobutanol, 200 mg	14b
90	1	EA	Chymosin, Recombinant Renin, 1L	1c
91	1	EA	Converter Plate, UV/White	5f, 5g, 6g, 8a, 8b
92	1	EA	COOMASSIE* Brilliant Blue R-250	5f, 5g, 6g, 9e
93	1	EA	Cotton, Non-Sterile, Absorbent, 1 Roll	10c
94	1	EA	Cotton, Non-Sterile, Non-Absorbent, 1 Roll	11c
95	1	EA	Cow Serum 100mL	14a
96	1	EA	Crystal Violet Staining Solution, 2% (Methanol), 100 mL, Flammable	Additional Laboratory Essentials
97	2	PK	Culture Tube with Screw Caps, 38 X 200 mm, 12/PK	2b
98	5	CS	Culture Tubes, Glass, 13 X 100 mm, 1000/CS	2a, 2f, 3a, 3e, 3f, 3g, 3h, 4c, 6b, 6f, 7a, 7b, 7f, 7g, 8d, 8e, 9c, 9d, 12c, 12e
99	8	EA	Cupric Sulfate 5-Hydrate, 500 g	2a, 3e, 3f, 3g, 3h, 4c, 5d
100	2	PK	Cups, Styrofoam, 6 oz, 25/PK	10d, 11a, 11b, 11d
101	1	EA	Cuvette, 50 µL Microcell, Masked, UV Silica, 10mm Pathlength	5d, 7h, 7i, 8f, 8g, 11f, 11g, 11i, 12a
102	1	EA	Cuvette, Standard, Masked, UV Silica, 10mm Pathlength	5d, 7h, 7i, 8f, 8g, 11f, 11g, 11i, 12a
103	1	EA	DEAE Sepharose (for columns)	9c, 9d
104	2	EA	Deoxyribonucleic Acid, Salmon Testes, 1.0 g	4b, 4c, 4d
105			Dialysed broth culture from previous lab (Lab 9c)	9d
106	2	PK	Dialysis Tubing, 1" width, 100 ft/PK	9b
107	1	EA	Digital Camera, Moticam 1000, with Adapter	2c, 2d
108	1	EA	Diphenylamine (DPA), 100 g	4c
109	1	PK	Disposable Tissues/Wipes	Additional Laboratory Essentials

continued

POP	Rec Qty	Unit	Description	Section
110	8	EA	Dissecting microscope, 2X, 4X	11j
111	1	EA	DNA Marker 100 bp ladder (DNA Sizing Standards), 250 µL	11k, 13e, 13g
112			DNA samples from additional sources	4j
113			DNA Synthesis PAGE Gel in the cassette from previous lab (Lab 13b)	13c
114	1	EA	DNA Synthesis Standard Size Markers, 150µL at 0.038pmol/µL	13b
115	1	EA	DNA Template 150µL at 1.5 pmol/µL	13a
116	1	EA	DNA, Yeast, 10 µg	4j
117	1	EA	DNeasy Plant Mini Kit	11g
118	1	EA	dNTP MIX	11k, 13e
119	1	EA	Dried Bees, about 70	10d
120	3	EA	Dry Block Heater (holds 2 blocks)	5f, 5g, 6c, 6d, 8e, 8f, 8g, 9a, 9b, 9e, 11k, 13a, 13b, 13f, 14b
121	1	EA	DTT, 100mM, 100 µL	14b
122	1	EA	DU 530 UV/Vis Spectrophotometer	5d, 7h, 7i, 8f, 8g, 11f, 11g, 11i, 12a
123			E. coli broth cultures from previous lab (Lab 4g)	4h
124			E. coli DNA samples from previous lab (Lab 4h)	4j
125	1	EA	E. coli JM109, 500 µL	2b, 4g, 6d, 8c, 8d
127			E. coli, JM109, transformed with pAmylase, from previous lab (Lab 8c)	8e, 8f, 8g
128	1	EA	EcoRI enzyme, 5000 U	8a
129	1	EA	EDTA Solution, 0.05M	13b, 13c, 13d, 14b
130	1	EA	EDTA, Disodium salt, 100 g	4a, 8f, 8g, 11f, 11i, 14b
131	2	EA	Electrode Stand	7c, 7d, 7e, 7f, 7g, 7h, 7i, 8g, 9b, 9c, 9d, 9e, 11d, 12e, 13d, 14a, 14b
132	1	EA	Electrophoresis Buffer Concentrate, 40X TAE	4i, 4j, 7c, 8a, 8b, 8f, 8g, 11f, 11k
133	1	PK	Elodea densa, 50/PK	2c
134	1	EA	Ethidium Bromide, 10 mL	4d, 4j, 8a, 8b, 8f, 8g, 11f, 13e, 13g
135	1	EA	F1 GgAa SEEDS	10c
136	1	PK	F1 Heterozygous Non-Purp Stem, Yell-Grn Leaf, GgAa seeds, PK of 200	10d
137	1	CS	Falcon Square Petri Dishes, 300/CS	10c, 13d
138	1	EA	Ferric Nitrate, Nonahydrate, 500 g	12c, 12e
139	1	EA	Fertilizer pellets, 1 lb package	10d
140	1	EA	Filter for UVP White Light Box/Imaging Imaging System	5f, 5g, 6g, 9e

continued

POP	Rec Qty	Unit	Description	Section
141	4	PK	Filter Paper, 12.5 cm, 100/PK	1c, 5b, 6d, 7a, 11c, 11j, 12c, 12e, 13c, 13d
142	1	PK	Filter Paper, 18.5 cm, 100/PK	10c
143	2	CS	Filtering Flasks, Nalgene 250 mL, 0.2 µm, 12/CS	4a, 8c, 8e, 9a, 13f
144	1	EA	Flaked ice machine (24 X 24 X 39 in)	Additional Laboratory Essentials
145	1	CS	Flask, Erlenmeyer, 1000 mL, 6/PK, 4 PK/CS	Additional Laboratory Essentials
146	1	CS	Flask, Erlenmeyer, 125 mL, 12/PK, 4 PK/CS	Additional Laboratory Essentials
147	1	CS	Flask, Erlenmeyer, 250 mL, 12/PK, 4 PK/CS	2b, 12e, Additional Laboratory Essentials
148	1	CS	Flask, Erlenmeyer, 500 mL, 6/PK, 6 PK/CS	Additional Laboratory Essentials
149	1	CS	Floating rack (1.7 mL tubes), 4/PK, 4 PK/CS	13a
150	16	EA	Forceps, Fine-tipped, Stainless Steel, 5 in Length	6d
151	32	EA	Forceps, Fine-tipped, Stainless Steel, 5" Length	10a, 10b, 10c, 10d, 11a, 11d, 11j, 13c, 13d
152			Forward primer 150µL at 10uM	11k
153	1	EA	Freezer, Compact, VWR	Additional Laboratory Essentials
154	1	EA	Fructose, 500 g	2e
155	1	EA	Galactose, 100 g	2e
156	4	EA	Gas Burner (Bunsen Burner)	4f, 4g, 6d, 8c, 8d, 8e, 9a, 11j, 12c
157	1	PK	Gauze Squares, 6 X 6 in, 100/PK	10c
158	16	EA	Gel Box, Horizontal, Owl Scientific - 7 X 8 cm (for agarose gels)	4i, 4j, 8a, 8b, 8f, 8g, 11f, 11k, 13e, 13g
159	8	EA	Gel Box, Vertical, Double-sided, for 10 X 10 cm PAGE	5f, 5g, 6g, 9e, 13b, 13e, 13g
160	1	PK	Gel Loading Dye, 10X, 10 X 250 µL	4j, 8a, 8b, 8f, 8g, 11f, 11k, 13e, 13g
161	1	EA	Gelatin, 500 g	2a, 3f, 4c, 6b
162	1	EA	Genesys 10 UV/VIS Spectrophotometer	5d, 7h, 7i, 8f, 8g, 11f, 11g, 11i, 12a
163	3	PK	Glass Rods, 200 mm, 12/PK	Lab Station Essentials, 3f, 4h, 5b, 5e, 6c, 8e, 9a, 9b, 11f, 12c
164	1	PK	Glass Rods, 200 mm, 144/CS	4a, 4b, 4e, 6e, 8c, 8d, 8e, 9a
165	1	CS	Glass Spreader, 50/CS	6d, 8c
166	32	EA	Glasses, Safety, Plastic	Lab Station Essentials, 4c, 4d, 4f, 4g, 4i, 4j, 5f, 5g, 6d, 6g, 8a, 8b, 8c, 8d, 8e, 8f, 8g, 9a, 9e, 11f, 11j, 11k, 12c, 13b, 13d, 13e, 13g, 14a, 14b
167	16 PK Gloves,	Large 100/PK	Lab Station Essentials, 4c, 4d, 4j, 5f, 5g, 6g, 8a, 8b, 8f, 8g, 9e, 11f, 11k, 12c, 13b, 13d, 13e,	13g, 14a, 14b

continued

POP	Rec Qty	Unit	Description	Section
168	4	EA	Glucose (Dextrose), 500 g, anhydrous	2a, 2b, 2e, 3c, 6b, 8g
169	1	PK	Glucose test strips, 50/PK	3c, 6c, 8e, 9a, 9b
170	1	EA	Gooseneck Stand (Flex Arm), for Digital Camera	2c, 2d
171	2	CS	Graduated Cylinder, 100 mL, 12/CS	4a, 12c
172	2	EA	Graduated Cylinder, 1000 mL	Additional Laboratory Essentials
173	2	CS	Graduated Cylinder, 25 mL, 12/CS	1c, 5b, 6g, 7e, 11c, 11j, 11k, 13d, 14b
174	2	EA	Graduated Cylinder, 250 mL	Additional Laboratory Essentials
175	2	EA	Graduated Cylinder, 500 mL	Additional Laboratory Essentials
176	1	EA	Grams Iodine, Biological Stain (Aqueous) (1.85% Iodine/3.05%Iodide), 1L	Additional Laboratory Essentials
177	1	EA	H+ Bond Nylon Membrane	13c
178	6	EA	Heat Block (for 1.7 mL tubes)	5f, 5g, 6c, 6d, 8e, 8f, 8g, 9a, 9b, 9e, 11k, 13a, 13b, 13f, 14b
179	1	EA	HinD III enzyme, 5000 U	8a, 8b, 8f, 8g
180	1	EA	Hood, Chemical Fume, Self-Contained System, 32" on 36" cart	4c, 12c, 12e
181	16	EA	Hot Hand, Hand Protector	Lab Station Essentials, 4e, 4i, 6e, 8c, 8d, 8e, 9a
182	8	EA	Hot Plate Stirrer, 7" X 7"	2a, 3f, 4c, 4e, 6b, 6e, 8c, 8d, 8e, 9a, 11d, 12c
183	1	EA	Hydrochloric Acid Solution, 6N, 1L	4a, 6h, 7d, 7e, 7f, 7g, 7h, 7i, 8g, 9b, 9c, 9d, 9e, 11d, 12e, 13d, 14a, 14b
184	8	EA	Hydrogen Peroxide, 3%, 500mL	6f
185	4	EA	Ice Pail/Bucket/Insulated, 4L	8a, 8b, 8c, 8f, 8g
186	2	EA	Incubator Oven, Analog, 2 shelves	2b, 4g, 6d, 6e, 8c, 8d, 9a
187	2	PK	Inoculating Loop, Ni/Cr wire, 24 GA, 4 mm, 12/PK	4g, 6d, 8c, 8d, 8e, 9a
188	2	EA	Invitrogen NUPAGE® 10% BIS-TRIS gel 1.5 mm, 10-well	14b
189	1	EA	Invitrogen XCELL SURELOCK ™ MINI-CELL CE MARK	14b
190	1	EA	Isopropanol, 1L	8f, 8g, 11k
191	1	EA	Kanamycin Sulfate, 25g	11j
192	1	EA	Kinetin, 99% 1G	11j
193	1	PK	Lab Gas Lighter, 10/PK	4f, 4g, 6d, 8c, 8d, 8e, 9a, 11j, 12c
194	16	EA	Lab marker pens, permanent fine-tipped	Lab Station Essentials
195	1	CS	Lab Mat Bench Liner, Box 20" X 50' 6/CS	Additional Laboratory Essentials
196	1	EA	Lab Rotator, 12 X 12 in, 60 rpm 120V	5f, 5g, 6g, 9e

continued

POP	Rec Qty	Unit	Description	Section
197	4	PK	Lab Scoop, Stainless Steel, 6/PK	3c, 3e, 3f, 3g, 3h, 4a, 4e, 4i, 5a, 5b, 5d, 5e, 5f, 5g, 6b, 6c, 6d, 6e, 6g, 6h, 7d, 7e, 7f, 7g, 7h, 7i, 8a, 8b, 8c, 8d, 8e, 8f, 8g, 9a, 9b, 9c, 9d, 9e, 11c, 11d, 11e, 11f, 11i, 11j, 11k, 12a, 12c, 12e, 13b, 13c, 13d, 13e, 13f, 13g, 14a, 14b
198	16	EA	Label Tape, White, 3/4" roll	Lab Station Essentials, 11c, 11d, 11j, 11k, 12c
199	1	EA	Lactose, 500 g	2e
200	6	EA	Lambda DNA	13e
201	1	EA	Lambda, cut w/HinDIII, 5X100 µg, 0.5 µg/µL	4j, 8a, 8b, 8f, 8g, 11f
202	1	EA	Lambda, uncut, 5X200 µg	4j, 8a
203	1	EA	Laminar Flow Hood, 3 X 3 X 2 ft	2b, 4f, 4g, 6d, 6e, 8c, 8d, 8e, 9a, 11d, 11j
204	4	EA	LB Agar Basße, Lennox, 500 g	2b, 4e, 4f, 5a, 6d, 6e, 8c, 8d, 9a
205	4	EA	LB Broth Base, Lennox, 500g	2b, 4e, 6d, 8c, 8d, 8e, 9a
206	1	EA	Lemon juice	2f
207	1	CS	Lid Lock, blue, Sorenson, 5000 locks/CS	6c, 8e, 9a, 9b, 13b, 13f
208	1	EA	Light System	10d, 11e, 11j
209	1	PK	Loop, Inoculating, Sterile, 20/PK, 0.55mm diameter	2b, 6e
210	1	EA	Lugol's Iodine Solution, 500 mL	2a, 2c, 2d, 6b, 6c, 8e, 9a, 9b
211	1	EA	Lysol® Disinfectant, conc 1 gallon	2b, 4f, 4g, 6d, 6e, 8c, 8d, 8e, 9a, 11j
212	1	EA	Lysozyme, 5 g	5e, 8f, 9c
213	1	EA	Magnesium Chloride, 1M, 100 mL	13d, 14b
214	16	ST	Magnetic Stir Bars, Assorted, 6/Set	Lab Station Essentials, 4e, 6e, 8c, 8d, 8e, 9a
215	32	EA	Magnifying Hand Lens, 6.5 cm dia, 2X	10a, 10b
216	1	EA	Maltose, 500 g	2e, 6b
217			Master Mix	13g
218	1	CS	Media Bottle, Wheaton, Grad. w/cap, 1000 mL 24/CS	4c, 5e, 5f, 5g, 9e
219	1	CS	Media Bottle, Wheaton, Grad. w/cap, 125 mL 48/CS	4a, 4e, 5f, 5g, 8c, 8d, 9e, 14b
220	1	CS	Media Bottle, Wheaton, Grad. w/cap, 250 mL 48/CS	4e, 4i, 6d, 6e, 8a, 8b, 8d, 8e, 8f, 8g, 9a, 11c, 11j
221	1	CS	Media Bottle, Wheaton, Grad. w/cap, 500 mL 24/CS	2b, 5a, 8c, 9a, Additional Laboratory Essentials
222	1	EA	MES Monohydrate, 100g	14b
223	1	EA	Methanol, Absolute 4 L	6d, 11i

continued

POP	Rec Qty	Unit	Description	Section
224	1	EA	Methylene Blue Stain, 1%, 100 mL	2c
225	1	EA	MgCl2	13e
226	1	EA	Microcentrifuge	3b, 4j, 5f, 5g, 6g, 8a, 8b, 8f, 8g, 9e, 11f, 11k, 13a, 13f, 14b
227	1	CS	Microcentrifuge Tubes, 1.7 mL, clear 500/PK, 10 PK/CS	3b, 4j, 5d, 5f, 5g, 6c, 6d, 6g, 7g, 7h, 7i, 8a, 8b, 8c, 8e, 8f, 8g, 9a, 9b, 9d, 9e, 10c, 11f, 11g, 11i, 11k, 13a, 13f, 14a, 14b
228	1	CS	Microcentrifuge Tubes, Assorted 1.7mL, 500/PK, 10 PK/CS	Additional Laboratory Essentials
229	1	EA	Microcentrifuge, VWR GALAXY, High Speed, 16K X G	8f, 8g, 9a, 11k, 14b
230	16	PK	Micropipet Tips, Blue, 220/PK, for P1000	Lab Station Essentials, 1c, 3b, 3d, 3f, 4b, 5b, 5d, 6b, 6c, 7i, 8c, 8e, 8f, 8g, 9a, 9b, 9c, 9d, 11g, 11k, 12c, 12e, 13f, 14a, 14b
231	16	PK	Micropipet Tips, White, 96/PK, for P10	Lab Station Essentials, 3b, 3d, 4d, 4j, 5f, 6g, 6h, 8a, 8b, 8c, 8f, 8g, 9e, 11f, 11g, 11k, 13a, 13b, 13d, 13e, 13g, 14a, 14b
232	16	PK	Micropipet Tips, Yellow, 192/PK, for P100	Lab Station Essentials, 2f, 3b, 3d, 4j, 5f, 5sg, 6c, 6g, 6h, 7e, 8a, 8b, 8c, 8e, 8f, 8g, 9a, 9b, 9d, 9e, 11f, 11g, 11k, 13a, 13b, 13d, 13e, 13f, 13g, 14a, 14b
233	16	EA	Micropipet, BioHit M-Line, P10, 0.5-10 µL	Lab Station Essentials, 3b, 3d, 4d, 4j, 5f, 6g, 6h, 8a, 8b, 8c, 8f, 8g, 9e, 11f, 11g, 11k, 13a, 13b, 13d, 13e, 13g, 14a, 14b
234	16	EA	Micropipet, BioHit M-Line, P100, 10-100 µL	Lab Station Essentials, 2f, 3b, 3d, 4j, 5f, 5g, 6c, 6g, 6h, 7e, 8a, 8b, 8c, 8e, 8f, 8g, 9a, 9b, 9d, 9e, 11f, 11g, 11k, 13a, 13b, 13d, 13e, 13f, 13g, 14a, 14b
235	16	EA	Micropipet, BioHit M-Line, P1000, 100-1000 µL	Lab Station Essentials, 1c, 3b, 3d, 3f, 4b, 5b, 5d, 6b, 6c, 7i, 8c, 8e, 8f, 8g, 9a, 9b, 9c, 9d, 11g, 11k, 12c, 12e, 13f, 14a, 14b
236	1	PK	Micropipets, Biohit, mLine 3/PK	Additional Laboratory Essentials
237	2	PK	Microscope Slide Coverslip, Glass 100/PK	2c, 2d
238	4	PK	Microscope Slides, Plain, 72/PK	2c, 2d
239	16	EA	Microscope, Advanced Compound, with oil immersion objective	2c, 2d
240	8	EA	Microwave oven	4f, 4i
241	1	ST	Mixed Algae, For 35 Students	2c
242	8	ST	Mortar and Pestle, 100 mL volume, 100 mm outer diameter	5g, 6d, 6g, 12e

continued

POP	Rec Qty	Unit	Description	Section
243	1	CS	Murashige and Skoog Basal Salts, 10/CS	11j
244	1	EA	Murashige and Skoog Multiplication Medium	11d
245	1	EA	Murashige and Skoog pretransplant medium for African Violets	11d
246	1	EA	N,N-dimethyl formamide, 500 mL	11j
247	1	EA	Nitrocellulose membrane	14b
248	2	EA	Novagen, Protein Markers 15-150 KD	5f, 5g, 6g, 9e, 14b
249	1	EA	O-Acetylsalicylic Acid 500 g	12e
250	1	EA	Oil immersion, cargill	Additional Laboratory Essentials
251	1	PK	Pack of 4 Colors, 4/PK	3a, 3b, 7b
252	1	CS	PAGE Gel Loading Tips, 200 µL 576/PK, 8PK/CS	5f, 5g, 6g, 9e, 13b, 13e, 13g, 14b
253	2	EA	PAGE gel, Invitrogen, 10% TG, 10 well	5f, 5g, 6g, 9e
254	1	EA	PAGE Sample Prep Buffer with SDS, 4X, 2 mL	Additional Laboratory Essentials
255	1	EA	pAmylase (0.2 µg/µL)	8b, 8f, 8g
256	1	EA	pAmylase (0.005 µg/µL)	8c
257	1	PK	Paper cups, 100/PK	2e
258	1	PK	Paper, Thermal, 4 Rolls/PK	4d, 4j, 5f, 5g, 6g, 8a, 8b, 8f, 8g, 9e, 11f, 11k, 13e, 13g
259	1	EA	Parafilm®, 125 ft, 4"	11c, 11d, 11e, 12e
260	1	EA	Paramecium caudatum Culture for 35 Students	2c
261	1	CS	Pasteur Pipet Bulb, 72/CS	5d, 7h, 7i, 8f, 8g, 11f, 11g, 11i, 12a, 12c
262	1	PK	Pasteur Pipets, 9", 250/PK	5d, 7h, 7i, 8f, 8g, 11f, 11g, 11i, 12a, 12c
263	1	EA	pBR322, 25ug	4j
264			PC01 PRIMER	13e
265			PC02 PRIMER	13e
266	1	EA	pCambria (0.005 ng/µL)	11k
267	1	PK	PCR tubes, 0.2 mL, 1000/PK	11k, 13e, 13g
268	1	PK	PCR Tubes, 0.5 mL, domed, 1000/PK	8f, Additional Laboratory Essentials
269	1	EA	Pectinase, 25 g	5b
270	1	CS	Peg Racks, Polypropylene, for 10-13 mm tubes, 24/CS	Lab Station Essentials, 2a, 2f, 3a, 3e, 3f, 6b, 6f, 7f, 7g, 8d, 8e, 9a, 9c, 9d, 12c, 12e
271	1	EA	Perlite, 4 cubic ft/bag	11j, 11k
272	1	CS	Petri Dishes, 100 X 15 mm, sterile, 20/PK, 25 PK/CS	4f, 6e, 8c, 8d, 9a, 10d, 11j
273	1	CS	Petri Dishes, 150 X 15 mm, sterile, 100/CS	5f, 5g, 6g, 9e, 12e

continued

POP	Rec Qty	Unit	Description	Section
274	1	CS	Petri Dishes, 60 X 15 mm, sterile, 20/PK, 25 PK/CS	2b, 2e, 5a, 6d, 11d, 11j, 11k
275	1	EA	Petroleum Ether, 1L	12e
276	1	EA	pH Buffer, Blue, pH 10.0, 500 mL	7c
277	1	EA	pH Buffer, Red pH 4.0, 500 mL	7c
278	2	EA	pH Buffer, Yellow, pH 7.0, 500 mL	7c, 7d, 7e, 7f, 7g, 7h, 7i, 8g, 9b, 9c, 9d, 9e, 11d, 13d, 14a, 14b
279	2	EA	pH Electrode, gelfill, plastic	7c, 7d, 7e, 7f, 7g, 7h, 7i, 8g, 9b, 9c, 9d, 9e, 11d, 12e, 13d, 14a, 14b
280	2	EA	pH Meter, digital student	7c, 7d, 7e, 7f, 7g, 7h, 7i, 8g, 9b, 9c, 9d, 9e, 11d, 12e, 13d, 14a, 14b
281	16	PK	pH Paper, Narrow-Range 0-6, 100 strips/PK	4a, 7c, 7d, 7e, 7f, 7g, 7h, 7i, 8d
282	16	PK	pH Paper, Narrow-Range 5-10, 100 strips/PK	4a, 7c, 7d, 7e, 7f, 7g, 7h, 7i, 8d
283	16	PK	pH Paper, Wide-Range 0-14, 100 strips/PK	Lab Station Essentials, 2f, 4a, 5d, 7c, 7d, 7e, 7f, 7g, 7h, 7i, 8d
284	1	EA	Phosphate Buffer,10X PBS Dry Mix,1L	14b
285	1	EA	Photo Imaging System Package	4d, 4j, 5f, 5g, 6g, 8a, 8b, 8f, 8g, 9e, 11f, 11k, 13e, 13g
286	1	EA	Pierce Brand BCA Kit	7h
287	1	EA	Pierce Brand Bradford Kit	7h
288	1	EA	Pig Serum, 100mL	14a
289	16	EA	Pipet Pump Blue, for 1-2 mL pipets	Lab Station Essentials, 1c, 3a, 4b, 4h, 5a, 5g, 6b, 6c, 6d, 6f, 6g, 7f, 7g, 8c, 8f, 8g, 9c, 9d, 11d, 11f, 11i, 12c, 12e
290	16	EA	Pipet Pump Green, for 5-10 mL pipets	Lab Station Essentials, 1c, 2a, 3a, 3c, 3e, 3g, 3h, 4g, 4h, 5b, 5e, 6d, 7b, 7f, 7g, 7i, 8c, 8d, 8e, 8f, 9a, 9b, 9c, 9d, 11c, 11f, 12a, 12c, 12e, 13b, 13f, 14a, 14b
291	1	EA	Pipet Pump Red, for 25 mL pipets	Additional Laboratory Essentials
292	1	CS	Pipet, 1 mL, individually-wrapped, 1000/CS	1c, 6d, 8c, 11i
294	1	CS	Pipet, 10 mL, individually-wrapped, 200/CS	1c, 6d, 8c, 9a, 9c, 9d, 11c
295	1	CS	Pipet, 2 mL, individually-wrapped, 500/CS	4b, 6f, 6g, 8f, 8g
296	1	CS	Pipet, 25 mL, multi-pack, 500/CS	Additional Laboratory Essentials
297	1	CS	Pipet, 5 mL, individually-wrapped, 200/CS	8d, 8e, 8f, 9b
298	1	CS	Pipets, 1 mL, multi-pack, 500/CS	Lab Station Essentials, 3a, 5a, 5g, 6c, 7f, 7g, 11f
299	1	CS	Pipets, 10 mL, multi-pack, 500/CS	Lab Station Essentials, 3a, 3c, 4g, 4h, 5b, 5e, 8c, 11f, 12a, 12c, 12e, 13b, 13f, 14b
300	1	CS	Pipets, 2 mL, multi-pack, 500/CS	Lab Station Essentials, 3a, 4h, 5g, 6b, 8f, 9c, 9d, 11d, 11f, 12c, 12e

continued

POP	Rec Qty	Unit	Description	Section
301	1	CS	Pipets, 5 mL, multi-pack, 500/CS	Lab Station Essentials, 2a, 3a, 3e, 3g, 3h, 5g, 7b, 7f, 7g, 7i, 9c, 9d, 11f, 12a, 14a
302	1	PK	Pipets, 5 mL, 12/PK	12c
303	2	PK	Pipets, Transfer, 3 mL, Graduated 0.25 mL, 500/PK	2c, 2d, 5a, 5f, 5g, 9e, 10c, 10d, 11a, 11j, 11k, 13b, 13c
304		EA	Plant DNA Samples	11i
305	3	PK	Plant labels, sticks or tape, 16/PK	10d
306	3	EA	Plant Support Stakes, Pack of 16	10d
307	1	EA	Plant Tissue Culture Agar	11d, 11j
308	4	EA	Planting quads (or pots, film tubes, or pods), 16 quads	10d
309	1	EA	Plastic bags, 1 gallon	11j
310	1	CS	Plastic beaker, 1L tripour 100/CS	Lab Station Essentials, 2b, 3a, 3b, 4b, 6g, 8a, 8b, 8c, 8f, 8g, 9b, 10d, 11a, 11d, 11j, 11k
311	2	PK	Plastic Funnels, short-stemmed, for 12.5 cm filter paper, 12/PK	1c, 5b, 6d, 11c
312	1	PK	Plastic teaspoons, 50/PK	2e
313	1	PK	Plastic tubing to connect pump to air stone 8FT/PK	11e
314	1	EA	Plastic wrap	2a, 11j, 11k, 13d, 14b
315	1	PK	Plug-Type Caps (for 13 X 100 mm tubes), blue 1000/PK	2f, 3a, 3f, 7f, 7g, 9c, 9d, 12c, 12e
316	1	EA	Potassium Acetate, Crystals, 500 g	8g
317	1	EA	Potassium Chloride, 500 g	5a
318	1	EA	Potassium Hydroxide, 500 g	11d
319	1	PK	Potato Dextrose Agar, 125 mL bottles, 6/pk	2b
320	1	EA	Potting Soil, 1 lb	10d
321	16	EA	Power Supply, 250 V	4j, 5f, 5g, 6g, 8a, 8b, 8f, 8g, 9e, 11f, 11k, 13b, 13e, 13g, 14b
322			Prepared Cheek Cell DNA Samples from previous lab (Lab 13f)	13g
323	16	EA	Prepared Slide, Allium sp. (Onion) Root Tip	2c
324	16	EA	Prepared Slides, Bacteria, Type No.1, three smears	2c
325	16	EA	Prepared Slides, Human Blood	2c
326	3	ST	Prepared Slides, Silk Thread Slides, Set of Six	2c
327			Primer Mix	13g
328	1	EA	Printer, Thermal, Video/Analog	4d, 4j, 5f, 5g, 6g, 8a, 8b, 8f, 8g, 9e, 11f, 11k, 13e, 13g

continued

POP	Rec Qty	Unit	Description	Section
329	1	EA	Protease, Pronase, 50 units	4h, 5b
330	1	EA	Protozoan Culture (Cereal Media)	2c
331	1	EA	PUREGENE Cell and Tissue Kit, Gentra	11g, 11k
332	2	PK	Pyrex Funnels, short-stemmed, for 12.5 cm filter paper, 12/PK	12c, 12e
334	4	PK	Quad Water Wick Strips, 70/PK	10d
335	1	PK	Rainbow label tape 1", 12/PK	Additional Laboratory Essentials
336	1	PK	Rainbow label tape 1/2", 24/PK	Additional Laboratory Essentials
337	1	EA	Refrigerator,Compact VWR, 4.9 cu. Ft.	Additional Laboratory Essentials
338	1	EA	Rennin, Bovine, 25 g	1c, 5b, 5e
339	1	CS	Replacement Flint Tips, 5/PK, 40PK/CS	4f, 4g, 6d, 8c, 8d, 8e, 9a, 11j, 12c
340			Reverse Primer, 150µL at 10uM	11k
341	1	EA	Ring Stand Clamp (Biuret Clamp)	12c
342	1	EA	Ring Stand, Rod/Base	12c
343	1	EA	RNase, 10 mg/mL solution, 1 mL	4h, 8f, 8g
344	1	LB	Rubber Stopper, Size 5, for 25 X 200 cm tubes, 29/LB	12c
345	32	EA	Ruler, Metric, Clear	Lab Station Essentials, 10b, 10c
346	1	EA	Safranin Solution, 1.0% (Aqueous), 100mL	Additional Laboratory Essentials
347	1	EA	Salicylic Acid, 500g	12c, 12e
348			Salmon Sperm DNA Extracts from previous lab (Lab 4b)	4c, 4d
349			Salmon Sperm DNA samples from previous lab (Lab 4h)	4j
350	1	PK	Sand, 5 lbs	11a
351	4	PK	Scalpel Blades, #22, 10/PK, for #4 Scalpel Handles	2a, 2b, 6f, 10a, 10b, 11a, 11c, 11d, 11j
352	32	EA	Scalpel Handles, #4	2a, 2b, 6f, 10a, 10b, 11a, 11c, 11d, 11j
353	1	EA	Scholar MSDS CD-ROM	12b
354	1	EA	Schultz Take Root Rooting Compound, 2 oz	11c
355	32	EA	Scissors, Stainless Steel, 4.5" straight	Lab Station Essentials, 11b, 11d
356	1	PK	Seeds, Broccoli, 4oz PK	10c
357	1	PK	Seeds, Cabbage, 4oz PK	10c
358	1	PK	Seeds, Carrot, 4oz PK	10c
359	1	EA	Sequenase (Polymerase) Version 2.0	13a
360	1	EA	Sheep Serum 100mL	14a
361	5	EA	Silent Air Pump, for 10 gallons	11e

continued

POP	Rec Qty	Unit	Description	Section
362	16	EA	Six-cell Planting Trays with Covers and water tray	11j, 11k
363	1	EA	Sodium Carbonate, anhydrous, 500 g	5a
364	4	EA	Sodium Chloride, 500 g, granules	2a, 4a, 4h, 5a, 7c, 8f, 9c, 9d, 12e, 13a, 13d, 13f, 14a, 14b
365	1	EA	Sodium Dodecyl Sulfate (SDS), 100 g	4h, 5e, 5f, 5g, 6g, 8g, 9e, 11f, 13d, 14b
366	4	EA	Sodium Hydroxide, 500 g, pellets	2a, 2f, 3f, 4a, 4c, 4e, 5d, 7c, 7d, 7e, 7f, 7g, 7h, 7i, 8g, 9b, 9c, 9d, 9e, 13b, 13c, 13d, 14a, 14b
367	1	EA	Sodium Monophosphate, Dibasic, Anhydrous	11j, 14a, 14b
368	2	EA	Sodium Phosphate, Monobasic, Monohydrate NaH2PO4 X H20, 500 g	5d, 6g, 6h, 7e, 9b, 9c, 11j, 13d, 14a, 14b
369	1	CS	Soil, Planting, 8qt/8lbs, 6/CS	11a, 11b, 11d, 11j, 11k
370	8	EA	Spectrophotometer, Spectronic 20 D+	3e, 3f, 3g, 3h, 7a, 7b, 7f, 7g, 8d, 8e, 9c, 9d
371	1	PK	Spider Plants, 3/PK	11b
372			Spinach Extraction Samples from previous lab (Lab 11f)	11h, 11i
373	1	EA	Starch, Soluble , 500 g	2a, 2e, 6b, 6c, 6e, 8c, 8d, 8e, 9a
374			Sterile LB agar plates from previous lab (Lab 4f)	4g
375			Sterile LB broth from previous lab (Lab 4f)	4g
376	1	EA	Sterilizer, Tabletop Autoclave, 12 X 18" inside chamber	4e, 6d, 6e, 8c, 8d, 8e, 9a, 11d, 11j, 11k
377	1	EA	Sterilzer Water System, Harvey DI	Additional Laboratory Essentials
378	1	EA	Still 1.4LPH	Additional Laboratory Essentials
379	1	EA	Streptavidin, use at 1 mg/mL	13d
380	1	EA	Sucrose, 500 g	2e, 5f, 5g, 6g, 8f, 9e, 11d, 11j, 14b
381	1	EA	Sudan III solution	2a
382	1	EA	Sulfuric Acid 2.5L	4c, 12c
383			Suspected actin seafood samples	14b
384	1	CS	Syringe Filter, 25 mm, Cellulose, Luer-lock, 0.2 μm, 50/CS	5e, 6d, 7d
385	1	PK	Syringe, Plastic, 10 mL, 100/PK	5e, 6d, 7d
386	1	EA	TBE Buffer Concentrate, 5X, 4L	7c, 13b, 13c, 13e, 13g
387	2	EA	TBE gel, 1.0mm, 10%, 10 well	13e, 13g
388	2	EA	TBE-Urea gel, 1.0mm, 10%, 12 well	13b
389	16	EA	Test Tube Holder (Stoddard)	Lab Station Essentials, 2a, 3f, 4c, 6b, 12c

continued

POP	Rec Qty	Unit	Description	Section
390	3	CS	Test Tube Racks, White, for 15 mL tubes, 8/CS	Lab Station Essentials, 1c, 3c, 3e, 3f, 3g, 3h, 4a, 4b, 4h, 5d, 5e, 5g, 6b, 6g, 7d, 7f, 7g, 7h, 7i, 8c, 9a, 9b, 9c, 9d, 11f, 12a, 12c, 14a, 14b
391	3	CS	Test Tube Racks, White, for 50 mL tubes 8/CS	2b, 3a, 3b, 4g, 5d, 8c, 8d, 11c, 11d, 11j, 11k
392	1	PK	Test Tube, Pyrex, 25 X 200 cm, 48/PK	12c
393	1	EA	Thermal cycler, Teche TC-512, 96 wells X 0.2 mL	11k, 13e, 13g
394	16	EA	Thermometer –20 to +150 C	13a, Additional Laboratory Essentials
395	4	EA	Thermometer, Mercury, -10°C- 260°C	
396	1	CS	Tissue Culture Tube Caps, 25 mm, 100/CS	11d
397	1	CS	Tissue Culture Tube, 25 X 150 mm , 72/CS	11d
398	1	EA	TMB Solution	6h, 14a
399	1	EA	Toothpicks, flat	2c, 10d
400	16	EA	Tray, Plastic, 1-1/2"H X 10"W X 13-1/2"D	2a
401	4	EA	TRIS	4a, 5e, 5f, 5g, 6c, 6g, 7d, 7e, 7f, 7g, 7h, 7i, 8f, 8g, 9d, 9e, 11f, 11i, 13b, 13c, 14b
402	1	EA	TRIS-HCl	13d, 14b
403	1	EA	TRITON X-100 10%, 100 mL	8f
404	4	CS	Tubes, 15 mL Sterile, Capped, Conical Centrifuge, 500/CS	1c, 3c, 3e, 3f, 3g, 3h, 4a, 4b, 4h, 5d, 5e, 5g, 6b, 6g, 7d, 7f, 7g, 7h, 7i, 8c, 9a, 9b, 9c, 9d, 11f, 12a, 12c, 14a, 14b
405	2	CS	Tubes, 50 mL Sterile, Capped, Conical Centrifuge, 500/CS	2b, 3a, 3b, 4g, 5d, 8c, 8d, 11c, 11d, 11j, 11k
406	1	EA	Tween	14b
407	1	EA	UV Crosslinker	13c
408	1	EA	UV/White Light Box/Imaging System, UVP	4d, 4j, 5f, 5g, 6g, 8a, 8b, 8f, 8g, 9e, 11f, 11k, 13e, 13g
409	1	EA	Vacuum pump and trap jar	4a, 8c, 8e, 9a, 13f, Additional Laboratory Essentials
410			Various samples of dialyzed broth from previous lab (Lab 9b)	9e
411	1	PK	Vermiculite	11a, 11j, 11k
412	1	CS	Vials, 5 mL, 250/CS	14a
413	1	EA	Vinegar, White (Clear), 473 mL	7c
414	1	EA	Vortex (Mini) Mixer	2a, 6b, 11k, 13f
415	2	PK	Watch Glass, Pyrex, 4" diameter, 12/PK	12c
416	1	EA	Water Bath, 6L, Analog	1c, 4h, 4i, 8a, 8b, 8c, 8f, 8g, 11f, 13a
417	1	EA	Water Bath, 6L, Digital	1c, 4h, 4i, 8a, 8b, 8c, 8f, 8g, 11f, 13a

continued

POP	Rec Qty	Unit	Description	
418	1	EA	Water Bath, Shaking	4g, 6d, 8c, 8d, 8e, 9a
419	2	PK	Water Mat, 2/PK	10d
420	2	EA	Water Reservoir/Tray	10d
421	2	EA	Watering System	10d
422	1	EA	Wax paper	3b
423	1	PK	Weigh boat 5.5" X 5.5" X 1" 500/PK	4i, 4j, 8a, 8b, 8f, 8g, 11f, 11k, 13e, 13g
424	4	PK	Weigh Boat, 3.5" X 3.5" X 1" 500/PK	3c, 3e, 3f, 3g, 3h, 4a, 4e, 5a, 5b, 5d, 5e, 5f, 5g, 6b, 6c, 6d, 6e, 6g, 6h, 7d, 7e, 7f, 7g, 7h, 7i, 8a, 8b, 8c, 8d, 8e, 8f, 8g, 9a, 9b, 9c, 9d, 9e, 11c, 11d, 11e, 11f, 11i, 11j, 11k, 12c, 12e, 13b, 13c, 13d, 13e, 13f, 13g, 14a, 14b
425	4	PK	Weigh Paper, 7.6 X 7.6 cm 500 SHT/PK	3c, 3d, 3e, 3f, 3g, 3h, 4a, 5a, 5b,5e, 5f, 5g, 6b, 6c, 7d, 7e, 7f, 7g, 7h, 7i, 8f, 8g, 9c, 9d, 9e, 10b, 11i, 11j, 12a, 12c, 13b, 13c, 13d, 14a, 14b
426	1	EA	Western Blot, Electroblotter tank 9 X 9 cm	14b
427	1	EA	White glue, 8 oz	10d
428	1	EA	White Willow Bark shreds, 1 lb	12e
429	2	KT	Wisconsin Fast Plants® Dihybrid Genetics Class Kit	10d
430	1	EA	XCELL II™ Blot Module CE MARK	14b
431	1	PK	Yeast Malt Agar, 125 mL bottles, 6/pk	2b
432	1	EA	Yeast, 100g	2b
433	1	EA	Zinc Chloride, 100 g	13d, 14b

Section

3

How to Set Up a Biotechnology Lesson

Although it seems that biotechnology is inherently interesting, students come into class each day with the distractions of their daily lives. To make the most of the instructional time, a lesson plan that is well thought out can help students focus on the lesson objectives and learn more effectively. This section describes how to create engaging lesson plans using the *Biotechnology: Science for the New Millennium* textbook and laboratory manual and presents sample lesson plans for the text and lab manual. Lesson plans for each section of the text and each lab activity in the laboratory manual are found in the *Course Planner*.

Lesson Model for Text

Many models of effective instruction and lesson delivery are available. One successful methodology uses an abbreviated version of Dr. Madeleine Hunter's seven-step lesson plan presented in *Instructional Theory into Practice* (a good summary of Dr. Hunter's model is at www.humboldt.edu/~tha1/hunter-eei.html#eei). Similar models are presented in *Exceptional Teaching,* a professional development resource published by EMC Corporation. In a biotech version, a new lesson begins with an anticipatory set to establish a platform for the learning, followed by instruction with active student participation, and ending with a check of understanding including high-order applications of knowledge. A version of the three-part lesson plan has also been called "the learning cycle."

Anticipatory Set

Begin each lesson with a question, discussion, or activity that will set the stage for new learning and give context to what is about to be presented. An anticipatory set may be some kind of directed question(s), a review of past work, or a discussion of experiences, knowledge, new discovery (news article/current event), or new observation. The anticipatory set is like a "hook" that increases a student's level of interest or curiosity, and reminds them of what they already know. The goal is to set the stage for new learning. An example of an anticipatory set for an activity on macromolecules is to ask students to analyze a food label for protein, carbohydrate, and lipid content. A set doesn't have to be long or complicated, but it should provide a link to the intended instruction.

Instruction/Concept or Skill Development

Providing new information or experience to students and allowing them to incorporate their knowledge is the goal of the "instruction" portion of a lesson plan. Instructional methods may include readings and lectures; laboratory activities and demonstrations with props or mega-manipulatives; discussions; videos, DVDs, and the Encore CD packaged with the text and lab manual; and Web-based activities, projects, review sheets, and/or homework. As you design each lesson, consider how students will practice what they have learned and apply it to the next task. Also, plan how you will check for student understanding during instruction (student responses, self-checks, product production, group-thinks, discussion of answers and/or misconceptions, and what comes next) as well as at the end of the lesson or unit.

Assessment/Check for Understanding

At the end of a lesson, allow students an opportunity to demonstrate and apply their new knowledge, skill, or understanding using one of several methods. Sometimes the check for understanding may be teacher evaluated, such as in things that are "turned in," but often it is appropriate and valuable for students to check their own understanding without the teacher immediately learning the results, such as when students are given questions to answer and they check their answers themselves. This personal feedback allows students to get into the habit of thinking about how they are doing, their level of understanding, and whether they need to review or ask for assistance.

If possible, connect their new understanding to future learning or experiences. Depending on the lesson or activity, answering either *Section Review* questions, end-of-chapter *Thinking like a Biotechnician* questions, or test bank questions may be used to check for understanding and application. The *Biotech Online* (found in each chapter section) and the *Biotech Live* activities at the chapter's conclusion allow students to extend and apply their knowledge. In the lab, oral exams are particularly useful in shedding light on how well students comprehend, synthesize, and apply their knowledge. Skills quizzes let students demonstrate a technique or manufacture a product, and are particularly good for helping students gain confidence. In biotech, each lesson is like a step in a staircase building on the steps below. The end of the lesson (assessment/check for understanding) is ideally the lift to the next lesson.

Correlation between Text Features and Lesson Plan Parts

The features of each chapter, as shown in the following chart, can be aligned to the three parts of the lesson plan model as presented above.

Parts of a Lesson Plan	Textbook Features/Resources
Anticipatory set	Learning Outcomes Biotech Careers (chapter opener) Definitions of key terms (in page margins) *Biotech Online* activities
Instruction	Reading prior to or after lecture/discussion/group work Definitions of key terms End-of-chapter *Concepts Summary* *Biotech Online* activities *Biotech Live* and *Bioethics* activities
Checking understanding and application	Section Review questions *Thinking Like a Biotechnician* questions *Biotech Live* and *Bioethics* activities Testbank questions

Sample Text Lesson Plan

Lesson Plan for Section 2.4

Anticipatory Set

Post the names of these diseases or disease-causing organisms on the screen or board:

tuberculosis	Alzheimer's disease	cancer	chlamydia	common cold
cytomegalovirus	drug abuse	*Escherichia coli* (*E. coli*)	*Helicobacter pylori* (*H. pylori*)	hepatitis
HIV/AIDS	human papilloma virus (HPV)	influenza	Lyme disease	malaria
meningococcal disease	yellow fever	plague	*Staphylococcus aureus* (*S. aureus*)	

Ask, "What do these have in common?" The answer is that they are all diseases for which biotechnology companies are trying to develop new vaccines. Many of the new vaccines will be available in the next decade. With vaccine protection, millions of lives will be saved.

For more information on these potential vaccines, go to www.immunize.org/newvaccines/#cytomegalovirus.

Instruction

Remind students that biotechnology is a broad term that describes several techniques to study and manipulate organisms or their components. Vaccine development is one application of some of the laboratory advances of biotechnology.

A big upturn in the amount and direction of R&D of biotechnology products came in the 1970s when rDNA techniques and cell transformation were first used for genetic engineering. Today, most products and advances in biotechnology can be traced back to the basic science of genetic engineering.

Use Figure 2.37 to describe step-by-step how recombinant human insulin (rhInsulin) was created through genetic engineering of bacteria cells.

Remind students of how scientists now engineer all types of cells to express new DNA sequences and produce new proteins.

Discuss the rDNA products presented in Table 2.3. Have students go online and determine the specifics of the genetic engineering process (organisms modified and genes expressed) that resulted in these products.

Additional Activities/Resources

Assign the *Biotech Online,* "Biotech Products Make a Difference."

Have students read and report on the article online, "Genetically Engineered Virus-Resistant Squash Approved for Sale" at: www.accessexcellence.org/RC/ AB/BA/Gen_Engineered_Squash.html

An outstanding rDNA bioethics activity (Recombinant DNA Strategy) is available at: http://nova.bsuvc.bsu.edu/~d000tadl/dna_case.html

Check Understanding/Applications

After reading Section 2.4, students should answer the Section 2.4 Review Questions.

1. What term is used to describe DNA that has been produced by cutting and pasting together pieces of DNA from two different organisms?
   Answer: The term, "recombinant DNA (rDNA)" is used to describe DNA that has been produced by cutting and pasting together pieces of DNA from two different organisms.
2. What organism was the first to be genetically engineered?
   Answer: *E. coli* was the first organism to be genetically engineered.
3. What was the first commercial, genetically engineered product?
   Answer: rhInsulin was the first commercial product made possible through genetic engineering.

4. Explain why South San Francisco, California, calls itself "The Birthplace of Biotechnology."
   Answer: South San Francisco, California, calls itself "The Birthplace of Biotechnology" because it is the city where the first biotechnology company, Genentech, Inc., was founded. Many other companies were quickly started there once Genentech's success became well known.

Ask the students to answer question No. 10 at the end of the chapter in "*Thinking Like a Biotechnician.*"

10. Restriction enzyme molecules cut DNA molecules into smaller pieces. DNA ligase molecules can paste cut pieces back together. Propose a method by which a scientist could create an rDNA molecule that carries genes for high levels of chlorophyll production and genes to resist frost damage. Into what kind of organism might you want to insert the new rDNA and why?

   Answers will vary. Theoretically, you could use a restriction enzyme to cut the chlorophyll genes from plant DNA. First, find a restriction enzyme that will cut out a frost-resistant gene from a bacterium that lives in frigid temperatures. Then find a plasmid vector. Cut it open using the same restriction enzymes used to cut open the other DNA molecules. Mix them all together and add DNA ligase to paste the DNA pieces together. Add this to a bacterial broth culture. Grow bacteria on plates that are in bright light at freezing temperatures. Bacteria that survive and grow with green color are likely to contain recombinant plasmids with the desired genes.

Planning Lessons Using the Laboratory Manual

Each lab activity in the laboratory manual can be conceptualized as an individual lesson plan with a beginning (anticipatory set), middle (instruction, or lesson), and end (application or check for understanding). However, in a laboratory-based program, lessons may not be restricted to a single class meeting but instead require several meetings to set up an experiment or activity, conduct it, and analyze the results.

For the purpose of building laboratory proficiencies, the anticipatory set, the instruction, and the check for understanding may look different than in lesson plans for a lecture-based course. The table that follows shows the correlation between lesson plan parts, lab manual chapter features, and textbook chapter features. This table is especially useful if you are teaching a combination concepts and skills-based (lab) course.

Parts of a Lesson Plan	Lab Manual Chapter Elements/Resources	Textbook Chapter Features/Resources
Anticipatory set	Chapter introduction, lab activity *Background* section, *Purpose* statement or question, lab vocabulary (see Part 4 of this IG)	*Learning Outcomes*, *Biotech Careers*, definitions of key terms (page margins), or *Biotech Online* activities
Instruction	*Procedures*, figures, tables, reflection/*Data Analysis/Conclusion* sections, lab vocabulary	Reading prior to or after lecture/discussion/group work, definition of key terms, chapter *Concepts Summary*, as well as *Biotech Online*, *Biotech Live*, *Bioethics* activities
Check for understanding and application	*Thinking Like a Biotechnician* questions, skills quizzes	*Section Review* questions, *Thinking Like a Biotechnician* questions, *Biotech Live* and *Bioethics* activities, plus test bank questions.

Sample Lab Manual Lesson Plan

Lab 3b: Measuring Very Small Volumes in a Biotechnology Lab

Objective: Students will develop and demonstrate proficiency using micropipets to measure, deliver, and mix very small volumes.

Timing

Pre-lab = One 50-minute period to teach how to read and use the micropipets. Instruction = One 50-minute lab period of micropipeting practice.
Post-lab = One 30-minute period of micropipeting skills quiz.

Student Groups

Student pairs for instruction and practice
Individuals for Micropipeting Skills Quiz

Materials

Tube rack for 1.7 mL tubes
Reaction tubes, 1.7 mL
Permanent lab marker pens
Pack of 4 colors, package of 4
Red dye (1 mL dye:499 mL dH_2O)
Blue dye (1 mL dye:499 mL dH_2O)
Green dye (1 mL dye:499 mL dH_2O)
Yellow dye (1 mL dye:499 mL dH_2O)
Micropipets and tips (P-10, P-100, P-1000)
Tubes, 50mL. sterile
Tube racks for 50 mL tubes
Plastic beaker, 1000 1L
Microcentrifuge
Wax paper

Safety Issues and Tips

Food coloring stains everything. Use two feet of paper towel as lab matting.

Text Support

Section 3.1 has an extensive discussion of volume measurement, conversion of metric units, and use of micropipets. There are several good diagrams and figures for illustrating proper micropipet handling and dispensing.

Encore CD Support

Show the student Encore CD Lab Tutorials demonstrating how to use micropipets.

Anticipatory Set

Set up a milligram balance to use in a demonstration. Tare it with a piece of weighing paper. Using a P-1000, dispense a mL (1000 µL) drop of deionized water onto the weighing paper. Remind students of the conversion that shows that these are unit equivalents. Point out that one milliliter (1000 µL) weighs 1 g. This is by design. The designers of the metric system decided that one cubic centimeter of water (a "cc") would be equivalent to a milliliter and weigh one gram.

Next, repeat the demonstration with different microlilter amounts. Ask the students to predict the weight of the dispensed amounts.

Instruction

Show students how the numbers in the display on each micropipet are read. Start with the P-100 since it is the easiest to read. Remind them to first look to determine the range of the micropipet and what the top of the range is. This will determine the numbers that will be displayed.

If, for example, the technician wants to use a P-100, the range is 100 µL down to 10 µL. The maximum is 100 µL and the numbers in the display should say 100. Decimal values are shown after a decimal point or along a scale on the bottom of the display.

Demonstrate how the displays on different micropipets may be read differently from each other.

Ask students, "What would a value of 73.3 µL look like on the display?" Show students how to dial in the desired volume on the brand of micropipet they are using. Show them how to add and eject tips.

Read through the lab's *Background* information with your students. Demonstrate how to pick up and dispense samples. Emphasize the importance of keeping the micropipet at eye-level to see that the take-up and dispensing is complete.

Remind students that a technician must be able to convert between units and measure with the appropriate instrument.

Remind students of the conversion factors:

$$\text{Liter (L)} \xleftrightarrow{1000} \text{milliliter (mL)} \xleftrightarrow{1000} \text{microliter (µL)}$$

Propose the following question: Suppose 1000 µL of reagent is needed for an experiment, but a P-1000 is too wide to retrieve a sample from a narrow tube. How can a pipet be used to get the sample?

Remind students to use the B$\leftrightarrow$S rule to convert between volume units (see text Figure 3.5).

Ask students to report several microliter values in milliliters and vice versa.

Assign the *Procedures* and have each student produce tubes A-D. Students should evaluate their micropipeting skill as directed in the *Procedures*.

Points to Stress with Students:

- Micropipets should always be kept in vertical position so solutions do not damage the internal chamber.
- Show students how to hold the micropipet so the number dial is visible. This means that the lip hangs over the index finger and the plunger is accessible by the thumb.
- Students must be aware of the proper technique for reading the measurement system on a micropipet. All micropipets are different so it is important to first examine the type of micropipet you have and to determine whether the number dial has three or four digits. It is easiest to begin with the P-100 or P-200, depending upon which type of micropipette, because these are the easiest models to read. For micropipets that have four digits, the volume desired is read exactly as it appears on the display. If the micropipet only has three digits then the screen would be read as follows:

  P-100 / P-200, 100 µL would be read as 100, but for 50 µL, the screen would read 050.

  P-10 / P-20, 20 µL would read as 200, but 5 µL would read as 050.

  P-1000, 1000 uL would read as 100, and 500 µL would read as 050.

- Have students locate the screw dial to adjust the volume, which can be between the plunger and the display or can actually be located on the top of the plunger, depending upon the model. Have them determine if it is necessary to hold down a button or lever when adjusting the volume. It is extremely important that students never force the dial, because extreme force can cause expensive damage to the micropipet. Once they have determined the actions necessary, they can proceed to adjust the dial to a volume you specify.
- Have students learn how to use the plunger on the top of the micropipet to extract and expel volumes. Students must be aware that they can depress the plunger to two stops, the first of which is depressed to take up a sample. Students should only push the plunger to the second stop when they desire to expel the sample from the tip into a container. Be certain students have a feel for how to use the first and second stops on the micropipet. Some micropipets actually have a third stop for tip ejection. Extra care is necessary with this type of micropipet.

- There are numerous sizes, brands, and colors of pipet tips and not all types fit all micropipets. Typically, if the pipet tip is yellow in color, it will fit on most types of P-10 / P-20 and P-100 / P-200 micropipets. Usually, if the tip is blue, it is for a P-1000 micropipet. Have students practice how to put on and take off micropipet tips. The tips come in small boxes that have been sealed in plastic and have a plastic cover to keep them free of contamination. To add a pipet tip, push the pipet end gently down over the tip. After using a tip, release it by depressing the release lever. This should only be done when the micropipet is pointing down and into a trash receptacle.
- To take up a specific volume it is important to depress the plunger to the first stop before placing the tip into the solution. This prevents bubbling and makes the volume more accurate. Once the tip is underneath the solution, students should slowly release the plunger until it stops, giving the tip time to fill. To expel the sample, slowly depress the plunger to the first stop and then further to the second stop. Hold the plunger down as the tip is dragged on the inside of the vessel. This allows surface tension to pull all of the sample out of the tip. It is extremely important that students change tips between different samples to prevent contamination.
- Remind students to have all recipient tubes prepared for delivery of samples. This will decrease loss of sample due to pipet dripping and will decrease contamination.
- Often there is a specific sequence for adding samples to a mixture. When there is no order specified, add the smallest volume first. Add progressively larger volumes, mixing each addition to the sample by pipeting up and down.
- Have students label all tubes with permanent marker, directly to the *top* of the sample tube. An appropriate label would include sample number, initials, date, and optional items.
- The larger the instrument (micropipet), the less accurate the measurement.

Tips, Tricks, and Hints

- Start with everyone having their own set of micropipets (P-10 / P-20, P-100 / P-200, and P-1000) in front of them. One by one, have students determine the maximum volume, the value of graduates, and how to read the micropipet. Have students draw a diagram in their notebook of each micropipet illustrating these points.
- Check students' understanding of how to read the micropipet by asking them to point out a value on the mciropipet.
- Teach students how to properly adjust, apply, and eject tips to the micropipet and have them practice measuring certain volumes that the instructor determines. Students can wrist flick samples down to the bottom of the tube; this pools the sample. Have students check the accuracy of their measurements by comparing their tubes to others and making sure the volumes are at equal heights.
- Once you are confident that students can read and measure using micropipets, allow them do the "Practicing with Micropipets" activity.
- If the micropipet leaks, check to make sure the tip is securely fastened to the micropipet.

Other Teaching Tools

Assign from Section 3.1 of the text the *Biotech Online* activity titled "Positive Displacement Pipet."

Assign from the text the Chapter 3 *Bioethics* activity titled "Is Honesty Always the Best Policy?" as part of a discussion about taking skills quizzes and how each student is expected to produce his or her own work.

The following Web site has a video link in which there is a video presentation on the use of micropipets: http://biosci191.bsd.uchicago.edu/labindex.html. This video requires Real Player to run.

Checking for Understanding

Assign the *Reflection/Analysis* section at the end of the lab activity.

In addition to a Micropipeting Skills quiz, assign students the *Thinking Like a Biotechnician* questions at the end of Lab 3b:

1. For most experiments, several reagents must be added to the same tube. Propose a method to keep track of the samples that have been added to a reaction tube.

Answer: Both of the following methods could and should be used to keep track of samples added to a tube.

Method #1 – On the reaction matrix, check off each sample added to the tube.

Method #2 – Unless instructions state otherwise, when adding several reagents to one tube, release each drop of reagent onto a new location on the inside wall of the tube. This will help keep track of what has been added.

2. Demonstrate the effect of micropipeting incorrectly by doing the following:
   a. Set a P-20 or P-10 to 2 μL.
   b. Purposely, misuse the P-20 or P-10 pipet and depress the plunger to the second stop.
   c. Suck up this apparent 2-μL volume and release onto a piece of wax paper.
   d. Now, correctly collect a 2-μL volume using the P-20 or P-10.
   e. Release it onto the wax paper next to the other drop. Are the drops noticeably different in size?
   f. How much more is there in the "misused" volume? (Use the pipet to suck up the misused volume in 2-μL increments.)
   g. If a balance or scale is available, and you have been trained to use it, make these measurements on it. Determine the percentage error that would occur if you were to accidentally misuse the pipet in this fashion.

   Answer: A 2 mL pipet is best to use because it has a smaller diameter, giving it less error in measurement (judging the meniscus).

3. Practice micropipeting samples to create mixtures by producing the four tubes in the table below.
   a. Measure all solutions into 1.7-mL microtubes. Label all tubes with the tube number, your initials, and the date.
   b. Although you may help each other, micropipeting as independently as possible is a better practice.

Tube No.	Red Dye Volume (μL)	Blue Dye Volume (μL)	Green Dye Volume (μL)	Total Volume (mL)
A	27.2	313.0	59.3	
B	555.0	222.0	7.8	
C	133.3	19.8	235.0	
D	9.4	.4.1	2.25	

- Use the smallest instrument possible for all measurements.
- Change tips every time.
- More than one pipet may be necessary to measure amounts.
- Total volumes may be checked by using a P-1000.
- Evaluation criteria: labels, final volume, and final color/mixing.

   Answer: Total volume in each tube is:
   Tube A = 399.5 μL
   Tube B = 784.8 μL
   Tube C = 388.1 μL
   Tube D = 15.75 μL

Extensions

Have students go to the VWR Scientific products Web site (www.vwrsp.com) and search for multichannel micropipets. Have them find at least three different brands of multichannel pipets. Have them make a chart for comparison, identifying the similarities and differences in these instruments. If photos are available, have them cut and paste a photo of each pipet.

Separate Comprehensive Lesson Plans Resource

Complete sets of lesson plans for both the text and lab manual are available in a separate printed resource (*Course Planner*) and on the Instructor's side of the Biotechnology Internet Resource Center at www.emcp.com.

Part
3

Assessment

Section

1

Authentic Assessment

The *Biotechnology: Science for the New Millennium* curriculum includes several evaluation methods to assess student progress in light of the program objectives presented in Part I:

- To better prepare biotechnology students for matriculation into higher education
- To better prepare biotechnology students for industry placement
- To provide biotechnology students with the resources necessary to make good educational and career choices
- To increase scientific literacy in biotechnology students

In addition to possessing scientific knowledge and skills, lab technicians working in a biotechnology facility must have excellent attendance, be prompt, and participate effectively as individuals and as team members. Self-direction, the ability to follow oral and written directions, and attention to detail are also expected. If biotech students are treated like employees and are expected to develop these qualities, they learn workplace etiquette and how to work in an environment where expectations are high. Evaluation methods that measure performance in these areas are truly "authentic assessment."

This section outlines the method of authentic assessment used to evaluate more than 2,000 adults and teenagers in the San Mateo Biotechnology Career Pathway (SMBCP). Many hundreds of SMBCP students have transferred their knowledge of laboratory skills and appropriate workplace behavior to internships, externships, and employment. As you design your program, you may choose to implement all or parts of this assessment model.

Some of the methods of assessment may seem traditional, and some may seem nontraditional, but each operates under the premise that the biotechnology courses prepare students to enter either a biotechnology workplace or an advanced educational setting. While preparing students for the academic rigors of university courses, teachers have a responsibility to prepare students to work in a business environment, with the traits valued by supervisors and lab managers.

If industry sites are to bring in students as interns or employees, the candidates must have an outstanding or above average skill set in comparison to other potential employees. To ensure that the biotech program produces potential employees of high caliber, instructors must require that students demonstrate excellent or above average performance (80 percent score) on every assessment tool. That means a minimum proficiency of 80 percent on all tests, concept quizzes, skills quizzes, projects, presentations, performance assessments, attendance, promptness, and participation evaluations.

Development of new skills and improvement of previously learned skills are expected. Students train, practice, test, then retrain and retest, if necessary, to demonstrate their proficiency. While they may train in pairs, students should take skills quizzes and most other evaluation tools individually.

Suggested Grading System

It is recommended that an evaluation system reflect a student's excellent behavior and skills by basing his/her grade on attendance/promptness, participation, record keeping (documentation), process development (lab skills), and concept mastery. In the San Mateo Biotechnology Career Pathway (SMBCP), each of these five areas equals 20 percent of a student's total grade. This grading method rewards students for the qualities that employers value, which is a major characteristic of authentic assessment.

Since this evaluation method is a bit nontraditional, consider asking students to read and sign an "Employment Contract" to guarantee that they understand and accept the evaluation method (see Figure 6).

To be placed at a job site for an internship, externship, or employment, a candidate must:

- Attend class regularly
- Arrive for class promptly
- Bring required materials daily
- Participate in all activities
- Maintain a complete notebook
- Be pleasant and positive
- Be diligent and self-directed

Regular evaluation and feedback is necessary if a student is going to progress. Formal evaluation of attendance, promptness, and participation is recommended every six weeks.

Evaluating Attendance and Promptness

One method of evaluating attendance is by assigning a point value to each hour of class time. "Excused" absences (as determined by the school site or instructor) would be deducted from the total attendance grade, hour per hour, and a maximum of four hours of excused class time could be "made up" in the lab. Absences beyond a total of four hours of class time per grading period may not be "made up."

For example, if there were 30 hours of class time in a grading period, 30 points would represent the maximum attendance score. If a student misses only two hours of class time during the grading period, and the absence was due to illness, he/she would receive a 28/30 for attendance. If that student worked in the lab for two additional hours during the grading period,

then two points would be reinstated to the attendance grade, resulting in a 30/30 score.

Students with unexcused absences are docked two hours for every hour of class time missed. The same makeup rules apply. Thus, if a student has two absences, one that is excused and one that is not, and he/she makes up one hour of lab time, that student is awarded an attendance grade of 28/30.

At the instructor's discretion, and as important tasks are needed in the lab, a "general amnesty" work period may allow students to make up or bank lab time. This is similar to providing students with "comp time." If students or employees are not "on the job" and not present at the scheduled start time, the productivity of a workplace will be negatively impacted. Being "on time" to the biotechnology classroom means being in the intended workplace (in one's seat or at the lab station), with materials, ready to go at "starting time."

Promptness evaluations may be calculated in a manner similar to the attendance evaluations. In this method, students may earn a total of 30 points representing the 30 times they can arrive "on time" to class. Students who are not on time, up to 20 minutes late, are docked two points for each infraction (tardy). A student may earn back one of the two-point promptness deductions with a 15-minute lab makeup. Thus, a student who is tardy to class two times during a grading period and who "made up" each tardy would earn a promptness grade of 28/30 points.

Evaluating Participation

Many students have never worked in a business environment, so they are not aware of the behavior that is expected from professionals in the workplace. Often, accepted student classroom etiquette is not the same as expected workplace etiquette, particularly if one will be working in a laboratory or manufacturing setting. A participation/evaluation rubric, such as the one in Figure 7, may be used to outline the expectations for appropriate biotechnology workplace behavior.

Use the participation/evaluation rubric to give students regular feedback on their behavior and participation. Distributing and discussing the participation/evaluation rubric the first week of class will encourage appropriate participation and workplace etiquette throughout the course. At the end of each grading period, students should receive a new copy with annotations and a score based on their performance that term.

Biotechnology 1 "Employee Contract"

Welcome to _Introduction to Biotechnology_

This course is designed to get you ready for positions and careers in the biotechnology industry. It is the first semester of a 6-semester career pathway. Its goals and expectations are different than in most courses.

PATHWAY GOALS:

A general knowledge of the goals and functions of the biotechnology industry —"The Big Picture."

Experience with the processes used in the biotechnology industry, including experimental design, use of scientific equipment, data analysis and interpretation, critical thinking, and communication.

The development of good business practices, organizational skills, and self-reliance.

COURSE REQUIREMENTS:

Biotechnology students are expected to be present and prompt to class every day.

Biotechnology students are required to maintain a legal, scientific notebook and develop a placement portfolio.

Biotechnology students are required to develop lab and industry skills with at least 80% competency.

CLASS PROCEDURES:

1. You are expected to be in class (at work), seated, with materials, ready to work when the bell rings.
2. Every day, you are expected to have the following materials:
   • your legal, scientific notebook • a black pen • a metric ruler • a calculator • a gluestick
3. You are expected to follow the directions of the instructor/supervisor the first time.
4. You are expected to use all equipment correctly, safely, and as directed.
5. You are expected to respect the rights of others to learn and work.
6. You are expected to participate in all labs and discussions, plus take notes during lectures.
7. You are expected to clean your work area. The teacher (supervisor), not the bell, dismisses you.
8. If you miss a class, it is your responsibility to make up the work/time in the required time period.

EVALUATION: Since Introduction to Biotechnology is designed to prepare you for the workforce, you will be evaluated in a fashion similar to the evaluation techniques used in industry. Your evaluation (grade) and continued participation are based on:

Attendance/ Promptness (20%)	If you miss a class (workday), you must make it up promptly. (* See below.)
	All tardies require make-up time, during lunch, within 1 week. ***
Record-keeping (20%)	All data and information will be kept in a legal, scientific notebook.
Participation (20%)	Subjective evaluation of effort, skills, and work production.
Process/Content (40%)	Objective evaluation of skill development, skills/content tests, and required projects.

*   Makeups are by appointment only, on _____ at _____, within one week of absence. Each absence affects your grade. You may "make up" up to 4 missed class hours/semester without penalty, after which each absence will affect your attendance grade proportional to the number of class hours/semester. Truancies will be counted as 2 absences.

*** _____ at lunch may be used for tutoring and assistance, by appointment. Tardy, truant, or disruptive students will be given detention. Each tardy is counted against the "promptness" grade. Detentions will be served at lunch only on either a ____ or ____. Unserved detentions will result in twice the number of promptness points docked from the "promptness" grade. Every 3 tardies results in additional lost points (5% of the total points) and recommendation of removal from pathway.

Biotechnology students will have opportunities not available to others, including sophisticated laboratory research, guest speakers, "meaningful" readings/activities/discussions/ lectures/ presentations, field trips, and workplace experiences. It requires a commitment from the students and the adults in his or her life. Because it is often hard to control the timing of experiments, occasionally students will be expected to be in the lab at unscheduled times.

I understand the commitment required for this course.

Student's Signature _____   **E-mail** _____

Parent's Name (printed), Signature/Phone No. (if under 18)_____

Teacher Name/E-mail _____

Figure 6. Example of a "Biotechnology Student Employee Contract." Biotechnology student rules and evaluation guidelines are agreed upon on the first day of class.

Employee/Student Participation Evaluation Rubric

Qualities Demonstrated by Student/Employee	Approximate Raise in an Industry Setting	Course Score
• Pleasant, positive attitude, easy to get along with. • Shows willingness to benefit from training. • Acts appropriately in the lab and meetings. • Acts in an alert and safe manner. • Participates in **all** lab work and discussions completely and appropriately. • Works well as a team member, sharing in the work distribution. • Completes assignment in a reasonable amount of time.. • Follows **all** written and oral instructions. • Asks appropriate questions. • Is self-directed, recognizing tasks which need to be done. • Reflects on work done and the values and applications of the work. • Maintains a clean and orderly lab station workspace. • Contributes to the organization and cleanliness of common lab areas.	15% merit raise Meant to encourage employee to stay long-term. This is a very valuable employee.	95%
• Pleasant, positive attitude, easy to get along with. • Shows willingness to benefit from training. • Acts appropriately in the lab and meetings. • Acts in an alert and safe manner. • Participates in **most** lab work and **most** discussions. • Works well as a team member, sharing in the work distribution. • Completes assignment in a reasonable amount of time. • Follows **most** written and oral instructions. • Usually asks appropriate questions. • Usually is self-directed, recognizing tasks which need to be done. • **Often** reflects on work done and its value and applications. • Maintains a clean and orderly lab station workspace. • Contributes to the organization and cleanliness of common lab areas.	10% merit raise Meant to encourage employee to stay long-term. Also meant to encourage the employee to reflect on slight improvements to increase effectiveness. A valuable employee.	90
• Pleasant, positive attitude, easy to get along with. • Shows willingness to benefit from training. • **Usually** acts appropriately in the lab and meetings. • **Usually** acts in an alert and safe manner. • Participates in **most** lab work and **most** discussions. • **Usually** works well as a team member, sharing in the work. • **Usually** completes assignment in a reasonable amount of time. • Follows **most** written and oral instructions. • **Usually** asks appropriate questions. • **Sometimes** is self-directed, recognizing tasks which need to be done. • **Rarely** reflects on work done and its value and applications. • **Usually** maintains a clean and orderly lab station workspace. • **Usually** contributes to the organization and cleanliness of lab areas.	5% "cost of living" raise. Meant to encourage the employee to reflect on improvements to increase effectiveness. A good employee.	85%
• **Usually** has a pleasant, positive attitude, easy to get along with. • **Usually** shows willingness to benefit from training. • **Usually** acts appropriately in the lab and meetings. • **Usually** acts in an alert and safe manner. • Participates in **most** lab work and **most** discussions. • **Usually** works well as a team member, sharing in the work. • **Usually** completes assignment in a reasonable amount of time. • Follows **most** written and oral instructions. • **Usually** asks appropriate questions. • **Sometimes** is self-directed, recognizing tasks which need to be done. • **Rarely** reflects on work done and its value and applications. • **Usually** maintains a clean and orderly lab station workspace. • **Usually** contributes to the organization and cleanliness of lab areas.	0% raise. Meant to encourage the employee to make significant improvements to increase effectiveness. A fair employee.	80%
Employee/student does not meet a significant number of the standards in the previous section.	0% raise. Employee is not demonstrating enough effectiveness or productivity. An ineffective employee in danger of being released.	Less than 80%

Figure 7. Student/Employee Participation Evaluation Rubric. Instructors can give positive feedback on a student's participation while suggesting areas in which a student might improve.

Evaluating Documentation and Record-Keeping

Documentation in a biotechnology facility may take several forms, including keeping records on loose-leaf charts or logs, maintaining computer databases, and most commonly, recording all work and analysis in a legal, scientific notebook. Maintaining a legal scientific notebook is critical in research and development labs but is also important in many manufacturing and quality control environments. In this biotechnology program, the primary method of record-keeping is the use of a legal, scientific notebook.

A legal scientific notebook must be maintained in a specific fashion to hold up under the scrutiny of disputes including those that may occur in a court of law. A legal scientific notebook must have pages that are sewn into the binding so that pages are permanently bound. All work that is done is recorded into the notebook, or a reference to where work can be found is noted. All work entered into the notebook must be signed and dated.

Corrections in the scientific notebook are made in a specific fashion. No erasures, inking-over, or whiting-out of errors is allowed. All errors and corrections must be readable. A mistake should be lined-out and the correction recorded. The technician's or scientist's initials are placed beside the correction.

A legal scientific notebook should have a table of contents pointing the user to the beginning of all major work. All directions, materials, quantities used, reactions, and operating conditions should be recorded in sufficient detail and clarity so that someone of equal skill could understand or repeat the procedures, if necessary. Abbreviations and codes should be avoided. Only abbreviations for metric measurements may be used universally.

As much original data as practical should be attached into the notebook. Where it is not practical to attach original data, examples should be included and clear reference to where the original data is stored should be recorded. All persons who provided assistance, data, or samples should also be cited.

Most importantly, legal scientific notebooks must be 100 percent correct and ready to review at all times. Instructors must train students to anticipate unexpected reviews by supervisors or regulatory agents, and to practice good notebook maintenance. The laboratory notebook policy used in this curriculum is found in Lab 1a or on the inside back cover of the legal scientific notebook available from the publisher.

Notebook Checks

Notebook checks (documentation evaluations) are recommended every four or five weeks. This is a tedious and laborious task for most instructors but the benefits far outweigh the negative aspects of the task.

Since students are required to keep everything in their notebooks and to present the work in a specific fashion, most students who maintain acceptable legal scientific notebooks develop good organizational skills that transfer to the workplace and to other educational settings.

The organization of a legal scientific notebook makes it fairly easy for an instructor to develop a spreadsheet to check it and to give meaningful feedback that the student will actually use. An example of a notebook check spreadsheet is shown in Figure 8.

Many students recognize the value of creating and maintaining legal scientific notebooks. They appreciate that all their work can be found in one place and is easy to access. Since the notebook is a reference and it may be used as such in most applications, they are motivated to keep it organized and current. For many students, their notebook is a significant point of pride.

Instructor Challenges in Working with Notebooks

Although there are several advantages to having students maintain notebooks, there are some drawbacks in demanding industry-quality notebooks. The main downside is that it takes a great deal of time to thoroughly evaluate a notebook, especially if it is from a student who lacks good organizational skills. Even with a grading spreadsheet, a "good" notebook may take 5-10 minutes to grade, and a poor quality one may take up to 20 minutes. The amount of time can be significantly cut if the objective, easy-to-grade items (worksheets, data tables, graphs, etc.) are graded by a teaching assistant, leaving subjective evaluation of conclusions, etc. to the instructor.

Another concern is if a student loses a notebook. Since such a large portion of the grade is dependent on the notebook, this could present the student or the instructor with a significant number of headaches. Or what if a student just never gets organized? Notebook grading could escalate into a difficult experience! On the other hand, a complete, organized notebook is a thing of beauty and a valuable tool in a biotechnology facility.

Honesty in Record-Keeping

Finally, an instructor must be vigilant about cheating and must set the tone for authenticity, trust, and honesty in all work and record-keeping in a scientific facility. The consequences of scientific fraud should be

Figure 8. Example of a Notebook Check Spreadsheet. A significant amount of feedback can be communicated with just a tiny bit of notation on the spreadsheet. Students are required to make corrections of all work that does not receive full credit.

Biotech 1 NB Check 10.17.03

Item	pts	Item	pts
Front Cover Info (T, N, D, P, S)	5	Average CurdlingGraph	
Class Procedures (in front cover)	3	- title	2
- student signature	5	- ruler	1
- parent name & signature & ph #	5	- labels (units)	3
- notes/corrections	5	- data	4
NB policy (on back, with notes)	2	stamp	3
- signed and dated	1	Cheese Production Lab-Conclusion	
Title page (T, N, D, P, S)	5	- results/evidence/explanation	20
Lab/computer group	1	- possible errors	10
Table of contents -up to date	20	- practical applications	10
"Go to" statements	5	stamp	5
"From" statements	5	Domains of Biotech/Notes	5
Signatures/dates on pages	20	Intro to Internet Worksheets	
Corrections (strikeout/initals only)	5	- answers to questions	10
No erasures, etc.	5	Bioethics - Animal Use Chart	5
Pen only	3	Bioethics - Personal Position	5
Loose Papers	5	Biotech Article/Active Reading	10
How to Set up NB	1	Article Sharing Notes	3
stamp (NB setup done on time)	2	Researching 2 Companies	20
Scope and Sequence Sheet (Notes)	3	Investing in Biotech (A.R./notes)	10
Cheese Production Background Notes	5	Intro to Slop - Volume Notes	20
Cheese Production Purpose Question	2	Pipeting Practice Matrix	5
Cheese Prod Materials/Proc Notes	5	Pipeting Quiz Matrix/score	10
Cheese Prod Lab-Indiv Data Table		Micropipeting Practice Matrix	5
- data	4	Micropipeting Quiz Matrix	10
- comments/names	4	Honesty is Best Policy Position	
Cheese Prod Lab-Class Data Table	2		
Average Timing Graph		Misc.	
- title	2		10
- ruler	1		
- labels (units)	3		
- data	4	Total	
stamp	3		300

discussed often. A good activity to use to begin a discussion on honesty in science is the *Bioethics* activity in Chapter 3 of the text. It presents students with a case of scientific fraud and what to do about it.

Evaluating Skill Development

Measuring skill development is something many teachers have thought about trying, but most have never learned how to implement such a program and do not know where to start. Assessing if a student has mastered specific skills is often challenging because it is difficult to separate tasks into measurable or observable events.

Many skills are important and fundamental for entry-level biotechnicians. Some of them have been mentioned earlier in this section. Several are difficult to create a quantitative assessment for, such as following written and oral instructions or maintaining a clean workstation. Other skills and behaviors can be rather easily evaluated in a quantitative fashion (such as how to use a pH meter properly) and are briefly discussed here.

Being Ready to be Productive

Materials checks can verify that students are coming to the workplace with the tools necessary to be productive. For some programs, these materials may include: a legal scientific notebook (which may be kept on site), a black pen, a gluestick, a metric ruler, and a calculator. It is quick and easy to have students open their notebooks to a particular assignment and check their required materials. This quick check lets the instructor know if a student is prepared to work and is staying current. It also reinforces to the student the importance of being prepared to work. Awarding points or stamping a notebook page may be the reward of being ready to work.

Skills Quizzes

Skills quizzes may be given after each new instrument or technique has been presented. Usually a skills quiz involves the production of "something" to be evaluated by the instructor, and often questions or an activity are included that demonstrate the understanding of a process. For example, students are trained to use micropipets. After a period of practice they are given a micropipetting skills quiz to measure both their micropipetting technique and their ability to produce a tube containing a specific volume of sample (see Figure 9).

Depending on the particular technique or instrument, skills quizzes must be passed with a minimum score of 80 percent or better. If students do not pass the skills quiz, they retrain and take another version of the skills quiz a few class meetings later. A variety of skills quizzes (pH meter use, spectrophotometer use, pipet

Micropipetting Skills Evaluation

1. Measure all solutions into 1.5 mL microtubes
2. Absolutely no talking. Working independently is required.

Tube #	Red Dye Volume (µL)	Blue Dye Volume (µL)	Green Dye Volume (µL)	Total Volume (µL)
A	754	3.26	143	
B	198.5	78.6	323	
C	53.7	84.6	2.75	
D	5.4	697	120.4	

- Use the smallest instrument possible for all measurements.
- Change tips every time.
- More than one pipet may be necessary to measure amounts.
- Grading criteria: labels, volumes, color, mixing.

Figure 9. Micropipetting Skills Quiz. Using the three micropipets (P-1000, P-100, and P-10) available in the laboratory, students work independently to produce four tubes of "product." Students are required to score 90 percent or higher on this skills quiz.

use, etc.) are available on the Instructor's page of the Biotechnology Internet Resource Center at www.emcp.com.

Skills quizzes are often informal and not even called "skills quizzes." This is the case when demonstrating that something can be made or treated properly. In media preparation, for example, LB agar and LB broth must be prepared. If the samples produced are not the correct volume, color, consistency, or if they are not labeled correctly, they must be remade by the student. Another example is when students must repeat their tissue culture preparations of African violet samples until they successfully produce clones in uncontaminated cultures.

Checking Concept and Process Development

An oral exam composed of a few questions, conducted as you walk around the laboratory, is useful in assessing laboratory skill and concept development in your students. While students are working in the laboratory, the instructor moves around the room, asking questions to check for comprehension and the ability to apply knowledge. Not all students are asked questions during a given lab activity, but periodically a student is "put on the spot" to show that he or she understands the tasks and their significance. Creating a spreadsheet with students' names and a column for questions and responses/comments helps the instructor keep track of students' assessment values.

An example of how to use oral exams for process assessment while a group of students are conducting a Biuret test of different solutions is provided in this list of questions:

To student 1, "What does Biuret test for?"
To student 2, "What chemicals make up a Biuret test reaction?"

To student 3, "What is the color of a positive Biuret test?'
To student 4, "Which of the tubes represents the negative control and why?"
To student 1, "What are your expected results and why?"
To student 2, "If this tube is more purple than expected, what may be the reasons for that result?"
To student 3, "How might this test be used in the future?"
To student 4, "How might this test be improved?"

Prior planning is not really necessary for oral quizzing. Just grab a clipboard to record notes and create questions as the situation at a lab station presents itself. Oral quizzing holds students accountable for what they are doing and helps them get comfortable sharing their knowledge and discussing protocols with supervisors. Of course, at a work site, a student/employee will have to communicate in this way with supervisors and colleagues. Thus this method becomes an excellent tool for authentic assessment.

What about Homework and Projects?

Additional items requiring assessment may include homework assignments and projects that are not laboratory–based. Depending on the nature of the assignment, they may be categorized under process/skill development or concept development. For example, the homework task "Research online the types of DNA extraction kits available for plant cell DNA extraction" may fall into one or the other category.

Each instructor should decide his or her own policy on the amount of work required outside of the regularly scheduled class time. In the biotechnology workplace, most work is done during the scheduled work hours, and if an employee is productive, extra take-home work is not routinely expected. Occasionally though, because science experiments do not always fit well into an eight-hour day, employees may be expected to stay late or to return to the lab to complete an activity or take readings.

It is appropriate, therefore, to run a biotechnology education program in the same way, meaning students should do some amount of work outside class hours. In the SMBCP, students are expected to spend a maximum of two hours per week doing biotechnology-related activities (homework, projects, or lab work) in addition to their regularly scheduled class hours. Homework assignments may be evaluated as part of a notebook check or, more likely, as a separate component of either a process-based or concept-based grading system.

Assessment Tools

Several structured types of assessment tools are available with the *Biotechnology* product:

- **Quizzes on Encore CD**
  Students can take a 15-item multiple-choice quiz for each chapter of the text. In the Review mode, students receive immediate feedback upon answering each item. In the Practice Test mode, students receive no feedback until they complete the quiz. Their scores are sent by e-mail to them as well as to the instructor. A book-level exam presents 56 items selected randomly from the chapters (four items per chapter). Both Review and Practice Test modes operate at the book-level also.

- **Text Section Review questions**
  Each section of the text chapters ends with a set of concept questions that check students' comprehension of the material. Consider using these questions as homework assignments that become part of the course grade. Answers are provided in Part 3 of the *Instructor's Guide* and in the *Course Planner* lesson plans.

- ***Thinking Like a Biotechnician* questions (text and lab manual)**
  These concept review questions assess students' understanding of key biotechnology principles, and most sets also include items that require students to apply their knowledge to practical situations. Answers are provided in Part 3 of the *Instructor's Guide* and in the *Course Planner* lesson plans.

- **ExamView test generator and item bank**
  Available as a separate product component, the ExamView test generator on CD allows you to create chapter, unit, midterm, and/or final exams. The bank includes 50 multiple-choice, matching, and short-answer questions for each chapter. Since the concepts in the text support the understanding of processes presented in the lab manual, many of the questions assess process comprehension. A User's Guide file on the CD provides clear directions about how to use the test generator.

- **Chapter and unit quizzes in IG**
  Included in this part of the IG are a quiz for each chapter and a test for each of the four units. These quizzes and tests have been created from the Exam View item bank.

Another type of assessment is instructors' evaluations of the *Biotechnology* text, lab manual, lab notebook, and the product ancillaries. The form presented below gives you the opportunity to relate your successes in using the course materials and to offer suggestions for improving the product. *Biotechnology: Science for the New Millennium* represents my life's work, but it is a "work in progress." My goal is to continually enhance its effectiveness based on your feedback. Your successes or any challenges you may experience in using the curricular materials are important data in that effort. Use this form (also available on the Instructor's side of the *Biotechnology* Internet Resource Center at www.emcp.com) to let me know specifically what successes you have had and what needs to be improved. You may also suggest new activities for the text, lab program, or ancillaries. Suggestions that result in new activities will be credited to you. Thank you in advance for taking time in your busy teaching schedule to provide this valuable information.

Sincerely,
Ellyn Daugherty
aeedaugher@aol.com
Fax (650) 369-1220

Your Name _____

School _____

School Address _____

City, State, Zip _____

E-mail Address _____

Dear Ellyn,

Here is some feedback on (check one):

___ *Biotechnology: Science for the New Millennium* textbook
___ *Biotechnology: Science for the New Millennium* laboratory manual
___ *Biotechnology: Science for the New Millennium* instructor's guide
___ *Biotechnology: Science for the New Millennium* student Encore CD
___ *Biotechnology: Science for the New Millennium* Internet Resource Center

Please note this error, or this suspected error, on page _____.
I think this should say:

You may want to check the reference I found at:

Please note this confusing or unclear language on page _____.

I think this should say:

You may want to check the reference I found at:

I am particularly fond of the activity on page _____ entitled _____.

Here are some comments that I have on this activity.

I found the activity on page _____ entitled _____ to be ineffective.

Here are some comments that I have on this activity.

Here are additional comments I have on your curricular materials.

Here is an alternative activity that I have used with my classes and think you should consider.

I think this is a worthwhile suggestion because it accomplishes the following:

Please feel free to use it in future revisions and cite the following as the source:

Signature _____ Date _____

Answers to Chapter Exercises and Activities

Textbook Section Reviews

Answers to Chapter 1 Section Review Questions

Section 1.1

1. What is biotechnology?

   Answer: Biotechnology is the study and manipulation of living things or their component parts. Biotechnology applies techniques from the disciplines of biology, chemistry, physics, and mathematics to understand processes and manufacture products.

2. Name a biotechnology product that has a medical use.

   Answer: Answers will vary. Some biotechnology products with medical uses include insulin (for treatment of diabetes), antibodies (for recognizing diseases, etc), or human growth hormone (hGH) (for treatment of short stature).

3. Where can biotechnologists work besides biotechnology companies?

   Answer: Besides biotechnology companies, biotechnologists can work in academic laboratories, such as at universities, governmental agencies (such as the National Institutes of Health (NIH), the Center for Disease Control and Prevention (CDC), fish and wildlife departments, forensics labs, police departments, and hospitals.

4. Biotechnology companies are grouped into four categories based on the products they make and sell. Name the four categories of products.

   Answer: Biotechnology companies are grouped into the following four categories based on the products they make: pharmaceuticals, agricultural products, industrial products, and instrumentation.

Section 1.2

1. Name two antibiotics used as medicines.

   Answers will vary. Penicillin and Cipro® are two antibiotics used as medicines.

2. The use of what kind of enzymes allows scientists to cut and paste pieces of DNA together to form recombinant DNA (rDNA)?

   Answer: Restriction enzymes and the enzyme DNA ligase allow scientists to cut and paste pieces of DNA together to form rDNA.

3. Explain how making human tissue plasminogen activator (t-PA) in Chinese hamster ovary (CHO) cells is an example of genetic engineering.

Answer: Human DNA carrying the genetic instructions for t-PA production is inserted into CHO cells in culture. The CHO cells will read the human DNA and make human t-PA.

Section 1.3

1. What potential products must be tested in clinical trials before they can be marketed?

Answer: Pharmaceutical products must be tested in clinical trials before they can be marketed.

2. A drug development process can take nearly 15 years. Explain why it takes so long to bring a new drug to market.

Answer: It could take nearly 10 years for R&D to work out the process for making and testing a product. After that, it could take another 5 or more years to conduct all the clinical trials/testing (Phases I, II, and III) required and file all the required documentation.

3. Which questions must be answered to the satisfaction of company officials before a product goes into R&D?

Answer: The following questions must be answered to the satisfaction of company officials before a product goes into R&D:

- Does the product meet a critical need? Who will use the product?
- Is the market large enough to produce enough sales? How many customers are there?
- Do preliminary data support that "it" will work. Will it do what the company claims?
- Can patent protection be secured? Can the company stop other companies from producing it?
- Can the company make a profit on the product? How much will it cost to make it? For how much can it be sold?

4. Does every product in R&D make it to market? Yes or no? Explain.

Answer: If a product does not show safety or effectiveness it is likely to be pulled from R&D or production. Auriculin® is an example of a product that was pulled after years of R&D. In fact, only a small percentage of products make it to market.

Section 1.4

1. Scientific methods used by scientists vary from lab to lab and situation to situation. One approach to scientific a study is to follow a five-step process in which a question is asked and answered. Outline these five steps.

Answer: One approach to scientific studies is to use the following five-step process: 1) state a testable scientific question: 2) develop a testable hypothesis; 3) plan a valid experiment; 4) conduct an experiment; and formulate a conclusion

2. Why do valid experiments contain many trials repeating the same version of an experiment?

Answer: Multiple replications of trials are conducted so that the data collected can be averaged and examined for reliability. An average of several trials better represents the data because it decreases the effect of individual readings, which may be very different from the rest of the individual trials.

3. In a conclusion, evidence for statements must be given. Describe the kind of evidence that is given in a conclusion statement.

Answer: Evidence used in concluding statements should include averaged numerical data collected during experiments with multiple replications, appropriate controls, and valid testing conditions.

4. Name two ways that scientists share their experimental results with other scientists.

Answer: Scientists share their experimental results with other scientists by presenting their results at scientific conferences or meetings, and they publish journal articles presenting their methods, materials, results, and conclusions.

Section 1.5

1. For which types of biotechnology employees is there currently a large demand? What are the educational requirements for these types of employees?

Answer: There is currently a shortage of lab technicians. Lab technicians must have a two-year college program certificate or a higher degree.

2. Scientific positions in most biotechnology companies fall into one of four categories. List them.

Answer: Scientific positions in most biotechnology companies fall into one of the following four categories: R&D, Manufacturing and Production, Clinical Research, or Quality Control.

3. Why might having laboratory experience be beneficial for a nonscientific employee at a biotechnology company?

Answer: Experience in a laboratory, short- or long-term, helps employees to work more productively with all members of the company.

Section 1.6

1. Define the term "bioethics."

Answer: Bioethics is the study of decision-making as it applies to moral decisions that have to be made because of advances in biology and technology.

2. Give an example of an event that might lead a lab employee to be faced with an ethical issue.

Answers will vary. Data collection and reporting, product manufacture or distribution, and safety concerns are just some of the areas in which concerns about appropriate and ethical practices may arise.

3. Describe how the Strategy for Values Clarification can be used to solve a problem such as the use of embryonic stem cells for basic genetic research.

Answer: An example of how the Strategy for Values Clarification can be used to solve such a problem is:

Read as much as possible about the uses of embryonic stem cells, and the advantages and disadvantages of using them for basic genetic research.

Make a list of all the possible policy positions to use or not use embryonic stem cells for basic genetic research.

Identify the pros and cons of each policy position.

Rank the policy positions from best to worst.

Decide what your position is on the use embryonic stem cells for basic genetic research, and be prepared to describe and defend it.

Answers to Chapter 2 Section Review Questions

Section 2.1

1. Give an example of a plant that has been produced by biotechnology.

Answer: Some examples of plants that have been produced by biotechnology are frost-resistant strawberries and Roundup® -resistant soybeans.

2. Knowledge of what other disciplines of science will improve the understanding of biotechnology?

Answer: Knowledge of biology, chemistry, physics, and mathematics will improve the understanding of biotechnology.

3. Describe two characteristics of living things.

Answer: The characteristics of living things include growth, reproduction, response to stimulus, use of food molecules (respiration), and production of waste products

4. Which of the following is considered to be "alive": organs, molecules, atoms, cells, or organisms?

Answer: The following are considered "alive": organs, cells, and organisms.

Section 2.2

1. Which of the following structures are found in prokaryotic cells: a nucleus, ribosomes, mitochondria, a plasma membrane, or one or more chromosomes?

Answer: Ribosomes, a plasma membrane, and a single chromosome are found in prokaryotic cells.

2. Which of the following structures are found in eukaryotic cells: a nucleus, ribosomes, mitochondria, a plasma membrane, or one or more chromosomes?

Answer: A nucleus, ribosomes, mitochondria, a plasma membrane, and one or more chromosomes are found in eukaryotic cells.

3. Describe the relationship between chromosomes, messenger RNA (mRNA), and proteins.

Answer: Chromosomes contain the DNA that codes for mRNA production. The mRNA molecule is translated into protein molecules.

4. Explain how so many cells from the same organism can look so different from each other.

Answer: All body cells from the same organism contain the same genetic information, but only certain genes in particular cell types are expressed, producing only certain proteins. The proteins of a cell allow it to function in a specific way and may give it a specific appearance.

Section 2.3

1. Which of the following are monosaccharides: cellulose, sucrose, glucose, lactose, fructose, or amylopectin?

Answer: Glucose and fructose are monosaccharides.

2. Which of the following molecules are proteins that function as hormones: estrogen, insulin, hGH, testosterone, or cholesterol?

Answer: Insulin and hGH are proteins that function as hormones.

3. What distinguishes one amino acid from another?

Answer: The R-group [of atoms], attached at the central carbon, is unique and distinguishes one amino acid from another.

4. How are the terms nucleotide, nitrogenous base, and nucleic acid related to each other?

Answer: A nucleic acid is composed of one or two chains of nucleotides. Each nucleotide has a sugar group, a phosphate group, and a nitrogenous base, either A, G, C, or T, if the nucleotide is in a DNA molecule, or A, G, C, or U, if the nucleotide is in an RNA molecule.

Section 2.4

1. What term is used to describe DNA that has been produced by cutting and pasting together pieces of DNA from two different organisms?

Answer: The term, "recombinant DNA (rDNA)" is used to describe DNA that has been produced by cutting and pasting together pieces of DNA from two different organisms.

2. What organism was the first to be genetically engineered?

Answer: *E. coli* was the first organism to be genetically engineered.

3. What was the first commercial, genetically engineered product?

Answer: rhInsulin was the first commercial product made possible through genetic engineering.

4. Explain why South San Francisco, California, calls itself "The Birthplace of Biotechnology."

Answer: South San Francisco, California, calls itself, "The Birthplace of Biotechnology" because it is the city where the first biotechnology company, Genentech, Inc., was founded. Many other companies were quickly started there once Genentech's success became well known.

Answers to Chapter 3 Section Review Questions

Section 3.1

1. What instrument would you use to measure and dispense the following volumes? Pick the instrument that is likely to give the least error for each measurement.

   23.5 μL, 6.5 mL, 125 mL, 7 μL, 2.87 mL, 555 μL

   Answer:

   23.5 μL = P-100

   6.5 mL = 10-mL pipet

   125 mL = 250-mL graduated cylinder

   7 μL = P-10

   2.87 mL = 5-mL pipet

   555 µL = P-1000

2. Convert the following units to the requested unit:

   1.7 L = _____ mL   235.1 µL = _____mL   2.37 mL = _____ µL

   Answer:

   1.7 L = <u>1700</u> mL   235.1 µL = <u>0.2351</u> mL   2.37 mL = <u>2370</u> µL

3. What numbers should be dialed into the P-10 display if a volume of 3.7 µL is to be measured?

0
3
7

4. What instrument should be used if a technician wants to fill four sets of 16 tubes all with identical volumes?

   Answer: A multichannel pipet should be used if a technician wants to fill four sets of 16 tubes all with identical volumes.

Section 3.2

1. What instrument should be used to measure and dispense the following solutes? Choose the instrument that is likely to give the least error for each measurement.

   3.5 g of salt   6.5 mg of DNA 12.5 g of gelatin

   Answer: The instruments that should be used to measure and dispense the following solutes are as follows:

   3.5 g of NaCl = electronic tabletop balance
   6.5 mg of DNA = analytical balance
   12.5 g of gelatin = electronic tabletop balance

2. What is the relation of solute to solvent as a solution becomes more concentrated?

   Answer: The amount of solute increases in relation to the amount of solvent as a solution becomes more concentrated.

3. Which of the following are concentration units?   mi/hr g/mL   mM °F/°C

   Answer: g/mL and mM are each units of concentration measurement.

4. Describe how glassware should be prepared before using it to prepare or store solutions.

   Answer: When preparing glassware for solution preparation, wash the vessel with laboratory soap and water until clean. Rinse with tap water until no evidence of soap remains. Then rinse five more times with tap water, and use deionized water for the final rinse, if available.

Section 3.3

1. Which of the following are mass/volume concentration units?

   mg/mL, g/mg, L/mg, µg/µL, or g/L?

   Answer: mg/mL, µg/µL, g/L are mass/volume concentration units.

2. What mass of the protein, gelatin, is needed to make 0.5 L of a 3 g/L gelatin solution?

   Answer: To make 0.5 L of a 3 g/L gelatin solution, set up the equation, 3 g/L × 0.5 L = 1.5 g of gelatin is needed. The gelatin is mixed with solvent (deionized water) until 0.5 L is reached.

3. What mass of sugar is needed to make 25 mL of a 25 mg/mL sugar solution?

   Answer: To make 25 mL of a 25 mg/mL sugar solution, set up the equation, 25 mg/mL × 25 mL = 625 mg of sugar are needed. Since the electronic balance measures in grams, 625 milligrams is converted to 0.625 g and that mass is weighed out. The sugar is mixed with solvent (deionized water) until 25 mL is reached.

4. What mass of salt is needed to make 150 mL of a 100 µg/mL salt solution? Describe how the solution is prepared.

Answer: To make 150 mL of a 100 µg/mL salt solution, convert the 100 µg/mL to 0.1 mg/mL so that units are similar and can be cancelled out. Set up the equation, 0.1 mg/mL × 150 mL = 15 mg of salt are needed. Since the electronic balance measures in grams, 15 milligrams is converted to 0.015 g and that mass is weighed out. The salt is mixed with solvent (deionized water) to a total volume of 150 mL.

Section 3.4

1. What is the decimal equivalent of the following percentages?

    10%   15%   25%   2%   1.5%   0.5%

    Answer:

    10% = 0.1   15% = 0.15   25% = 0.25   2% = 0.02   1.5% = 0.015   0.5% = 0.005

2. What mass of gelatin (a protein) is needed to make 0.5 L of a 3% gelatin solution?

    Answer: Convert 3% to 0.03 g/mL and 0.5 L to 500 mL. Then set up the equation, 0.03 g/mL × 500 mL = 15 g of gelatin is needed. The gelatin is added to a container and solvent (deionized water) is slowly mixed in until 0.5 L (500 mL) is reached.

3. What mass of sugar is needed to make 25 mL of a 2.5% sugar solution?

    Answer: Convert 2.5% to 0.025 g/mL. Then set up the equation, 0.025 g/mL × 25 mL = 0.625 g of sugar is needed. The sugar is mixed with solvent (deionized water) until 25 mL is reached.

4. What mass of salt is needed to make 150 mL of a 10% salt solution? Describe how the solution is prepared.

    Answer: Convert the 10% to 0.1 g/mL. Set up the equation, 0.1 g/mL × 150 mL = 15 g of salt is needed. The salt is mixed with solvent (deionized water) to a total volume of 150 mL.

Section 3.5

1. What is the molecular weight of each of the following compounds?

    NaOH $MgCl_2$ MgO   HCl

    Answer: The molecular weight of each of the following compounds is:

    NaOH = 40 amu   (Na = 23, O = 16, H = 1)

    $MgCl_2$ = 95 amu   (Mg = 24, Cl = 35.5 each × 2 atoms = 95)

    MgO = 40 amu   (Mg = 24, O = 16)

    HCl = 36.4 amu   (H = 1, Cl = 35.4)

2. What mass of NaCl is needed for 0.5 L of a 0.5M NaCl solution?

    Answer: The mass of NaCl needed for 0.5 L of a 0.5M NaCl solution is:

    0.5 L × 0.5 mol/L × 58.4 g/mol = 14.6 grams of salt are mixed with water and brought to a final volume of 500 mL.

3. What mass of MgO is needed for 200 mL of a 0.25M MgO solution?

    Answer: The mass of MgO needed for 200 mL of a 0.25M MgO solution is:

    Convert 200 mL to 0.2 L, then 0.2 L × 0.25 mol/L × 40 g/mol = 2 grams of MgO needed

4. What mass of sodium hydroxide (NaOH) is needed to make 750 mL of a 125 mM NaOH solution? Describe how to prepare the solution.

    Answer: To prepare 750 mL of a 125 mM sodium hydroxide solution, convert 750 mL to 0.75 L. Then convert 125 mM to 0.125 M. Next, set up the equation,

    0.75 L × 0.125 mol/L × 40 grams/mol = 3.75 grams of NaOH with solvent in a total up to 750 mL. Careful. It heats up.

Section 3.6 Review Questions

1. How do you prepare 40 mL of 2 mg/mL protein solution from 10 mg/mL protein solution?

    Answer: To prepare 40 mL of 2 mg/mL protein solution from 10 mg/mL protein solution:

    C_1 = 10 mg/mL

    V_1 = the volume of the 10 mg/mL to be used to make the diluted sample

$C_2 = 2$ mg/mL

$V_2 = 40$ mL

Set up the $\boxed{C_1 V_1 = C_2 V_2}$ equation and solve for V_1:

10 mg/mL $\times V_1 = 2$ mg/mL $\times 40$ mL

$$V_1 = 2 \text{ mg/mL} \times \frac{40 \text{ mL}}{10 \text{ mg/mL}}$$

$V_1 = 80/10$ mL $= \boxed{8 \text{ mL}}$

So, to dilute the 10 mg/mL to 2 mg/mL, mix 8 mL of 10 mg/mL protein with 32 mL of solvent.

2. How do you prepare 200 µL of 2X enzyme buffer from 10X enzyme buffer solution?

Answer: To prepare 200 µL of 2X enzyme buffer from 10X enzyme buffer solution:

$(10X) \times V_1 = (2X) \times 200$ µL

$$V_1 = (2X) \times \frac{200 \text{ µL}}{10X}$$

$V_1 = 400/10$ uL $= \boxed{40 \text{ µL}}$

Mix 40 uL of 10X enzyme buffer with 160 uL of solvent.

3. How do you prepare 500 µL of 50 µM NaCl solution from 5 mM NaCl solution?

Answer: To prepare 500 µL of 50 µM NaCl solution from 5 mM NaCl solution:

Convert 5 mM NaCl to 5,000 µM

$(5,000 \text{ µ}M) \times V_1 = 50 \text{ µ}M \times 500$ µL

$$V_1 = 50 \text{ µ}M \times \frac{500 \text{ µL}}{5,000 \text{ µ}M}$$

$V_1 = 25,000/5,000$ µL $= \boxed{5 \text{ µL}}$

Mix 5 µL of 5mM NaCl with 495 µL of solvent.

4. How do you prepare 3L of 1X TAE buffer from 50X TAE buffer stock solution?

Answer: To prepare 3L of 1X TAE buffer from 50X TAE buffer stock solution:

$(50X) \times V_1 = (1X) \times 3L$

$$V_1 = (1X) \times \frac{3L}{50X}$$

$V_1 = 3L/50 = 0.06L = \boxed{60 \text{ mL}}$

Mix 60 mL of 50X TAE buffer concentrate with 2,940 mL of solvent (deionized water).

Answers to Chapter 4 Section Review Questions

Section 4.1

1. Describe the relationship between genes, mRNA, and proteins.

Answer: Small sections of DNA called genes store the coded message for how amino acids should be assembled into a protein. The genes are read and transcribed into a messenger molecule, mRNA. The mRNA code is decoded (translated) at the ribosomes. During translation, the mRNA code is used to assemble the correct amino acids, in the correct order, into a protein.

2. Name the four nitrogen-containing bases found in DNA molecules, and identify how they create a base pair (bp).

Answer: The four nitrogen-containing bases found in DNA molecules are adenine, guanine, cytosine, and thymine. Adenine always pairs with thymine, and guanine always pairs with cytosine.

3. The strands on a DNA molecule are said to be "antiparallel." What does antiparallel mean?

Answer: The two strands in a DNA molecule are oriented in opposite directions (antiparallel) with the nucleotides facing in one direction on one side and the other direction on the other side. The antiparallel nature of the molecule causes it to be decoded differently on each side.

4. During cell division, DNA molecules are replicated in a semiconservative manner. What happens to the original DNA molecule during semiconservative replication?

Answer: The DNA molecule unzips, and each original strand becomes the template for a new strand. On completion, the two new molecules have a strand from the original DNA molecule and a newly synthesized piece. Since half of the molecule was conserved from the original in the replication, this is called "semiconservative replication."

Section 4.2

1. Plasmids are very important pieces of DNA. How do they differ from chromosomal DNA molecules?

Answer: Plasmids are different than chromosomal DNA in that they are relatively small pieces of DNA, only few thousand base pairs in size and coding only for a few genes. Usually plasmids contain genes that are nonessential for the cell's survival under normal circumstances. Plasmids can be used as vectors to shuttle genes into cells.

2. Bacteria cell DNA is divided into operons. Describe an operon using the terms promoter, operator, and structural gene.

Answer: An operon is one or more structural genes (sections that code for a protein) and the controlling elements that regulate the gene's expression. On the DNA strand adjacent to the structural gene is the promoter, which is where the RNA polymerase enzyme binds before reading the structural gene to make mRNA. If a repressor attaches at the operator, the gene is blocked and essentially "turned off."

3. Describe the human genome by discussing the number and types of chromosomes, genes, and nucleotides.

Answer: 46 chromosomes in 23 pairs of varied length, and over 30,000 genes containing over 3 billion bp.

4. What is gene therapy? Cite an example of how it can be used.

Answers will vary. Gene therapy includes techniques that correct faulty genes. Cystic fibrosis is one genetic disorder that is a target of gene therapy R&D.

Section 4.3

1. Genetic engineering by any method requires certain steps. Put the following steps in the correct order:
   - Isolate the instructions (DNA sequence/gene).
   - Harvest the molecule or product and market it.
   - Manipulate the DNA instructions.
   - Identify the molecule to be produced.

   Answer: Genetic engineering, by any method, requires the following steps:
   - Identify the molecule to be produced.
   - Isolate the instructions (DNA sequence/gene).
   - Manipulate the DNA instructions.
   - Harvest the molecule or product, and market it.

2. What "naming" designation is used with recombinant products made through genetic engineering?

Answer: The naming designation used with recombinant products made through genetic engineering is to place an "r" for recombinant in front of the name of the product, as in rAmylase for recombinant amylase.

3. What is the smallest change in a DNA molecule that can occur after site-specific mutagenesis? What effect can this change have?

Answer: The smallest change in a DNA molecule that can occur after site-specific mutagenesis is the change or elimination of a single nucleotide (an A, T, G, or C). Depending on the location of the nucleotide in a codon, an amino-acid change could occur, and possibly change the shape and function of the protein for which the sequence codes.

4. What gene has been the target of gene therapy for cystic fibrosis (CF)? What does this gene normally do?

Answer: One target for CF gene therapy is the cystic fibrosis transmembrane conductance regulator (CFTR) gene, which is defective in CF patients. It regulates the flow of chloride ions into the epithelial cells lining the respiratory and digestive systems. When defective, mucus builds up in patients as cells die.

Section 4.4

1. Agarose gels can be used to study what size of DNA fragments?

   Answer: Agarose gels can clearly resolve only DNA fragments between 500 and 25,000 bp length.

2. If agarose gel material is labeled 1%, what does the 1% refer to?

   Answer: 1% refers to the agarose concentration in the buffered gel matrix. So, a 1% gel would have 1 g of agarose mixed with gel electrophoresis to buffer up to a total volume of 100 mL.

3. What causes molecules to be separated on an agarose gel?

   Answer: If molecules have a net charge on them, then they will move in a gel toward either the positive electrode or the negative electrode when the gel box is conducting electricity.

4. Name two common DNA stains that are used to visualize DNA on agarose gels.

   Answer: The most commonly used DNA stain is EtBr solution. Another DNA stain is methylene blue solution.

Answers to Chapter 5 Section Review Questions

Section 5.1

1. How many different types of amino acids are found in proteins? What distinguishes one amino acid from another?

   Answer: There are 20 different amino acids in proteins. The R-group, attached at the central carbon of the amino acid, distinguishes one amino acid from another. R-groups can be polar, have no charge, a positive charge, or a negative charge.

2. What causes polypeptide chains to fold into functional proteins?

   Answer: Interactions between amino acids whose atoms share electrons through hydrogen bonds cause a polypeptide to form alpha helical coils and beta-pleated sheets. Additional folding is due to tertiary interactions between charged or uncharged R-groups, as well as hydrophobic and hydrophilic behavior. Disulfide bonds between cysteine molecules stabilize the final structure.

3. How many polypeptide chains are found in an antibody, and how are they held together in a protein?

   Answer: An antibody is composed of four polypeptide chains: two long and two short. The chains are held together mainly by disulfide bonds between cysteine molecules and noncovalent bonds (ie, hydrogen bonds or polar bonds) on opposite chains.

4. What is the value of monoclonal antibody technology?

   Answer: Monoclonal antibody technology produces large amounts of identical antibodies in cells that are "immortal"; they grow and divide to make more and more cells that make many identical antibodies. The monoclonal antibodies are instrumental in genetic testing and research.

Section 5.2

1. Distinguish between transcription and translation.

   Answer: During transcription, an mRNA molecule is made using the information from a DNA section. During translation, a peptide sequence is made using the information from an mRNA molecule.

2. If a structural gene's code is "TAC GGC ATG CCC TTA CGC ATC," what will the mRNA transcript be?

   Answer: If a structural gene's code is "TAC GGC ATG CCC TTA CGC ATC," the mRNA transcript will be "AUG CCG UAC GGG AAU GCG UAG."

3. If the mRNA transcript from question No. 2 were translated into a peptide, what would the amino-acid sequence of the peptide be?

   Answer: If the mRNA transcript from question #2 were translated into a peptide, the amino-acid sequence of the peptide would be as follows:

   methionine – proline – tyrosine – glycine – asparagines – alanine – !stop! (no AA added).

4. What is the name of the machine that can make small sections of amino-acid chains?

   Answer: The machine that can make small sections of amino-acid chains is called a protein synthesizer or peptide synthesizer.

Section 5.3

1. Name three examples of enzymes and their substrates.

    Answers will vary. Some possibilities are amylase-amylose (starch), cellulase-cellulose, lactase-lactose, sucrase-sucrose, protease-proteins or polypeptides, peptidyl transferase-amino acids, DNA polymerase-nucleotides, DNase-DNA, and lipase-lipids,

2. What happens if an enzyme is significantly above or below its optimum temperature?

    Answer: If it is high enough, the enzyme will denature (unravel) and not function.

3. What happens if an enzyme is at a pH significantly above or below its optimum level?

    Answer: If it is too high or too low, the enzyme could denature (unravel) and not function. Also, the protein's net charge may change, resulting in a big impact on how it behaves.

4. What would an enzyme be called if it moved methyl groups ($-CH_3$) between molecules?

    Answer: An enzyme that moves methyl groups ($-CH_3$) between molecules would be called methyl transferase.

Section 5.4

1. What does "PAGE" stand for, and what kind of samples are studied using PAGE?

    Answer: PAGE stands for polyacrylamide gel electrophoresis. Proteins (and small DNA molecules) are studied using PAGE.

2. What separates molecules on a PAGE gel?

    Answer: Negatively charged samples are loaded into wells on the top of the gel. They move to the bottom (positive end) when the power is turned on.

3. PAGE gels are usually run at what amount of current?

    Answer: PAGE gels are usually run at about 35 milliamps (mA) of current.

4. A technician has a stock protein solution with a concentration of 1 mg/mL. He or she prepares a 1:4 serial dilution of the stock and runs the samples on a PAGE gel. What is the preferred method of staining and why?

    Answer: If five tubes representing a 1:4 serial dilution of a protein estimated at stock concentration of 1 mg/mL are run on a PAGE gel, the preferred method of staining would be silver stain. The serial dilution would bring many of the samples to microgram amounts in the gel. Therefore, the gel would require the most sensitive method of staining (silver stain).

Section 5.5

1. What causes the difference between normal and sickled cells in sickle cell disease?

    Answer: One nucleotide mutation results in one erroneous amino-acid placement, which causes an incorrect hemoglobin structure, which causes the red blood cells to sickle.

2. Give an example of proteins studied to understand evolutionary relationships.

    Answers will vary, but one example of a protein studied to understand evolutionary relationships between species is hemoglobin.

3. What is NCBI? How can you access it? What important information is found there?

    Answer: NCBI stands for The National Clearinghouse for Biotechnology Information. It is accessible at: http://www.ncbi.nlm.nih.gov. Sequences of proteins and nucleic acids are posted there, as well as other biotechnology information and protocols.

4. Do all protein scientists work at biotechnology companies? Explain.

    Answer: No. Many protein scientists work at universities, government agencies, and private foundations.

Answers to Chapter 6 Section Review Questions

Section 6.1

1. Why are antibiotics important biotechnology products?

    Answer: Antibiotics are important biotechnology products because they have improved the lifespan and the quality of life of patients by treating some life-threatening diseases.

2. What is the function of the enzyme, amylase?

Answer: Amylase speeds the breakdown of starch to sugar (maltose).

3. Why might a company be interested in producing amylase as a product?

Answer: A company might be interested in producing amylase as a product because starch breakdown and sugar production are important to many industries. Amylase is a potential product to sell to these industries.

4. Summarize the criteria that a potential product must meet in a CPDP review.

Answer: Answers will vary. The criteria that a potential product must meet in a CPDP review include a critical need for a large enough market. It must "work" or be effective. The company must be able to secure a patent for the product and be able to make enough profit on it. The safety of some products must also be demonstrated.

Section 6.2

1. What kind of assay would use Bradford reagent in the test?

Answer: Bradford reagent may be used in a protein concentration assay to indicate the concentration of protein in solution.

2. For what purpose would a technician use an enzyme-linked immunosorbent assay (ELISA)?

Answer: A technician would use an ELISA to recognize the presence and concentration of a specific molecule within a mixture. It is can distinguish between very similar protein molecules.

3. What does a stability assay measure?

Answer: A stability assay measures the shelf life of a compound, in other words, how long it remains active and effective.

4. In a large company, which department would have several employees developing and conducting assays?

Answer: Assay Services and/or Quality Control would have several employees developing and conducting assays.

Section 6.3

1. From where do scientists expect that most of the remaining naturally occurring biotechnology products will come?

Answer: Scientists expect that most of the remaining naturally occurring biotechnology products will come from the equatorial rainforests.

2. How can a technician know if a certain type of bacteria is sensitive to an antimicrobial substance?

Answer: A technician can test a type of bacteria's sensitivity to an antimicrobial substance by growing bacteria in the presence of antibiotic disks. The bacteria that are sensitive will have halos or no growth around the disk.

3. A few herbal products that claim to have therapeutic value against depression include pantothenic acid, magnesium, St. John's Wort, vitamin-B complex, and ginkgo.

Answer: List a few herbal products that claim to have therapeutic value against depression.

4. How can molecules be extracted from plant samples for testing purposes?

Answer: A common method of extracting chemicals from plant samples involves grinding the sample with a solvent, such as distilled water, alcohol, or acetone.

Section 6.4

1. Distinguish between phenotype and genotype using examples.

Answer: The genotype of an organism is the actual genes it contains for a trait. For example, a pea plant might have two genes for dented seeds that it inherited from the parent plants. The plant's phenotype, on the other hand, is the observed expression of those genes, in this case, dented seed coats.

2. What does GMO stand for? Explain how Monsanto Canada, Inc.'s Roundup Ready® soybeans are an example of a GMO.

Answer: **GMO** stands for "genetically modified organism." Monsanto's Roundup Ready® soybeans have a gene inserted into them that produces a protein that breaks down Roundup Ready® herbicide to make it nontoxic to that plant.

3. What is the most challenging part of trying to isolate plant DNA or plant proteins from cells?

Answer: The most challenging part of trying to isolate plant DNA or plant proteins from cells is removing the cell wall so that the cells can be burst open. This can be accomplished through mechanical means or enzymatic digestion.

4. Of what value are plant cell protoplasts?

Answer: Plant cell protoplasts are cells within the cell wall that are removed, making it easier to inject them with foreign DNA. They are also easily burst open to access the cell's DNA or proteins.

Section 6.5

1. What are CHO cells and what are they used for?

Answer: CHO stands for "Chinese hamster (*Cricetulus griseus*) ovary" cells, and they are used for mammalian genetic engineering and protein production.

2. How long does it take to develop, test, and market a typical rDNA protein product?

Answer: It takes approximately 15 years to develop, test, and market a typical rDNA protein product.

3. What does GMP stands for, and what does it cover?

Answer: GMP stands for Good Manufacturing Practices, and it includes all the guidelines to ensure the safety and purity of biotechnology products. GMP is practiced during manufacturing, purification, and formulation.

4. Biotechnology products must be formulated before they can be marketed. Name two formulations of a pharmaceutical product other than tablet form.

Answer: Two other formulations for a pharmaceutical product beside tablet form could be any two of the following: an injectable liquid, an aerosol inhaler, a patch, or a cream.

Answers to Chapter 7 Section Review Questions

Section 7.1

1. What is measured in a spectrophotometer?

Answer: A spectrophotometer measures the amount of light transmitted through a sample. It reports the percent transmittance, or the amount of light absorbed by the molecules in the sample, calculated using $A = 2 - log_{10} \%T$.

2. What is the difference between a UV spectrophotometer and a VIS spectrophotometer?

Answer: A UV spectrophotometer produces UV light that interacts with and detects colorless molecules. A visible spectrophotometer produces light from the visible spectrum that interacts with and detects molecules that exhibit color.

3. What happens to the absorbance of a sample as the concentration of a sample increases or decreases?

Answer: Molecules do the absorbing in a sample, so if the number of molecules increase, the absorbance of the sample increases. If the number of molecules in a sample decreases, the absorbance of the sample decreases.

4. What color of light has a wavelength of 530 nm? If a molecule absorbs light at 530 nm, what color could it be? What color do we know that it is not?

Answer: Green light has a wavelength of 530 nm. If a molecule absorbs at 530 nm, it could be any color, except green.

Section 7.2

1. If a sample has a pH of 7.8, is it considered an acid, a base, or neutral?

Answer: If a sample has a pH of 7.8, it is considered a base, a weak base, but a base, nevertheless.

2. What does pH paper measure?

Answer: pH paper measures the H+ concentration of a solution.

3. Before a pH meter can be used, it needs to be calibrated. To measure the pH of most solutions, the pH meter is calibrated to what pH?

Answer: To measure the pH of most solutions, the pH meter is calibrated to pH 7.0.

4. If the pH of a hot tub is too high, say pH 8.0, what should be added to bring it to a neutral pH?

Answer: To bring the pH of a solution from pH 8.0 to 7.0, add an acid.

Section 7.3

1. Why must DNA and proteins be stored in a buffered solution?

   Answer: A buffered solution resists changes in pH. Protein and DNA molecules must be buffered to maintain their structure and function

2. In what kind of buffer should a DNA sample that was isolated from human cheek cells be stored?

   Answer: A DNA sample isolated from human cheek cells should be stored in a TRIS buffer.

3. The formula weight of TRIS is 121.14 g/mol. How is 100 mL of 0.02 M of TRIS at pH 8.0 prepared?

   Answer:

   To prepare 100 mL of 0.02 M of TRIS at pH 8.0:

   Measure 0.24 g of TRIS

   0.1 L × 0.02 mol/L × 121.14 g/mol = 0.24 g of TRIS

   Mix it with solvent (dH_2O) to about 70 mL.

   Adjust the pH to 8.0 (with 1 M of HCl)

   Fill to a final volume of 100 mL with dH_2O.

Section 7.4

1. What is lambda$_{max}$, and why is it important?

   Answer: For a particular sample, the wavelength that gives the highest absorbance value is the lambda$_{max}$. It is the wavelength that is "most sensitive" to the protein, so it should be used to detect it.

2. What is the lambda$_{max}$ for colorless proteins?

   Answer: The lambda$_{max}$ for a colorless protein is 280 nm.

3. How is Bradford reagent used to detect the presence of a specific protein in solution?

   Answer: Bradford reagent cannot be used to detect the presence of a specific protein in solution. If a solution has many different proteins in it, a Bradford protein reagent will not distinguish between them. An ELISA might be used to detect and measure the protein in a mixture. Or, an indicator specific to just one protein might be used.

4. Which graph is used to determine the concentration of unknown protein samples?

   Answer: A standard curve of absorbance versus the concentration of known proteins can be used to determine the concentration of unknown samples.

Answers to Chapter 8 Section Review Questions

Section 8.1

1. What is the name of the genetically engineered rennin molecule? Why is it desirable to produce genetically engineered rennin instead of harvesting rennin from nature?

   Answer: The name of the genetically engineered rennin molecule is chymosin. It is desirable to produce chymosin because rennin is expensive to harvest from calves.

2. What is the name of the process that occurs when complementary pieces of DNA or RNA locate and bind to each other? How is that technology used in the laboratory?

   Answer: It is called hybridization when complementary pieces of DNA or RNA find each other and bind. Hybridization is used in probe technology, such as when a small piece of DNA or RNA is used to find a complementary sequence.

3. What is a Southern blot, and how is it used?

   Answer: A Southern blot transfers DNA from a gel to a membrane. The membrane can be probed and/or stained.

4. What does a thermal cycler do?

   Answer: A thermal cycler is used to run a PCR in which a tiny piece of DNA is copied repeatedly to make millions of copies for use in research diagnostics.

Section 8.2

1. What is the name of the process in which bacteria receive and express recombinant plasmid DNA and recombinant viral DNA? What is the name of the process in which mammalian cells receive and express rDNA?

   Answer: Transformation occurs when bacteria receive and express recombinant plasmid DNA. Transduction occurs when bacteria receive and express recombinant viral DNA. Transfection occurs when mammalian cells receive and express rDNA.

2. Which two types of enzymes are needed to produce an rDNA molecule?

   Answer: Some kind of restriction enzyme and DNA ligase are needed to produce an rDNA molecule.

3. What name is used for the differences in gel banding patterns in DNA samples that result from a restriction enzyme's activity?

   Answer: Restriction fragment length polymorphisms (RFLPs) are the differences in gel banding patterns in DNA samples as a result of a restriction enzyme's activity.

4. Which two techniques are used to increase transformation efficiency?

   Answer: To induce competency and increase transformation efficiency, the two techniques used are 1) a calcium chloride or magnesium chloride treatment; and 2) heat and cold shocks.

Section 8.3

1. What is a spinner flask and where is it used?

   Answer: Spinner flasks are sterile glass fermentation bottles that have a spinning blade (for aeration) in the base. They are used to grow 1- or 2-L cell cultures early in scale-up.

2. What type of environmental conditions must be monitored in cultures as they are scaled-up?

   Answer: Temperature, pH, nutrient concentration, oxygen content, and protein concentration and activity of the culture must be monitored during scale-up.

3. How are ELISAs utilized during manufacturing?

   Answer: ELISAs are used during manufacturing to confirm that the concentration of protein product is high enough.

4. How is a QC department involved in the manufacturing process?

   Answers will vary. The Quality Control department tests products for all the characteristics important to a regulatory agency, such as the FDA. These can include effectiveness, purity, concentration, stability, potency, safety, and more.

Section 8.4

1. Distinguish between the processes of alcoholic and lactic-acid fermentation. Give an example of a product made by each process.

   Answer: Alcoholic fermentation breaks down sugar for energy, and produces ethanol and carbon dioxide. Wine and beer are two products made by alcoholic fermentation. Lactic-acid fermentation breaks down sugar for energy and produces lactic acid. Yogurt and sauerkraut are examples of products made by lactic-acid fermentation.

2. Manufacturing teams want to keep cell cultures in exponential growth. What is exponential growth?

   Answer: Exponential growth occurs when the number of cells doubles with each generation. So, if there are 1 million *E. coli* cells in culture and they divide every 20 minutes, there would be 2 million cells in 20 minutes and 4 million cells in 40 minutes, and so on.

3. Place these events in order, from early to late in the product pipeline.

   transformation
   fermentation
   assay development
   scale-up
   manufacturing
   R&D
   QC

Answer: The order of events from early to late in the product pipeline is as follows:

R&D

assay development

transformation

scale-up

fermentation

manufacturing

QC

4. Which federal agency is responsible for setting cGMP guidelines?

Answer: The FDA is the agency responsible for setting guidelines for GMP.

Section 8.5

1. What is the name of the procedure in which plasmids are extracted from cells?

Answer: When plasmids are extracted from cells it is called a plasmid preparation (mini-, midi-, or maxi-prep).

2. How is plasmid DNA precipitated in the final steps of a plasmid prep?

Answer: Plasmid DNA is precipitated in the final steps of a plasmid prep using alcohol.

3. Once plasmid is extracted from a cell, how can a technician know that it is the "correct" plasmid?

Answer: A restriction digestion pattern can confirm the presence of a particular plasmid.

4. If a DNA sample gives a 260-nm reading of 0.8 au and a 280-nm reading of 0.5 au, what are its concentration and purity? Is this purity acceptable?

Answer: If a DNA sample gives a 260-nm reading of 0.8 au and a 280-nm reading of 0.5 au, its concentration would be 50 μg/mL × 0.8 = 40 μg/mL and its purity would be 0.8/0.5 = 1.6. This indicates a small amount of protein contamination. For most purposes, a purity value of 1.6 may not be acceptable.

Answers to Chapter 9 Section Review Questions

Section 9.1

1. When harvesting broth cultures, how are cells separated from the broth?

Answer: When harvesting broth cultures, cells are separated from the broth by filtering or centrifugation.

2. In a column chromatography, what accomplishes the separation of molecules in a mixture?

Answer: In a column chromatography, interaction of the molecule of interest with the resin beads is what separates molecules in a mixture.

3. What are the samples called that are collected from a column?

Answer: The samples collected off a column are called fractions.

4. What happens during a dialysis? Why is a dialysis an important technique in protein purification?

Answer: During a dialysis, molecules that are small enough pass through the pores of the dialysis bag from a high concentration to a low concentration. It is a method by which a protein solution's buffer can be changed.

Section 9.2

1. What is the solid phase for each of the following types of chromatography?

paper

thin-layer

gel-filtration (size exclusion)

ion-exchange

affinity

Answer: The solid phase for each of the following types of chromatography is as follows:

paper chromatography: filter paper

thin-layer chromatography: silica gel

gel-filtration chromatography: sizing resin beads

ion-exchange chromatography: charged resin beads

affinity chromatography: antibody resin (or some other shape- or function-recognizing resin)

2. If a molecule is the smallest in a mixture, will it be the first or last molecule to come off a size-exclusion column?

   Answer: The smaller the molecule, the faster it elutes off a size-exclusion column. The smallest molecule in the mixture should be in one of the earliest fractions.

3. Diethylaminoethyl (DEAE) sepharose is a type of ion-exchange resin. At a pH of 7.5, it has a positive charge. What would be expected if a sample containing one positively charged protein and one negatively charged protein were put on a DEAE column? Where should the proteins end up?

   Answer: In a DEAE sepharose column, at a pH of 7.5, the positively charged protein should be repelled by the positively charged DEAE and run through the column. The negatively charged protein should bind to the positively charged resin and held until it is eluted.

4. What is the value of a fraction collector?

   Answer: A fraction collector automates the fraction collection process. A column produces so many fractions that it would take too long to collect them all by hand.

Section 9.3

1. A technician wants to quickly determine whether an antibody affinity resin will bind [to?] a particular protein for purification. Which type of chromatography should he or she use to test the resin?

   Answer: If a technician wants to quickly determine whether an antibody affinity resin will bind [to?] a particular protein for purification, he or she should use open-column chromatography to test the resin.

2. Which instrument, FPLC or HPLC, is used for large-scale protein separations/purifications?

   Answer: FPLC is used for large-scale protein separations/purifications.

3. Why are spectrophotometers hooked up to most FPLC or HPLC units?

   Answer: Spectrophotometers can measure the absorbance (concentration) of proteins as they come off the column and are delivered to fraction tubes.

4. You are asked to dialyze 10 mL of a protein extract in a PAGE running buffer into a sodium monophosphate buffer before running an FPLC ion-exchange column. Into what volume of sodium monophosphate buffer should you place the dialysis bag?

   Answer: If 10 mL of a protein extract in a PAGE running buffer is to be dialyzed into a sodium monophosphate buffer before running an FPLC, the dialysis bag should be placed in at least 100 mL of sodium monophosphate buffer for several hours, followed by three treatments of fresh buffer.

Section 9.4

1. What type of biotechnology product undergoes clinical testing/clinical trials?

   Answer: Pharmaceutical products must go through clinical testing and clinical trials.

2. How many people (subjects) are usually involved in Phases I, II, and III of a clinical trial?

   Answer: The numbers of people usually involved in Phases I, II, and III clinical trials are as follows:

   Phase I: tens of people
   Phase II: hundreds of people
   Phase III: thousands of people

3. In which phase of a clinical trial, is product safety tested?

   Answer: Safety is tested in all three phases of clinical trials.

Section 9.5

1. What are some of the reasons that a product in development may not make it to the marketplace?

   Answers will vary, but some of the reasons that a product in development may not make it to the market place include the following: it may be ineffective, it may have harmful side effects, its production is not economical, it cannot be FDA approved, or it cannot be patent-protected.

2. What is covered in an "employee's proprietary-rights contract?"

   Answer: In an employee's proprietary rights contract are the rules for employees to keep the company's R&D secret.

3. Why must a company gain patent protection on a product?

Answer: A company must gain patent rights to protect against other groups using or selling a similar product or technology.

Answers to Chapter 10 Section Review Questions

Section 10.1

1. How many parent plants are necessary for an offspring to be produced by sexual reproduction? How many parents are necessary for an offspring to be produced by asexual reproduction?

Answer: Two parents are necessary for an offspring to be produced by sexual reproduction. One parent is necessary for an offspring to be produced by asexual reproduction.

2. Which two cells fuse to make a zygote? From where do the chromosomes of a zygote come?

Answer: Sperm and egg cells fuse to make a zygote. The chromosomes come to the zygote from the parent plants, carried by the sperm and egg cells.

3. How does a plant cutting become a functioning, independent organism?

Answer: A cutting grows the missing parts to become an independent organism. For example, a stem cutting grows roots and leaves.

4. What is the smallest number of cells required to clone a plant through tissue culture?

Answer: Theoretically, the smallest number of cells required to clone a plant through tissue culture is a single cell. However, in practice, usually a few hundred cells are used.

Section 10.2

1. List some foods that are examples of the following plant organs: stems, roots, leaves, flowers, fruits (ovaries), and seeds (fertilized ovules).

Answers will vary, but some foods that are examples of plant organs include the following:

    stems: celery, asparagus, and potatoes
    roots: carrots and radishes
    leaves: spinach, cabbage, and lettuce
    flowers: broccoli and cauliflower
    fruits (ovaries): apples, zucchini, bananas, and watermelon
    seeds (fertilized ovules): peas, beans, and nuts

2. Which plant tissue type is the source of cells for tissue culture?

Answer: Meristematic tissue is the source of cells for tissue culture.

3. Give an example of a plant that has been modified through genetic engineering.

Answers will vary, but examples of plants that have been modified by genetic engineering are the FlavRSavR® tomato or Roundup Ready® soybeans.

Section 10.3

1. Name the parts of the plants that contain actively dividing cells.

Answer: Root tips, shoot tips, branch tips, flower buds, leaf buds, and the vascular cambium all contain meristematic (actively dividing) cells.

2. After a mitotic division, how many chromosomes do daughter cells have compared with the parent cell?

Answer: After a mitotic division, daughter cells have the same number of chromosomes as the parent cell?

3. When a seed germinates, what is the first plant part to emerge from the sprouting seed?

Answer: The first plant part to emerge from the sprouting seed is the radicle, also called an embryonic root.

4. There is vast diversity among plant cells and plant tissues. What are the chemicals called that trigger much of the cell and tissue specialization in plants?

Answer: Plant hormones are the chemicals that trigger much of the cell and tissue specialization in plants.

Section 10.4

1. Which of the following are diploid (2N), and which are haploid?

    egg, zygote, embryo, parent plant, sperm, and seed

   Answer: egg = haploid (1N), zygote = diploid (2N), embryo = diploid (2N), parent plant = diploid (2N), sperm = haploid (1N), seed (embryo = 2N and the endosperm filling the rest of the seed is actually 3N).

2. A plant has purple flowers and hairy stems. Is this description its genotype or phenotype? Propose some allelic symbols for purple flowers and hairy stems.

   Answer: The description "purple flowers and hairy stems" are phenotypes. Answers may vary, but P and H are logical alleles to use for these traits.

3. Consider a cross between two *Brassica rapa* parent plants known to be heterozygous tall. Using the same allelic symbols as those in the text, show the entire cross (problem), including the chances for this breeding to result in short plants.

   Answer: For a cross between two *Brassica rapa* parent plants known to be heterozygous tall:

   Parents' genotypes: Tt   ×   Tt
   Alleles possible in gametes: T or t   T or t

   Punnett Square of the Cross

Genotypes of Male/Female Gametes	T	t
T	T T	T t
t	Tt	t t

   Expected genotypic results of crossing these gametes:
       1/4 of offspring = TT
       1/2 of offspring = Tt
       1/4 of offspring = tt
   Expected phenotype(s) of the offspring:
       3/4 of offspring = tall (since TT and Tt genotypes result in tall phenotypes)
       1/4 of offspring = short (since the tt genotype results in a short phenotype)

Section 10.5

1. A set of plant DNA extractions is measured on the UV Spec. There are 13 samples, and the average concentration is 18.7 µg/mL. One sample has a value of 17.2 µg/mL. Using the 10% rule, is the sample's value valid and acceptable?

   Answer: 10% of 18.7 is 1.87, thus, values between 18.7 + 1.87 and 18.7-1.87 would be considered acceptable, that is, values between 16.83 and 20.57. A sample concentration of 17.2 µg/mL is considered acceptable.

2. An experiment is conducted to determine the number of kindergarten children with attention deficit disorder (ADD) in the United States. The result shows that 80 of 1000 students, on average, with a standard deviation (SD) of 5, exhibit symptoms of ADD. A town near a nuclear power plant has an average of 84 students per 1000 with ADD. Should the citizens be concerned? Why or why not?

   Answer: No, 84 of 1000 falls within 1 SD of the expected average. There appears to be no difference between the numbers.

3. A family had 22 children: 14 boys and 8 girls. Calculate the chi-square value for such a cross, and determine whether the results are due to a random mating, or an environmental or genetic disorder.

   Answer: $(11-14)^2 /11 + (11-8)^2 /11 = 9/11 + 9/11 = 0.82 + 0.82 = 1.64 = X^2$ with 1 df

   The χ^2 value is at 0.20, which is higher than 0.05. Therefore, the number of boys and girls appears to have occurred by chance and is within expectations.

Answers to Chapter 11 Section Review Questions

Section 11.1

1. Which of the following are examples of asexual plant propagation: plant tissue culture, selective breeding, stem cuttings, leaf cuttings, or runners?

   Answer: Plant tissue culture, stem cuttings, leaf cuttings, and runners are examples of asexual plant propagation.

2. How is length or width added to a plant?

   Answer: Cell division in meristematic regions adds more cells to length and width.

3. Leaf or stem cuttings must include at least some of what kind of tissue to form new roots?

   Answer: To form new roots, leaf or stem cuttings must include some of kind of meristematic tissue.

Section 11.2

1. What is another name for plant hormones?

   Answer: Another name for plant hormones is plant growth regulators.

2. Auxin is responsible for what kind of plant growth regulation? Cytokinin is responsible for what kind of plant growth regulation?

   Answer: Auxin is responsible for cell elongation. Cytokinin is responsible for cell division.

3. How can a plant tissue culturist know that an explant is beginning to respond to the hormones in the plant tissue culture media?

   Answer: A plant tissue culturist knows that a plant-tissueculture explant is starting to respond to the hormones in the plant tissue culture media if the explant starts to swell and callus begins to form.

Section 11.3

1. What is it called when very closely related animals are bred? Why is it discouraged?

   Answer: Inbreeding occurs when very closely related animals are bred. It is discouraged because "bad" recessive disorders show up in offspring more often because it is more likely that relatives will share similar genes (the smaller the gene pool, the less variation).

2. Name two advantages of growing plants hydroponically.

   Answer: Advantages of growing plants hydroponically include the use of less space, easier regulation, and the ability to grow plants almost anywhere.

3. How are plant-based pharmaceuticals related to genetically engineered organisms?

   Answer: Plant-based pharmaceuticals are genetically engineered plants, that is, engineered to produce human pharmaceuticals. Plant-based pharmaceuticals have altered genetic codes to produce human proteins for harvest from the transformed plants.

Section 11.4

1. Which is larger, genomic DNA (gDNA) or plasmid DNA (pDNA), and by how much?

   Answer: Genomic DNA is much larger than plasmid DNA with base pairs in the billions. Plasmid DNA may have up to several thousand base pairs in the strand.

2. Plant DNA is difficult to extract from plant cells. List a few "tricks" that biotechnologists use to isolate plant DNA.

   Answer: Answers will vary, but a few "tricks" that biotechnologists use to isolate plant DNA include freezing plant tissue with liquid nitrogen, using a chloroform/isoamyl alcohol mixture, or using commercially developed plant DNA isolation kits.

3. Why is the bacterium, *Agrobacterium tumefaciens*, of interest to biotechnologists?

   Answer: *Agrobacterium* is a naturally occurring bacterium that will transfer plasmids into plant cells.

4. Why is Ti plasmid of interest to biotechnologists?

   Answer: Ti plasmid is the naturally occurring plasmid in *Agrobacterium* that is transferred during plant genetic engineering. Scientists can cut and paste genes of interest into the Ti plasmid and use the recombinant Ti plasmid to carry genes of interest into cells.

Section 11.5

1. What are the names of the naturally occurring bacterium and the plasmid that can infect plants and transfer DNA molecules?

   Answer: The bacterium that can infect plants and transfer DNA molecules is called *Agrobacterium,* and the plasmid is the Ti plasmid.

2. Name at least two selection genes that are used to confirm that Ti plasmid transformation has occurred.

   Answer: Answers may vary, but selection genes that may be used to confirm that Ti plasmid transformation has occurred could include any of the following: neomycin phosphotransferase (NPT II), GUS, or GFP.

3. How does GUS act as a selection gene?

   Answer: The GUS gene produces β-glucuronidase, which breaks down X-Gluc from a colorless to a blue product. A blue precipitate forms in colonies that are transformed with the GUS gene and that are responsible for the glucuronidase reaction.

4. Why are so many plant genetic-engineering experiments conducted with *Arabidopsis,* even though it has little, if any, economic value?

   Answer: Many plant genetic-engineering experiments are conducted with *Arabidopsis* because it is hoped that once mechanisms of genetic engineering are understood in *Arabidopsis,* the technology can be transferred to other plants of economic or ecological importance.

Answers to Chapter 12 Section Review Questions

Section 12.1

1. What kinds of organisms cause disease?

   Answer: Bacteria, fungi, protozoa, and viruses cause disease.

2. Where are drugs discovered?

   Answer: Drugs are discovered and isolated from natural sources, or created in the lab through chemical combination or genetic engineering.

3. How is aspirin an example of combinatorial chemistry?

   Answer: Aspirin is acetylsalicylic acid. It is synthesized when an acetyl group is added to salicylic acid.

Section 12.2

1. What is the value of combinatorial chemistry?

   Answer: The value of combinatorial chemistry is that it allows for the production of new versions of compounds that might have medicinal value.

2. How are chemical compound libraries related to high-throughput screening?

   Answer: Compound libraries are hundreds, thousands, or millions of versions of compounds that must be tested. When they are tested in large batches, it is high-throughput screening.

3. What is the value of microarray technology?

   Answer: Microarray technology allows thousands, even millions. of DNA samples to be screened at one time.

Section 12.3

1. What are three uses for peptides in medicinal biotechnology?

   Answer: In research and therapeutics (medicinal biotechnology), peptides are used to purify other molecules to be used as possible vaccine molecules or regulatory molecules.

2. How does a peptide synthesizer make peptides?

   Answer: A peptide synthesizer makes peptides in the following way: A column in the synthesizer binds the first amino acid. Another amino acid is added. A reaction binds the two amino acids. The column is washed. Another amino acid is added. A reaction binds it to the second amino acid. The column is washed. The process is repeated over and over until the peptide is the desired length, with the desired amino acids in the desired order.

3. How does a DNA synthesizer make oligonucleotides?

Answer: A DNA synthesizer makes oligonucleotides in the following way: A column in the synthesizer binds a nucleotide. Another nucleotide is added. A reaction binds the two nucleotides. The column is washed. Another nucleotide is added. A reaction binds it to the second nucleotide. The column is washed. The process is repeated over and over until the oligonucleotide is the desired length, with the desired nucleotides in the desired order

4. Of what value are oligonucleotides?

Answer: Oligonucleotides are used as primers or probes that recognize other pieces of DNA. They are critical for research to identify genes involved in diseases or disease prevention.

Section 12.4

1. How are antibodies used in flow cytometry?

Answer: Antibodies are used in flow cytometry as follows: Fluorescently-tagged antibodies attach to antigens on cells of interest. They flow through the cytometer, which counts the tagged cells and separates them into groups.

2. How does a vaccine increase the number of antibodies in a person?

Answer: A vaccine increases the number of antibodies in a person. An antigenic agent is injected into a person. The person's immune system produces large numbers of the antibodies to the antigen and antibody-producing cells.

3. How does a vaccine provide immunity?

Answer: After vaccination, antibody numbers increase and rid the body of antigen-bearing invaders. Many of the antibody-producing cells live for a long time and remember the invader (memory cells) upon future infections. This is called immunity.

Answers to Chapter 13 Section Review Questions

Section 13.1

1. How many chromosomes does an *E. coli* cell contain? How many chromosomes does a human body cell contain?
   Answer: *E. coli* has one chromosome. A human body cell has 46 chromosomes.

2. What are homologous pairs, and where do they come from?

   Answer: A homologous chromosome pair is two chromosomes that each contains the same genes in the same order, although they may contain different forms, or alleles, of the gene. One each of the homologues originally came from a parent.

3. Name six enzymes involved in *in vivo* DNA replication.

   Answer: The six enzymes involved in DNA replication *in vivo* are DNA helicase, topoisomerase, RNA polymerase (primase), DNA polymerase, RNase H, and DNA ligase.

4. How is *in vitro* DNA synthesis in a test tube different than *in vitro* DNA synthesis on an automated synthesizer?

   Answer: During *in vitro* DNA synthesis in a test tube, an enzyme synthesizes a complement on a template strand. On a DNA synthesizer, nucleotides are chemically added onto a resin bead, which creates a growing chain of nucleotides. The order of the chain is dictated by the sequence entered into the program.

Section 13.2

1. What is it called when DNA samples are transferred to a membrane for staining or probing?

   Answer: It called a Southern blot when DNA samples are transferred to a membrane for staining or probing.

2. How are probes used in microarrays?

   Answer: Probes, with some kind of visualization tag, are added to the wells of microarray slides that contain DNA fragments of varying sequences. The probes that are complementary to a DNA sequence will bind to the sequence. A microarray scanner evaluates the degree of target binding of a probe to a sequence.

3. Design a primer that would be good for recognizing the beginning of the following "sequence of interest." Describe why your primer is a good one.

   3'ACACAGGATACGTGCTGCTCAATGCCATGATAGCCGGTCACAAGCTAATCCGATTATCGCG-
   CAATTCCTAAATTCGCTAAAGCGAATCTTCAGGAAGGAACCCCGAAGGCCTTTT-5', and so on.

Answers will vary. However, a good primer should include the following criteria: "good" length, about 50% A-T, and not many Gs or Cs at the ends of the primer.

Section 13.3

1. Why is Taq polymerase used in PCR instead of some other DNA polymerase?

   Answer: Taq polymerase is used in PCR because it can withstand the high temperatures used to denature DNA in the first cycle step. Other DNA polymerases will denature and become inactive at such high temperatures.

2. What are the three parts to a thermal cycling reaction, and what are the differences in temperatures between them?

   Answer: The three parts to a thermal cycling reaction are denaturation (about 95°C), annealing (about 60°C), and extension (about 72°C)

3. What is it called when a PCR technician determines the best conditions for running a PCR protocol?

   Answer: What is it called when a PCR technician determines the best conditions for running a PCR protocol?

Section 13.4

1. Restriction-fragment length polymorphism (RFLP) technology was formerly used for DNA fingerprinting. What technology is currently used for DNA fingerprinting?

   Answer: The technology currently being used for DNA fingerprinting is PCR.

2. For a DNA fingerprint, many PCR targets are used. Each target is its own VNTR. What is a VNTR?

   Answer: A VNTR is a variable number of tandem repeats, a section of DNA that is a different length (due to the addition or deletion of a repeating DNA sequence) in different people, sometimes in 10 to 20 different forms.

3. Why would looking for the persons responsible for sneaking endangered species (rare birds, for example) into the United States be considered a job for a forensic scientist?

   Answer: A forensic scientist might be called in on an endangered-species smuggling case because it is against the law to smuggle endangered species and a crime has been committed. Animal DNA sequences can be used to prove that a particular animal has been imported illegally.

Answers to Chapter 14 Section Review Questions

Section 14.1

1. How is a ddNTP different from a "regular" ddNTP?

   Answer: A ddNTP is different from a "regular" dNTP in that a ddNTP is missing an oxygen atom from carbon number three of the deoxyribose molecule. This prevents it from bonding to the next nucleotide in a synthesis strand, which terminates of the strand synthesis.

2. When preparing sequencing-reaction tubes, each of the four dNTPs are added, but only one kind of ddNTP. Which are used in the highest concentrations, the dNTPs or the ddNTPs, and why?

   Answer: In the sequencing reactions, the dNTPs are used in the highest concentrations because the ddNTPs are only intended to be added occasionally to ensure that strands of all lengths are produced.

3. Where on the Internet may one go to compare DNA sequence data?

   Answer: On the Internet, one may compare DNA sequence data at the BLAST web site found at: http://www.ncbi.nlm.nih.gov/BLAST/.

4. What additional instrument is required for cycle sequencing?

   Answer: For cycle sequencing, a thermal cycler is used.

Section 14.2

1. How much of the human genome was sequenced using shotgun cloning?

   Answer: All of the human genome was sequenced using shot-gun cloning. The entire genome was chopped up and put into plasmid libraries for cloning and sequencing.

2. Name a plant and an animal whose entire genome has been put on a GeneChip® microarray for the purpose of studying gene function and expression.

Answer: Any of the following animals or plants has had their entire genome put on a GeneChip® microarray for the purpose of studying gene function and expression: dog, Rhesus macaque, Medicago trancatula (legume), Brassica, tomato, citrus, poplar and sugar cane.

3. MicroRNA, RNAi, and siRNA all operate in a similar fashion. What do they do?

    Answer: MicroRNA, RNA interference (RNAi), and short-interfering RNA (siRNA) all interfere with DNA or RNA to block RNA production or function and protein production.

Section 14.3

1. What is the technique called that uses an x-ray to study the structure of a protein crystal? What is the picture called?

    Answer: The technique that uses an x-ray to study the structure of a protein crystal is called x-ray crystallography or protein crystallography. The picture that is formed is called an x-ray diffraction pattern.

2. What causes proteins to crystallize out of solution?

    Answer: Proteins crystallize out of solution during salting-out. During salting-out, water moves from where it is high in concentration to where it is low in concentration due to differences in salt and protein concentrations.

3. What binds to what during an ELISA? How can a technician know that a protein is present during an ELISA?

    Answer: An antibody binds directly to an antigen (protein) in an ELISA, or an antibody binds to another antibody that binds to an antigen. A technician knows that a protein is present during an ELISA when an enzyme that is linked to [one of] the antibodies undergoes a color change.

4. What binds to what during a Western blot? How can a technician know that a protein is present during a Western blot?

    Answer: During a Western blot, antigens on a protein are blotted to a membrane using a blot transfer kit. An antibody binds directly to an antigen (protein) on the membrane, or an antibody binds to another antibody that binds to the antigen on the membrane. A technician knows that a protein is present during a Western blot when an enzyme that is linked to [one of] the antibodies and undergoes a color change.

Section 14.4

1. What is the name of the process by which strategies are used to solve environmental problems, such as oil spills, soil erosion, or fertilizer pollution?

    Answer: Bioremediation is the correction of environmental problems to reestablish an environment to a previous condition.

2. What is the function of the Autonomous Pathogen Detection System?

    Answer: The Autonomous Pathogen Detection System uses molecular and microbiological tests to detect biological threats, such as anthrax, plague, and botulism bacteria toxin, plus several other bacteria, fungi, and viruses.

3. What is the approximate size of the instruments and products used in nanotechnology?

    Answer: Instruments and products synthesized in biotechnology are approximately 1 billionth of a meter in size.

4. Give an example of a personalized medicine.

    Answers will vary, but examples might include a product that works best when the genetic and protein information of a patient is taken into consideration, such as special antibodies made from a person's own tumor cells, or a vaccine based on the antigens present in a person's own blood.

Answers to Thinking Like a Biotechnician Questions (Textbook)

Chapter 1, Thinking Like a Biotechnician

1. The following are stages in product development and manufacturing. Rearrange them in the order in which they take place:

   Testing for safety and efficacy
   Sales and marketing
   Product identification
   Small-scale manufacturing
   Research and development

Manufacturing

   Answer:

   1. Product identification
   2. Research and development
   3. Small-scale manufacturing
   4. Testing for safety and efficacy
   5. Manufacturing
   6. Sales and marketing

2. Match each of the descriptions or examples below with one of the five steps in the approach to scientific methodology presented in the chapter.

   a. scientific question
   b. hypothesis
   c. experimental plan
   d. conduct experiment
   e. analyze and report data

   ___collect numerical data
   ___create graphs of averaged data
   ___ask a testable question
   ___repeat trials
   ___try to answer questions based on the experience of others
   ___answer questions based on data collected during a valid experiment
   ___step-by-step instructions of how to test a scientific question

   Answer:

   d. collect numerical data
   e create graphs of averaged data
   a ask a testable question
   d repeat trials
   b try to answer questions based on others'
      experience
   e answer questions based on data collected during a valid experiment
   c step-by-step instructions of how to test a scientific question

3. As a biotechnologist, employment opportunities can be found in many areas. In addition to biotechnology companies, where can a scientist with a biotechnology background find employment?
   Answers may vary, but governmental agencies, such as the NIH, CDC, FDA, EPA, USDA, could be included, as well as universities.

4. In the fabric-bleaching experiment in Section 1.4, all samples lost all of their coloration in the 1-minute time period. Review the proposed procedure for the experiment, and suggest a change in the experiment's design so that you might see a difference in the degree of color fading due to the bleach concentration.

Answers may vary. A change in the experiment's design to allow the possibility of a difference in the degree of color fading due to the bleach concentration could include lowering the concentrations of all of the bleach solutions, or decreasing the soaking or treatment time.

5. When writing a conclusion, use the method of "Results with Evidence and Explanation (REE), Possible Errors (PE), and Practical Applications (PA) method" to ensure that all important data, evidence, and applications are discussed. Expand on the definitions or meanings of the terms represented by "REE", "PE", and "PA."

Answer:

"REE": Results with Evidence and Explanation. Answer the purpose question giving numerical data and explanations about how the data support the hypothesis.

"PE": Possible Errors. Identify the sources of experimental-design errors that could lead to misleading data and make recommendations of how to improve the experiment to minimize these sources of errors.

"PA" = Practical Applications. Discuss the meaning of the experiment and the value of the findings? Make recommendations about the applications of the new information.

6. After working for months repeating experiments, your data show that purifying a particular medicinal protein works better at a certain temperature. You want to share this scientific information with the rest of the scientific world. Name two commonly used ways that scientists share this kind of information.

Answer: Findings could be presented at a scientific meeting and/or submitted in the form of an abstract or article to a journal for consideration.

7. A large amount of the human protein collagen is needed so that it can be used to decrease the amount of wrinkling on people's faces. Describe, in a few steps, how genetic engineering could be used to make large amounts of human collagen for the dermatology market.

Answer: To produce large amounts of human collagen, the DNA instructions for human collagen could be isolated from human cells and transferred to production cells, like CHO cells, using a plasmid. The genetically engineered cells could be grown in large volumes and the human recombinant collagen purified from them, could be packaged and sold.

8. Consider the first five products in Figure 1.24. What is the market (who uses them) for these products? Consider the market size for each of these products. Which one do you think has the largest market (could make the most money), and which one do you think has the smallest market?

Answers will vary, but Roundup Ready ® soybeans have the largest market by far. The market for soybeans is one of the largest. Even though many people are infected with genital warts, treatments for this condition may have the smallest market of the pharmaceutical products listed. The DNA synthesizer probably has the smallest market. Scientists who need to make short pieces of DNA, mainly for research purchase it.

9. Getting a pharmaceutical product approved for sale in the United States takes much longer than it does to gain approval for an industrial product, such as a laundry enzyme. This is because of the required clinical testing. Explain why clinical testing slows down the approval process for pharmaceutical products.

Answer: During each phase of clinical testing, human subjects have to be recruited, tested, studied, and evaluated, which may take many months to many years.

10. Consider this scenario: You work for a company that has developed an AIDS drug that can prevent transmission of the HIV virus from an infected mother to a nursing baby in 990 of 1000 cases. However, in 10 out of 1000 cases, the drug causes a severe reaction and possibly death to the mother or the baby. Scientists want to conduct Phase III clinical trials in an area of Africa where the incidence of AIDS has doubled each year for the past 5 years. As a company employee, you are a member of a committee that will decide whether or not to support and fund the trial. Use the Strategy for Values Clarification model to determine what position you will take when meeting with the committee on this issue.

Answers will vary, but should include the following:

a. A statement of the problem or issue.
b. A list of possible solutions to the issue.
c. A list of the pros and cons of adopting each solution, ranked from best to worst.
d. Based on the pros and cons of each solution, a ranking of all solutions from best to worst.
e. A statement of position and the reason for it.

Chapter 2, Thinking Like a Biotechnician

1. List three examples each of prokaryotic and eukaryotic cells.

   Answer: Examples of prokaryotic cells include all bacteria, including, *Escheria coli (E. coli*, *Streptococcus sp*, and *Staphylococcus sp*. Examples of eukaryotic cells include plant cells, animal cells, fungal cells, and protists.

2. Identify the four groups of macromolecules found in living things. Give a specific example of a molecule and its function from each group.

   Answer: The four groups of macromolecules found in living things are as follows:

   - polypeptides, such as cellulose, which is the structural component of plant cell walls.
     lipids, such as phospholipids, which are structural components of cell membranes.
   - proteins, such as hemoglobin, which transports oxygen through the bloodstream.
   - nucleic acids, such as DNA, which stores genetic information about protein production.

3. Describe the relationship between amino acids, polypeptides, and proteins.

   Answer: Amino acids are connected together into long polypeptide chains. When the polypeptide chain folds into a functional molecule, it is called a protein.

4. Explain how differences in protein structure allow one protein molecule to recognize another protein molecule.

   Answer: Proteins interact with each other if amino acids in their chains interact with each other. Amino acid interactions are mainly due to attractions or repulsions between R-groups. Thus, depending on the amino-acid sequence, certain parts of a protein will be attracted to certain parts of other proteins.

5. If more than 75 percent of a cell's dry weight is protein, what makes up the remaining 25 percent of its dry weight?

   Answer: The remaining dry mass of a cell is a mixture of carbohydrates, lipids, nucleic acids, and simple organic compounds, such as urea, and inorganic compounds, such as salt (NaCl).

6. DNA molecules can be unzipped down the center and each side replicated. Look at Figure 2.34 (DNA structure). Propose a method by which two new strands could be produced from an existing DNA strand.

   Answer: H-bonds between complementary bases on each strand are broken and the sides are unzipped, revealing the nitrogenous bases. The nitrogenous base pattern is read on each strand, and a new complementary strand is built on each original strand.

8. It is often difficult to get large molecules to dissolve in a watery solution. Based on size, which of the following molecules should dissolve in water most readily: cellulose, hemoglobin, glucose, or amylose?

   Answer: Glucose is the smallest of the molecules and should go into solution (dissolve) most easily.

9. Look at Figure 2.29 (molecular structure of amino acids). Based on similar R-groups, propose a scheme to divide the 20 amino acids into four smaller groups based on similarities in their structure.

   Answers will vary, but amino acids are grouped in to four groups based on their R-groups: polar, nonpolar, positively charged, and negatively charged.

10. Restriction enzyme molecules cut DNA molecules into smaller pieces. DNA ligase molecules can paste cut pieces back together. Propose a method by which a scientist could create an rDNA molecule that carries genes for high levels of chlorophyll production and genes to resist frost damage. Into what kind of organism might you want to insert the new rDNA and why?

    Answers will vary. Theoretically, you could use a restriction enzyme to cut the chlorophyll genes from plant DNA. Find a restriction enzyme that will cut out a frost-resistant gene from a bacterium that lives in frigid temperatures. Find a plasmid vector. Cut it open using the same restriction enzymes used to cut open the other DNA molecules. Mix them all together, and add DNA ligase to paste the DNA pieces together. Add this to a bacterial broth culture. Grow bacteria on plates that are in bright light at freezing temperatures. Bacteria that survive and grow with green color are likely to contain recombinant plasmids with the desired genes.

Chapter 3, Thinking Like a Biotechnician

1. What is the best instrument to use to measure these volumes: 12.5 mL, 25 µL, 8.3 µL, 250 mL, and 571 µL?

   Answer: The best instrument to use is as follows:

   12.5 mL = 25-mL graduated cylinder or 25-mL pipet

   25 µL = P-100 micropipet

   8.3 µL = P-10 micropipet

   250 mL = 250-mL graduated cylinder

   571 µL = P-1000 micropipet

2. Convert the following values:

   12.5 µL = ___ mL

   3.05 mL = ___ µL

   0.45 L = ___ mL

   1.25 g = ___ mg

   989 µg = ___ mg

   Answer:

   12.5 µL = 0.0125 mL

   3.05 mL = 3050 µL

   0.45 L = 450 mL

   1.25 g = 1 250 mg

   989 µg = 0.989 mg

3. What numbers will be displayed on a P-20 micropipet if it is set to measure and dispense 14.8 µL?

   Answer: The number displayed on a P-20 micropipet if it is set to measure and dispense 14.8 µL is

1
4
8

4. Maple syrup solution is more concentrated with sugar than iced tea.

5. To make 15 mL of 12 mg/mL gelatin solution, set up the equation,

   12mg/mL × 15 mL = 180 mg = 0.18 g of gelatin are needed.

   The gelatin is mixed with solvent (deionized water) until 15 mL is reached.

6. To make 50 mL of 2.5% glucose solution, convert the 2.5% to 0.025.

   Set up the equation, 0.025 × 50 mL = 1.25 g of glucose is needed.

   The glucose is mixed with solvent (deionized water) until 50 mL is reached.

7. To make 125mL of 0.55 M $CaCl_2$ solution, convert 125 mL to 0.125 L.

   Then set up the equation,

   0.125 L × 0.55 mol/L × 111 grams/mol = 7.63 grams of $CaCl_2$. Add solvent up to 125 mL.

8. To prepare 200 mL of 5 mM $CaCl_2$ solution from 2M $CaCl_2$ solution:

   Convert 2M $CaCl_2$ to 2,000 mM

   (2,000mM) × V_1 = 5 mM × 200 mL

   V_1 = 5 mM × $\underline{200\ mL}$

   2,000mM

   V_1 = 1,000 mL/2,000 = 0.5 mL.

   Mix 0.5 mL of 2M $CaCl_2$ with 199.5 mL of solvent.

9. a. From 5X solution to 0.1X solution = diluting

b. From 25 mM solution to 1M solution = concentrating

c. From 3% solution to 0.2 % solution = diluting

d. From 0.1X solution to 0.15X solution = concentrating

e. From 2M solution to 10 mM solution = diluting

10. The new concentration of the sample is:

$$(50X) \times 10 \, \mu L = C_2 \times 20 \, mL$$

$$(50X) \times 0.01 \, mL = C_2 \times 20 \, mL$$

$$C_2 = (50X) \times \frac{0.01 \, mL}{20 \, mL}$$

$$C_2 = 0.5X/20 = 0.025X$$

Chapter 4, Thinking Like a Biotechnician

1. Name the four nitrogenous bases found in the nucleotides of the DNA molecule. List two ways in which these bases are similar to or different from each other.

Answer: The four nitrogenous bases found in the nucleotides of the DNA molecule are adenine, guanine, cytosine, and thymine. The answers for similarities and differences will vary, but could include the following:

a. the number of rings in the molecule (adenine and guanine with two, cytosine and thymine with one)

b. the placement of nitrogen in the rings

c. the additional functional groups, such as thymine, have a methyl group ($-CH_3$)

2. If a piece of one strand of a DNA molecule has the following code on it, what would be the nitrogen base code on the opposite DNA strand?

ATG CCC GTG TTA AAA TGT GGG ATC CCC GGT GTG CCC TTA

Answer: If a piece of one strand of a DNA molecule has the code

ATG CCC GTG TTA AAA TGT GGG ATC CCC GGT GTG CCC TTA,

the nitrogen base code on the opposite DNA strand would be

TAC GGG CAC AAT TTT ACA CCC TAG GGG CCA CAC GGG AAT.

3. A sample contains three DNA fragments with sizes of 3000, 20,000, and 80,000 bp. The sample is loaded onto a gel and run for the same amount of time as the gel diagramed in Figure 4.30. After staining, what will the samples look like on the gel?

Answer: After staining, the 3000 bp and the 20,000 bp fragments will be visible on the gel. The 3000 bp fragment will move faster and farther than the 20,000 bp fragment. The 80,000 bp piece will not be able to load into the gel because it is too large. It may be visibly stuck in the well.

4. A DNA molecule has a constant width. This is due to the nitrogenous base pairing. Explain how the nitrogen base pairing maintains the double helix's constant width.

Answer: Adenine binds to thymine, and guanine binds to cytosine. Since a two-ringed nitrogen base (called a purine), A or G, is bound to a single-ringed nitrogen base (a pyrimidine), T or C, the width of the base pair is constant.

5. The adenovirus has been genetically engineered to act as a vector to bring genes into cells for human gene therapy. Suggest a virus that could be used as a vector to carry genes into plants for plant gene therapy.

Answer: Tobacco mosaic virus infects certain plants. It or other plant viruses might be used as a vector to carry genes into tobacco or tomatoes to give them some new or improved characteristics.

6. When working in the lab, a sample is thought to contain DNA. What method could be used to test for DNA in the sample?

Answer: To test for DNA, a sample could be mixed with a DNA indicator, such as EtBr, and checked with ultraviolet (UV) light to look for a color change (some degree of glowing orange). The sample could be run on a gel and stained with EtBr.

7. Suppose that the DNA code in question 2 is part of the DNA sequence for an enzyme involved in milk digestion. What effect could a change (mutation) in this sequence have in the cell or in the organism?

   Answer: The mutation could cause a beneficial or detrimental change or no change in the resulting milk-digesting protein. It depends on which amino acids in the protein are affected.

8. Positive feedback occurs when the presence of something causes an increase in some other molecule or process. Negative feedback occurs when the presence of something causes a decrease in some other molecule or process. Lactose molecules turn on the lac operon in bacteria contain it. Is this an example of positive or negative feedback? Explain why.

   Answer: The cell needs to make beta-galactosidase to breakdown lactose to use for food. So, the more lactose there is in the cell, the more it binds to the repressor of the Lac Operon, thereby removing it and turning on production of beta-galactosidase. Lactose (positive feedback) turns on the operon to make more of an enzyme.

9. A sample has a mixture of 10 pieces of DNA that are very close in size (between 700 and 1000 bp). You want to separate them on an agarose gel. What can you do to increase the chances for good separation?

   Answer: Answers will vary, but one good idea to increase the chances for good separation of DNA molecules on a gel is to use a higher concentration of agarose in the gel and set the electrophoresis for a longer amount of time. By making a 2% to 3% solution, the molecules will better separate as they struggle to make it through the gel matrix.

10. A biotechnologist attempts to genetically engineer a cell to make a certain protein. It appears that the transformed cell is making the protein, but only in small amounts. Suggest a method to increase protein production in the transformed cell.

    Answers will vary. There are many good techniques to attempt. One good idea to increase protein production in the transformed cell is to use site-specific mutagenesis to modify the promoter to be better recognized by the RNA polymerase.

Chapter 5, Thinking Like a Biotechnician

1. How do the 20 amino acids differ from each other?

   Answer: An amino acid is different from other amino acids in the type of R-group attached at the central carbon. The R-group can be charged, uncharged, or polar.

2. What bonds or forces hold a protein together in a functional three-dimensional shape?

   Answer: Several types of bonds or forces hold a protein together in a functional three-D shape. The hydrogen bonding between amino acids results in alpha helices and beta pleated sheets. Charged attractions and repulsions cause loops and folds in the polypeptide chain. Nonpolar and polar interactions also cause loops and folds. Disulfide bonds between cysteine molecules fold and bend the chain.

3. Enzyme solutions are always prepared using a buffer at a specific pH as the solvent. Why is a buffered solvent important for enzymes and other protein solutions?

   Answer: A buffered solvent is important for enzymes and other protein solutions because changes in pH may cause proteins to denature and lose their function. For enzymes, suboptimal pH values will cause a loss in activity.

4. Describe the relationship between an antibody and an antigen. Explain how the human body can make so many antibodies.

   Answer: An antibody recognizes and binds to specific antigens. The body produces thousands of different antibodies by shuffling the DNA code for the tips of the antibodies.

5. A technician needs to determine the size and shape of a protein. Which of these methods could be used to gain the appropriate data to determine protein size and shape?

   mass spectrophotometry
   PAGE
   protein indicator testing
   x-ray crystallography
   protein sequencing

protein synthesis
visible spectrophotometry

Answer: The following methods could be used to gain data to determine protein size and shape: PAGE, x-ray crystallography, and protein sequencing.

6. If a structural gene has the code "TAC CCC ATG GGG TAA GGC GTC," which mRNA transcript will be made, and which peptide will be produced?

Answer: If a structural gene has the code "TAC CCC ATG GGG TAA GGC GTC,"

the mRNA transcript will be "AUG GGG UAC CCC AUU CCG CAG."
The peptide will be as follows:
methionine – glycine – tyrosine – proline – isoleucine – proline – glutamine
This assumes no posttranscriptional modification of the mRNA.

7. If a mutation occurs, substituting the "A" with a "G" at the seventh nucleotide in the structural gene, what are the consequences of the mutation?

Answer: If a mutation occurs, substituting the "A" with a "G" at the seventh nucleotide in the structural gene, the consequences of the mutation are that the third codon would be changed to "CAC," which codes for histidine. Substituting histidine in the chain could have no impact or could cause important changes in peptide folding and protein function. The change could cause improved or worsened protein function, or have no impact on function at all.

8. A technician prepares a 1 mg/mL of hemoglobin solution and leaves it on the lab bench over the weekend. When the concentration of the sample is checked on Monday, its value is significantly less than expected. What might have caused the difference in concentration from Friday to Monday? How should the solution have been stored?

Answers will vary, but some possibilities are that the decrease in protein concentration is due to the protein being degraded or denatured to some extent because of bacterial of fungal contamination (using the protein as a food source) or elevated temperatures. The solution should have been stored at 4°C or lower.

9. DNase is an enzyme that chops DNA into tiny pieces. It is evident that DNase is working when a thick mucus-like, DNA-containing solution becomes watery and runny. Design an experiment that would determine the optimum temperature for DNase activity.

Answers will vary, but an experiment that would determine the optimum temperature for DNase activity should include samples tested at different temperatures, all samples should have the same reagent (volume, mass, and concentration), all samples should be treated (except for the temperature) and measured in the same way, and runniness/viscosity should be measured in some numerical fashion

10. Protein is an important food nutrient. A technician working at a food company is interested in the nutritional content of seeds/nuts. She runs a PAGE gel with samples from two different seed extracts. She runs multiple lanes of the samples. The gel is stained with Coomassie Blue. Seed Extract No. 1 has three faint bands at 25 kD, 30 kd, and 35 kd; and Extract No. 2 has two bands at 25 kd and 35 kd, and the bands are very dark. What might she conclude from her results about the nutritional value of the seed extracts?

Answers will vary. The amount of blueness from the staining is an indication of the concentration of protein in the sample. The total protein content, an important nutritional issue, appears to be higher in Extract No. 2, even though it has fewer bands.

Chapter 6, Thinking Like a Biotechnician

1. A researcher wants to insert a gene into strawberry cells to prevent strawberries from freezing. Propose how that could be done using protoplast technology.

Answers will vary, but to get a gene into strawberry cells using protoplast technology, a researcher might start with mashed strawberry cells and treat them with an enzyme, like cellulase, to destroy the cell walls. The resulting protoplasts might accept foreign DNA using a needle or "gene gun."

2. Name a naturally occurring amylase producer that might be a source of an amylase gene.

Answer: The bacteria, Bacillus *subtilis* makes amylase. So do several herbivores.

3. A company is producing a diabetes medication with a new form of insulin. Part of the development includes designing multispecies pharmacokinetic/pharmacodynamic (PK/PD) assays. What are multispecies PK/PD assays, and why do they need to be developed in a human insulin product pipeline?

   Answer: Multispecies PK/PD assays show the activity of a protein in humans as well as other test organisms. These assays are conducted to understand the protein's presence and activity in monkeys, mice, rabbits, or other animals before the human tests are performed.

4. Conducting an ELISA can be cumbersome because there is so much pipeting involved. Suggest some instruments that might make an ELISA easier to conduct.

   Answers will vary, but to make an ELISA assay easier to conduct, one might use a multichannel pipet, or an ELISA plate washer or reader.

5. Propose a method for testing the effectiveness of an antiseptic, such as rubbing alcohol, on inhibiting *E. coli* growth.

   Answer: To test the effectiveness of an antiseptic, the test could be identical to the one for used for antibiotics except that antiseptics are substituted for the antibiotics. Petri dishes are spread with bacteria. Then antiseptic-soaked disks are laid on the agar. Each disk has a different antiseptic on it. The clarity of the zone (halo) shows the effectiveness of the antiseptic in inhibiting the bacteria.

6. Amylase breaks down starch to sugar. What indicators could be used in an activity assay to see if a sample contains some active amylase?

   Answer: An iodine indicator could be used to see if starch decreases in the presence of amylase. Or, a maltose indicator could be used to see if maltose concentrations increase in the presence of a suspected amylase sample.

7. If a cell extract is thought to contain a specific protein, how might a technician check to see if the protein is present?

   Answers will vary, but to check a cell extract for the presence of a specific protein, a technician could use a PAGE, if the molecular weight of the protein is known, or an ELISA.

8. Herbal therapies contain molecules that some people consider safe and effective. What argument can be made against herbal therapies being safe and effective?

   Answers will vary. Herbal therapies do not have to demonstrate concentration, safety, or efficacy. Most do not undergo clinical trials or FDA approval.

9. A CPDP committee recommends that the development of a product should be halted because an injectable liquid formulation has a short shelf life. After many years of R&D, you are disappointed. What suggestion might you make?

   Answers will vary, but if a formulation has a short shelf life, then an approach might be to try to reformulate the product as a tablet, powder, cream, or patch, which may make it more stable.

10. Propose how antibody therapy could be used to treat someone who is allergic to peanuts.

    Answers will vary. One idea for creating a therapy for peanut allergies is based on an allergic response being an overreaction to an allergen. One solution might be to take a serum sample and isolate the peanut-recognizing antibody, and then make an antibody (through genetic engineering) to that peanut antibody to rid it from your body when it is overexpressed.

Chapter 7, Thinking Like a Biotechnician

1. What color is the light of the following wavelengths: 600 nm, 525 nm, and 475 nm?

   Answer: 600 nm = orange light, 525 nm = green light, and 475 nm = blue light.

2. A colorless protein is purified from a cell extract. What kind of spectrophotometer should be used to detect its presence and concentration?

   Answer: To detect a colorless protein, a UV spec can be used, set at 280 nm, or, alternatively, if an indicator can make the protein solution colorful, a VIS spec can be used.

3. The concentration of H+ in a solution that has a pH of 6.0 is 1×10^{-6} moles/liter. The concentration of OH- in a solution that has a pH of 6.0 is 1×10^{-8} moles/liter.

4. If a solution has a pH of 5.3, add a base such as NaOH, to bring it to a pH of 7.1.

5. To prepare 5 liters of 0.25*M* TRIS buffer at pH 7.4, measure 151.43 grams of TRIS.

> 5 L × 0.25 mol/L × 121.14 grams/mol = 151.43 grams of TRIS
> Mix it with solvent (dH$_2$0) to about 3.5 L.
> Adjust the pH to 7.4 (with 1*M* HCl)
> Fill to a final volume of 5 L with dH$_2$0.

6. To prepare 250 mL of 0.01*M* sodium monophosphate monobasic buffer at pH 5.5, measure 0.35 grams of sodium phosphate monobasic.

> 0.25L × 0.01 mol/L × 137.99 grams/mol = 0.35 grams of sodium phosphate monobasic
> Mix it with solvent (dH$_2$0) to about 200 mL.
> Adjust the pH to 5.5 (with 10% NaOH)
> Fill to a final volume of 250 mL with dH$_2$0.

7. To prepare 600 mL of 50 m*M* sodium monophosphate monobasic buffer at pH 6.5, measure 4.14 grams of sodium phosphate monobasic.

> 0.6L × 0.05 mol/L × 137.99 grams/mol = 4.14 grams of sodium phosphate monobasic
> Mix it with solvent (dH$_2$0) to about 500 mL.
> Adjust the pH to 6.5 (with 10% NaOH)
> Fill to a final volume of 600 mL with dH$_2$0.

8. To prepare 100 mL of 0.5*M* TRIS, 0.05 *M* CaCl$_2$ buffer at pH 7.2, each buffering compound/salt mass is calculated independently of the other.

> Measure 6.06 grams of TRIS
> 0.1L × 0.5 mol/L × 121.14 grams/mol = 6.06 grams of TRIS
> Measure 0.56 grams of CaCl2
> 0.1L × 0.05 mol/L × 111 grams/mol = 0.56 grams of CaCl2
> Mix both soluted with solvent (dH$_2$0) to about 70 mL.
> Adjust the pH to 724 (with 1*M* HCl)
> Fill to a final volume of 100 mL with dH$_2$0.

9. A molecule has a lambda$_{max}$ of 475 nm. What wavelengths would probably not be good to use for testing samples for the presence of the molecule?

   Answer: The farther away from lambda $_{max}$ a wavelength is, the more likely it is that the absorbance of a molecule will be poor. To measure a molecule with a lambda $_{max}$ of 475 nm, wavelengths in the orange and red parts of the spectrum should be avoided, such as 590 to 700 nm.

10. A set of standards is prepared by diluting a stock sample in a 1:2 ratio. If the stock solution has an absorbance of 1.2 au, and the 1:2 dilution has an absorbance of 0.6 au, what would be the expected amount absorbance of the 1:4, 1:8, and 1:16 dilutions? If the absorbance of the dilutions is not as expected, what might be the reason?

   Answer: The expected absorbance of the 1:4, 1:8, and 1:16 dilutions are 0.3 au, 0.15 au, and 0.075 au, respectively. If the dilutions are not prepared correctly, the absorbance will be different than expected.

Chapter 8, Thinking Like a Biotechnician

1. Answer: In a DNA isolation, lysozyme breaks down bacterial cell walls and weakens the cells. RNase breaks down RNA molecules. Protease breaks down proteins. Cellulase breaks down plant cell walls and weakens the cells.

2. A technician is attempting to transform cells with a rather large plasmid, and the transformation efficiency is very low. What might he or she do to increase the transformation efficiency?

   Answers will vary, but to increase transformation efficiency, he or she might try several things, including adjusting the calcium or magnesium chloride concentration during competency. Or, he or she could adjust the time or temperature of the heat and cold shock. Also, cutting out the gene of interest on the plasmid and putting it into a different vector, such as a smaller plasmid, could be tried.

3. How can a technician obtain the current GMP regulations?

Answer: The GMP guidelines and regulations are on the FDA's web site. A technician can go to the site to learn the current GMP regulations.

4. A plasmid has a gene of interest that you would like to transfer to another plasmid that is a better vector for transformation. How would you know which restriction enzymes to use to make the rDNA?

    Answer: To determine which restriction enzyme should be used on a plasmid that has a gene of interest you would like to transfer to another plasmid, you would look for one restriction enzyme (or a combination of restriction enzymes) that opens both the donor and the recipient plasmid in only one place (hopefully, not in the gene of interest). Confirm this through gel electrophoresis. After digestion, ligate the pieces and transform the cells with the new rDNA. Look for colonies that have the "desired" characteristics.

5. A technician has found a section of DNA that is responsible for an antifreeze phenotype in an ocean fish. She wants to make several copies of the gene for genetic-engineering purposes. What technique(s) and instruments could be used to make multiple copies of the gene?

    Answer: DNA isolation, PCR, and a thermal cycler could be used to make multiple copies of the gene.

6. You are interested in finding the insulin gene in some human chromosomal DNA. Propose a method by which you could accomplish this.

    Answer: A method by which you could find the insulin gene in some human chromosomal DNA might include using mRNA for insulin as a probe. The insulin mRNA may bind to a certain section of the gene, but probably not the entire gene, because introns may interrupt the coding section. To obtain insulin mRNA molecules, one might look in pancreas cells whose primary function is insulin production.

7. A cell culture is in a 2-L spinner flask. Overnight, the growth rate of cells slowed, and the culture is no longer in a state of exponential growth. The density of cells in the culture is not high enough to "seed" another flask. What might the technician check?

    Answer will vary, but if a cell culture is not growing fast enough, a technician might try measuring and adjusting the pH and/or checking and adjusting the temperature, food source (ie, glucose), and the oxygen content, and/or looking for contamination.

8. If a DNA sample gives a 260 nm reading of 0.085 au and a 280 nm reading of 0.06 au, its concentration would be 50 µg/mL × 0.085 = 4.25 µg/mL and its purity would be 0.085/0.06 = 1.42, which indicates a significant amount of protein contamination.

9. In a given transformation, only a relatively low number of cells are transformed. How can a technician tell if a transformation, such as transforming *E. coli* into amylase producers, actually occurs?

    Answer: A technician can tell if a transformation has occurred by growing the cells in or on selection media. In the case of transforming *E. coli* into amylase producers, there should be starch in the agar. Any colonies that break down and remove starch from the agar would be considered transformed. Original, untransformed cells should also be grown on separate starch plates for comparison.

10. Answers will vary. The only real disadvantage of purchasing plasmid isolation kits is the cost. Each kit is hundreds of dollars. But, the time and trouble of gathering and preparing all the reagents and solutions is a big advantage of purchasing plasmid isolation kits.

Chapter 9, Thinking Like a Biotechnician

1. What are the advantages of pressure-pump chromatography (FPLC and HPLC) compared with open-column chromatography?

    Answers will vary, but the advantages of pressure-pump chromatography (FPLC or HPLC) compared with open-column chromatography might include the following: 1) it is automated and a technician does not have to stand over it; or 2) it can handle greater volumes in a relatively shorter time.

2. What is the difference between Phases I, II, and III of a clinical trial?

    Answer: The differences in between Phases I, II, and III include the number of people in the study and what must be demonstrated (safety and efficacy).

3. A gel-filtration column, containing resin with a 60-kd pore size is run with two proteins: one is 48 kd and the other is 100 kd. At the end of the column run, one of them is in fraction 10, and one is in fraction 15. Which protein would be in which fraction? Explain why.

   Answer: In a gel-filtration column containing resin with a 60-kd pore size, the 48-kd protein will become hung up in the resin channels and take longer to come down than the 100-kd protein. So, the 100-kd protein is probably in fraction 10, and the 48-kd protein is probably in fraction 15.

4. A small sample of valuable protein with a molecular weight of 58 and positively charged at pH 7.5 needs to be confirmed on a column. Which type of column chromatography should be used?

   Answer: For a small sample of valuable protein, an HPLC column should be used to confirm the protein's presence.

5. A mixture of proteins was separated on a sizing column. One 2-mL fraction has two proteins left in it, and the technician wants to run an ion-exchange column. First, he or she has to dialyze it into the appropriate buffer. How much ion-exchange buffer is needed for the dialysis?

   Answer: The amount of ion exchange buffer needed for the dialysis is 10×2 mL for each round of buffer exchange. At least 20 mL, preferably 30 mL, if time allows.

6. A technician sets up a negatively charged ion-exchange column and puts a small volume of a protein mixture on it. What should happen to the positively charged proteins in the mixture? What should happen to negatively charged molecules in the mixture?

   Answer: The positively charged proteins in the mixture should bind to the resin beads, and the negatively charged molecules should flow through the column and collected into fractions. Later, the positively charged proteins can be eluted off the column.

7. Propose a method of purifying recombinant amylase from transformed *E. coli* cells and their proteins.

   Answers will vary, but a method of purifying recombinant amylase from transformed *E. coli* cells and their proteins should include something about centrifuging cells out of broth and discarding the cells, since amylase is secreted into broth. The broth proteins then should be dialyzed into a buffer for chromatography: gel-filtration chromatography first (because amylase has a molecular weight of 61 kd), then ion-exchange chromatography.

8. How can you tell if the protein purified in No. 7 actually is amylase?

   Answer: You can tell if the protein purified in No. 7 really is amylase by running the column fractions on a gel. This should confirm the presence and purification of amylase. Activity assays can confirm that it breaks starch to sugar. An ELISA, using an antibody to amylase, could recognize it specifically in a sample. Running an HPLC will show a peak for amylase.

9. As a sample elutes from a column, the technician wants to determine the concentration of protein in the sample fractions. What instrument can be used to determine the concentration of the fractions, and at what setting(s) should it be operated?

   Answer: A UV spec can be used to determine the protein concentration, if absorbance readings are taken at 280 nm and compared with a set of standards.

10. How do the QC and QA departments in a company differ from each other?

    Answers will vary. The QC department is responsible for testing the quality of products and communicating within the company about how to improve the quality, if necessary. The QA department is more responsible for setting product quality goals and presenting product quality beyond the company, and for communicating with regulatory and consumer groups about product quality.

Chapter 10, Thinking Like a Biotechnician

1. It takes approximately 5 years for an orchid to breed, produce seeds, grow into the offspring plants, and flower. It takes about 2 years for an orchid tissue culture to grow from a protocorm (an undifferentiated mass of cells) until it matures and flowers. Why would plant scientists at an orchid company breed plants instead of propagating them through stem cuttings?

   Answer: Breeding creates new versions or variety in offspring. It is the way new and different (beautiful) orchids are developed. If tissue culture of protocorms is the only method of propagation, all their orchids would always be the same.

2. Why is meristematic tissue needed for tissue culture and other asexual propagation?

   Answer: Meristematic tissue is the only actively dividing, undifferentiated tissue. Plant cells do not easily revert back to dividing cells once they have specialized into specific tissues.

3. Why must a plant tissue culture be conducted under sterile conditions?

   Answer: Any fungi or bacteria contamination will out grow or grow over and destroy the small sample of plant cells used in the tissue culture.

4. Why must meiosis occur to produce plant sex cells? Use the terms "diploid" and "haploid" in your answer.

   Answer: Meiosis is cell division that starts with a diploid parent cell and results in haploid sex cells. If meiosis did not happen during sex-cell development, the chromosome number would still be diploid. When pollen (containing the sperm nucleus) and eggs fuse, the resulting zygote would be 4N, which is usually fatal to the plant.

5. Why might it be more difficult to get stem cuttings from a woody plant, such as an *Azalea*, to root versus the cuttings of an herbaceous plant, such as a *Coleus*?

   Answers may vary, but one reason may be that it is harder for everything (hormones, roots, and other nutrients) to penetrate thick woody tissue.

6. A sample of cellulase is used to release juice from apple cells. After 50 trials, the average amount of juice produced by a 1000-μL volume of cellulase in a 50-mL volume of crushed apples is 7.8 mL. One sample has a juice extraction value of 7.2 mL. Using the 10% rule, is the sample's value valid and acceptable?

   Answer: 10% of 7.8 is 0.78, thus, values between 7.8 + 0.78 and 7.8 - 0.78 would be considered acceptable, that is, values between 7.02 and 8.58. A sample concentration of 7.2 mL is acceptable.

7. An experiment is conducted to determine how the amount of the plant hormone, indoleacetic acid (IAA), affects bean-plant stem growth. Untreated bean stems grow to an average height of 100 cm. When 1 mL of 20 ng/mL of IAA was sprayed on bean plants, 120 plants grew an average of 115 cm with a SD of 17 cm. Two plant samples gave readings that looked questionable to the technician. One had a value of 125 cm, and the other had a value of 93 cm. Should these two plants' growth data be considered valid? Why or why not?

   Answer: 115 +/- 17 cm is considered acceptable, that is, values between 98 and 132 cm. The plant growth to 125 cm is accepted, and the plant growth to 93 cm should not be accepted as valid.

8. Consider a cross between two parent plants carrying genes for purple stems. Purple (P) is dominant to green (p) stems. One parent is heterozygous for the trait, and one is homozygous dominant. Show the cross (problem), including the chances for this breeding to produce green-stemmed plants.

   Answer:

   Parents' genotypes: Pp   ×   PP

   Alleles possible in gametes: P or p   P

   Punnett Square of the Cross

Genotypes of Male/Female Gametes	P
P	PP
P	Pp

   Expected genotypic results of crossing these gametes:

   1/2 of offspring = PP
   1/2 of offspring = Pp
   Expected phenotype(s) of offspring:
   100% purple-stemmed plants are expected.
   No green-stemmed plants are expected.

9. Consider a cross between two parent plants carrying genes for purple stems and yellow flowers. Purple (P) is dominant to green (p) stems. Yellow (Y) is dominant to white (y) flowers. One parent is heterozygous for purple stems but homozygous recessive for yellow flowers. The other parent is homozygous recessive for purple stems

but heterozygous for flower color. Show the cross (problem), including the chances of this breeding producing green-stemmed, white-flowered plants.

Answer:

Parents' genotypes: Ppyy   ×   ppYy

Alleles possible in the gametes: Py, or py   pY or py

Punnett Square of the Cross

Genotypes of Male/Female Gametes	Py	py
pY	PpYy	ppYy
py	Ppyy	ppyy

Expected genotypic results of crossing these gametes:

    1/4 of offspring = PpYy
    1/4 of offspring = Ppyy
    1/4 of offspring = ppYy
    1/4 of offspring = ppyy

Expected phenotype(s) of offspring:

    1/4 of offspring = purple-stemmed, yellow-flowered plants
    1/4 of offspring = purple-stemmed, white-flowered plants
    1/4 of offspring = green-stemmed, yellow-flowered plants
    1/4 of offspring = green-stemmed, white-flowered plants
    25% of offspring are expected to be green-stemmed, white-flowered plants.

10. A cross of plants with the genotypes given in problem No. 9 results in 200 offspring plants as follows:

    51 have purple stems and yellow flowers
    53 have purple stems and white flowers
    41 have green stems and yellow flowers
    55 have green stems and white flowers

Conduct a chi-square analysis of the cross, and determine whether the results show that a valid dihybrid cross was conducted.

Answer:

$(51-50)^2 / 50 + (50-53)^2 / 50 + (50-41)^2 / 50 + (50-55)^2 / 50$
$= 1/50 + 9/50 + 82/50 + 25/50$
$= 0.02 + 0.18 + 1.64 + 0.5$
$= 1.85 = X^2$ with 3 df

The X^2 value is between 0.70 and 0.50, which is higher than 0.05. Therefore, the dihybrid cross results are considered valid.

Chapter 11, Thinking Like a Biotechnician

1. Name at least five transgenic plants of economic value.

Answers will vary, but they might include Bt corn, Roundup Ready® soybeans, virus-resistant papayas, virus-resistant bananas, and FlavRSavR® tomatoes.

2. Alcohol is used in virtually every DNA isolation. What is the purpose of alcohol in these protocols?

Answer: Alcohol precipitates DNA out of solution. It is used in one of the final steps in DNA isolation to pellet DNA out of the liquid it is in.

3. What are the changes that one can expect to observe as a plant tissue culture develops?

Answer: The following should appear several weeks after the preceding one: explant, callus, shoot development, root development, and transplantable plantlet.

4. Besides using the Ti plasmid, name another way that foreign genes might be transferred to plant cells.

    Answer: Answers will vary, but two possibilities are, 1) using a virus as a vector; or 2) using a "gene gun" to inject DNA into protoplasts.

5. A horticulturist has a supply of several different plant growth regulators (hormones), including zeatin (a cytokinin), IAA (an auxin), ethylene, gibberellin, and abscisic acid (ABA). Which of the growth regulators would be a logical choice to test for its potential to do the following?

    a. produce an ivy plant with extra large leaves

    b. produce corn seeds that germinate after only a 4-week dormancy period

    c. produce an apple tree bearing fruit that ripens in half the normal time

    Answer: a. IAA (auxin) b. giberrellin c. ethylene

6. Sunflower plants are of great economic importance. They have a main stem that grows straight and tall. Design an experiment to test how the concentration of auxin affects stem elongation in sunflower plants. Use a stock auxin sample at a concentration of 100 parts per million (ppm)

    Answers will vary, but they should include some type of dilution (1:10 or perhaps 1:100) of the stock auxin solution. Each variation group should include several plants, but all plants are treated exactly the same (application method, volume of auxin, etc.) except for the hormone concentration. Measure the stem height in the same way in all of the plants.

7. Suggest a method for creating a recombinant soybean plant that contains and expresses a human insulin gene.

    Answers may vary. One approach could be that a recombinant Ti plasmid could be constructed with an inserted human insulin gene. The new plasmid could be inserted into *Agrobacterium* and *Agrobacterium* used to inoculate soybean tissue with the recombinant Ti plasmid. If the Ti plasmid transforms the soybean tissue, and the tissue is cultured on plant tissue culture media, transformed plantlets may arise.

8. Suggest a method for screening soybean tissue that has been inoculated with *A. tumefaciens* for the purpose of inserting a recombinant Ti plasmid.

    Answer: Grow tissue that has been inoculated with *Agrobacterium* (containing a Ti plasmid) on selected (depending on the plasmid, perhaps with kanamycin or X-gal) tissue culture media.

9. What might be the value and application of plants such as the one discussed in question No. 7?

    Answer: The plant parts (soybeans) could be given or fed to diabetic persons as medicine, or the plants could be ground up and the insulin purified for use as a pharmaceutical.

10. How might insulin be purified from the recombinant insulin soybean plant discussed in question No. 7?

    Answer: Ground plant samples could be treated with solvents to extract proteins from the plant cells. The protein extracts could be purified using column chromatography (see Chapter 9).

Chapter 12, Thinking Like a Biotechnician

1. What is the approximate maximum length of a peptide made on a peptide synthesizer?

    Answer: The approximate maximum length of a peptide made on a peptide synthesizer is 30 amino acids.

2. Why are the peptides created on a peptide synthesizer not called proteins?

    Answer: Peptides created on a peptide synthesizer are not called proteins because proteins are longer, folded peptide chains that are biologically active.

3. If scientists are screening thousands of samples daily or weekly, how can they process so much data?

    Answer: If scientists are screening thousands of samples daily or weekly, they use computers with special programs to handle all the data.

4. How might a genetic disorder be detected on a microarray?

    Answer: Only genetic disorders due to rather large mutations (change in DNA) may be detected on a microarray. Ways to detect them include the following: 1) the probes do not recognize or hybridize a sample; or 2) DNA is recognized by a probe looking for a specific mutated sequence.

5. Using a DNA synthesizer, suppose you want to make a primer that will recognize the following sequence: TAC CCG GGC AAT TCC AGT. What will the sequence on the primer have to be?

   Answer: The sequence on the primer should be ATG GGC CCG TTA AGG TCA, if the primer target is TAC CCG GGC AAT TCC AGT.

6. Allergies are caused by an overreaction of an antibody to an antigen. Suppose you are allergic to peanuts. Suggest an antibody therapy that might help you.

   Answer: An antibody to the antibody that recognizes peanuts should remove the overreacting antibody from the body and serve as a peanut-allergy antibody therapy.

7. Explain how the antibody technology works on a pregnancy test strip.

   Answer: On a pregnancy test strip, a pregnancy protein in urine must react with the antibody against that pregnancy protein, causing a color change, or vice versa.

8. How do scientists acquire enough antibodies to purify antigenic proteins for vaccine trials?

   Answer: Scientists can genetically engineer cells to produce antibodies to produce enough antibodies to purify antigenic proteins for vaccine trials.

9. How might the active ingredient from the Foxglove plant (digitalis) be isolated from the plant? How would a technician know if it were isolated?

   Answers will vary, but to extract the active ingredient from Foxglove, some type of solvent extraction could be tried, such as alcohol or water. Assays might measure an increase in the heart rate of an organism (mouse) or cells (heart cells in culture). UV spectrophotometry (lambda $_{max}$), mass spectrometry (MW determination), or melting-point determination, etc, would indicate to a technician that the active ingredient had been isolated.

10. If a vaccine is needed for a certain cancer, such as breast cancer, what type of vaccine antigen might cause an immune response and possibly be a therapeutic candidate?

    Answer: A unique protein found on the breast cancer cells and *only* on the breast cancer cells, wound be a good candidate for a breast cancer vaccine.

Chapter 13, Thinking Like a Biotechnician

1. People with Down's syndrome have an extra chromosome No. 21 in all of their cells (called trisomy 21). How can chromosome abnormalities such as these be identified in the lab?

   Answer: A karyotype shows the chromosomes of a cell. When homologous pairs are lined up, chromosome abnormalities, such as an extra chromosome No. 21, may be observed.

2. If an E. coli chromosome is approximately 4.6 million bp long with approximately 4400 genes, what is the average length of an E. coli gene?

   Answer: If an E. coli chromosome is approximately 4.6 million bp long with approximately 4400 genes, then the average length of an E. coli gene is about 1045 bp.

3. DNA strands are antiparallel. Why is this important for PCR?

   Answer: The antiparallel nature of DNA strands is important for PCR because it must be considered when picking or designing primers. To get a primer to recognize and attach at the correct spot, you need to know which of the two sides of the DNA strand is of interest, 3' to 5' or 5' to 3'.

4. Six enzymes are needed for DNA replication in cells. How many are needed for DNA synthesis in a tube?

   Answer: Only one of the five DNA replication enzymes is required for DNA synthesis in a tube, DNA polymerase. Helicase is not needed because the DNA is either single-stranded or is made so by heating. Primers are added, so no RNA primase is needed. The strands are short enough that the functions of topoisomerase and ligase are not needed.

5. A microarray is set up to recognize a DNA sequence only found in men with a rare type of prostate cancer. The array reaction is run. Five wells with samples from five men (out of 1000 men tested) glow 30% more than the negative controls. What do you conclude?

Answers will vary, but more glowing in a microarray hybridization means more probe-binding to the DNA target sequence. This may mean that 30% more DNA target is present and that the sample is representative of the rare form of prostate cancer.

6. DNA synthesis reactions are run with the goal of producing strands between 60 and 100 bases long. How might these be visualized in a lab?

   Answer: DNA samples that are smaller than 500 bp are usually run on a PAGE (vertical gels). They can be stained with EtBr, or blotted (Southern blot) and visualized.

7. Southern blot membranes are positively charged. Considering what they are used for, why might that be important?

   Answer: Southern blot membranes are positively charged so that they will attract and bind to the negatively charged DNA samples. The Southern blot membrane has an opposite charge to the DNA molecules.

8. In PCR, special thin-walled microtest tubes are used. Why might it be valuable for PCR tubes to be thin-walled?

   Answers will vary, but one value of thin-walled PCR tubes is that the contents will heat and cool rapidly.

9. In a PCR reaction, every variable needs to be tested to determine the optimum condition to produce the maximum amount of PCR product. Design an experiment in which the primer-annealing temperature will be optimized.

   Answers will vary, but a PCR primer-annealing optimization experiment would include multiple PCR tubes in groups whose only difference would be the primer-annealing temperature. That means that the technician would test perhaps three tubes each at five different annealing temperatures, such as 50° C, 55° C, 60° C, 65° C, or 70°C. All other volumes, concentrations, temperatures, times, and conditions would be the same from tube to tube.

10. Here is a DNA sequence that must be located in a genomic DNA sample. Below is a possible primer sequence. Evaluate the appropriateness of using this potential primer given the criteria in Section 13.2.

    Sequence of interest:

    3'ACATGCTGCTGCCGGTCACAAGGCAATTCCTAAAAAGGGAAGGAACCCCGAAGGCCTTTT-.5'...

    Possible primer to the sequence of interest:

    5'-TGTACGACGACGGCCAGTGTTCCGTTAAGGAT-3'

    Answer: The proposed primer appears to be a good primer to recognize this sequence of interest. It is a "good" length—30 bases. Of the 30 bases, 17 are Gs or Cs, which is good. There are no Gs or Cs at the ends of the primer, and there are no long repeats.

Chapter 14, Thinking Like a Biotechnician

1. In an ELISA, the last step is to add acid to stop the reaction. Why does adding acid stop the horseradish peroxidase (HRP)/tetramethylbenzidine (TMB) reaction?

   Answer: Acid is added because it denatures the HRP enzyme, so it does not do any further TMB color conversion. It stops the blue color development.

2. If a genome contains 4 billion bp, and a typical sequencing reaction can determine the code of about 500 bp, how many sequencing reactions are needed for a computer to begin piece together the entire genetic code?

   Answer: If a genome contains 4 billion bp, and a typical sequencing reaction can determine the code of about 500 bp, 8 million sequencing reactions are needed for a computer to begin piecing together the entire genetic code! And each sequencing reaction usually overlaps areas and multiple checks. That represents a lot of people doing a lot of sequencing.

3. DNA sequencing requires millions of exact copies of the same DNA strand. How does a technician obtain millions of copies of the same strand to sequence?

   Answer: A technician can get millions of copies of the same DNA strand to sequence in one of two ways: PCR; or cloning cells with plasmids that contain the sequence of interest.

4. Zookeepers want to breed two koalas from different zoos. Another zookeeper is declining, saying that the koalas are two different subspecies. How could that be checked?

   Answer: Theoretically, to determine whether koalas are of different species, DNA fingerprinting through PCR or sequencing of the individual koalas must be conducted. This produces a large set of genetic screens (fingerprints) from known members of each subspecies to be compared.

5. What would an x-ray diffraction pattern look like if the protein crystal used to make the x-ray pattern were not pure?

   Answer: The bands would not be symmetrical around the center and they might be fuzzy. Impurity leads to less resolution (less clarity in bands).

6. Which test could determine whether a fish, such as a salmon, were genetically modified?

   Answer: When DNA is transferred, it is usually accomplished using a plasmid that will have one or more selection or reporter genes. To check whether a fish is transgenic, PCR or sequencing for the foreign reporter or selection gene could be done.

7. What is the minimum number of various types of antibodies needed to develop an ELISA for the protein, amylase?

   Answer: Only one antibody is absolutely required for an amylase ELISA. If an antiamylase antibody can be found, with an enzyme reporter conjugated to it, it is all you would need.

8. Propose an assay to test for oil-eating bacteria (a possible candidate for bioremediation).

   Answers will vary, but to perform an assay for oil-digesting bacteria, one could prepare agar with a concentration of oil high enough to kill all average bacteria. Streak hundreds of the oil-agar plates with samples from the soil and water. Look for healthy bacteria colonies. Some of these may be oil-digesting bacteria.

9. A protein assay is needed to determine which bacteria produces cellulase. What should be bound on [or to?] the protein chip? And, what should be added to detect what is on the protein chip?

   Answer: Cell extracts from all the bacteria samples should be bound on [or to?] the chip, and anticellulase antibodies, with a reporter molecule attached, should be put on the samples to search for cellulase in the bacterial extracts.

10. You are given a solution suspected to contain a very high concentration of protein. How can you use a dialysis bag to crystallize the protein out of solution?

    Answer: Answers will vary. To crystallize a protein, the technician could try to place the protein solution in a dialysis tube and place the bag in a high-molarity salt solution. Then, every hour or so, the technician should add more salt to the beaker so that water will rush out of the bag and force the protein in the bag out of solution into the forming crystals.

Answers to Thinking Like a Biotechnician Questions (Lab Manual)

Lab 1c, Thinking Like a Biotechnician

1. In your notebook, make a chart similar to Table 1.3 that has at least eight rows and four columns. You will use the table to analyze the variables in this experiment that need to be controlled if a technician were to have confidence in the results.

   Answer: Tables will vary but some factors to be analyzed include: temperature, timing, shaking, measurement of reagents, measurement of product, etc. For example:

   Shaking, so curds have time to form and are not broken up, keep still in a test tube rack.
   Accurate measurement, so precise amount of curdling agent or milk (substrate) is added, practice pipeting and micropipeting.
   Filtering, paper absorption affects the amount of whey that filters through, use in the same way each time, and transferring curds and whey to filter more completely, maybe after centrifuging samples.

2. In this experiment, each curdling agent is tested multiple times and an average result is determined. Look at the class data. Does it appear that the number of replications for each curdling agent experiment was sufficient? Yes or no? Explain your answer.

   Answer: Some curdling groups contain replications with numbers that are very dissimilar. Without a formal statistical analysis it is hard to determine exactly how many replicate samples are needed. Increasing the number of replications until the number of dissimilar values is very small will give more confidence in the averaged data.

3. Do you think that the whey-o-meter instrument was adequate for an accurate determination of whey volume and, indirectly, the curd volume? Why or why not? If yes, explain why. If no, propose a better system to determine the volume of curds or the volume of whey.

   Answer: The whey-o-meter instrument was not adequate for an accurate determination of whey volume and, indirectly, the curds volume. It is hard to transfer all the curds and whey to the filter paper and the filter paper absorbs the whey to different degrees in each replication.

Lab 2a, Thinking Like a Biotechnician

1. Describe how you would test kidney bean seeds for the presence of glucose, starch, and protein. Include all reagents, volumes, and testing conditions. Describe the results that you would expect to occur.

   Answer: In four separate test tubes, add the equivalent of 2 mL of chopped kidney beans. Conduct a Benedict's solution test for sugar following the protocol in Part III of the procedures. Beans have a relatively low amount of sugar so a color change of the Benedict's to a greenish-yellow color would be expected. Conduct an iodine test for starch following the protocol in Part 3 of the procedures. Beans have some starch and a color change of some of the iodine to a blue-black would be expected. Conduct a Biuret reagent test for protein following the protocol in Part 3 of the procedures. Beans contain protein and a color change of the Biuret to a blue-violet color would be expected.

2. Which type of molecule(s) tested strongly in all of the egg component samples? Why?

   Answer: The Biuret testing showed protein in all of the samples. This is not surprising since protein makes up approximately 75% of the dry weight of cells.

3. If a pea green color resulted for a sample that was tested with Benedict's solution, what would you conclude about the sugar content? Propose a quantitative method by which the amount of sugar could be determined.

   Answer: A green Benedict's result indicates a relative low amount of sugar. To better estimate the quantity of sugar in a sample, a set of sugar samples of known concentrations (quantities) could be made and tested with Benedict's. Then the unknown sample's color could be compared to the known samples and the concentration estimated.

4. An enzyme is thought to have starch-digesting activity. What indicator might you use to show that starch is being broken down to glucose by an enzyme? How would you measure the reaction? What data would you collect?

Answer: Either a decrease in the starch content could be measured using an iodine test or an increase in sugar production could be measured using a Benedict's test.

5. Why is it necessary to have a negative control group for each test (testing water with each indicator)? What does the negative control result tell you?

Answer: The negative control shows you a negative test, such as when no sugar, starch, or protein is in a sample. The negative result gives a basis for comparison against another color change or positive test.

6. In what ways are these procedures a "controlled" experiment? List the parameters that must be kept constant to obtain meaningful variations in results.

Answer: All the variables in each of the macromolecule experiments, from tube to tube, are the same except one—the sample being tested. For example, the volume tested, the amount of reagent, and the amount of heating are the same for each trial of an experiment.

7. Propose some other use by scientists or consumers for any one of these indicator tests.

Answer: Answers will vary. Indicator tests such as these could be used to test for nutritional content of foods or supplements. Lab samples could be tested for sugar, starch, or protein products using test similar to these.

Lab 2b, Thinking Like a Biotechnician

1. In this experiment, you averaged the results of three technicians' individual experiments. Based on your analysis of the growth data, discuss the advantages and disadvantages of using multiple replications from different technicians.

Answers will vary. One of the advantages is that more readings lessen the effect of erroneous readings. The results are statistically more valid. One of the disadvantages is that reading of an unskilled or careless technician could cause the average to be skewed in one direction.

2. In this experiment, potential biohazards are used (*E. coli* – although we used a safe laboratory strain, *Aspergillus*, yeast). Describe the measures that should be taken by a lab technician or lab manager to protect workers and the public from biohazard contamination.

Answer: Surfaces and equipment must be disinfected before and after use of the biohazard. Petri plates, bottles and instruments containing biohazards must be autoclaved or treated with 10% bleach before disposal. Technician must wash hands with soap and water before and after working with a biohazard. Technician should wear protective garments such as goggles and gloves. No eating or drinking in the laboratory is allowed.

3. In addition to temperature, many other variables will affect *E. coli*'s growth and reproduction. Consider three other variables that could be varied and tested to determine their effect on *E. coli* growth. For each variable you suggest, describe the way an experiment would be conducted to test response to the variable. Include the measuring instruments to be used and the type of data to be collected. Report the variables to be tested, experimental plan, and data collection on a chart.

Answers will vary but might include the type of growth media, the pH of the growth media, the amount of light, or the amount of aeration.

4. *Aspergillus sp.*, like many fungi, is light sensitive. Design an experiment to test the effect of different light levels on *Aspergillus* growth. Propose step-by-step instructions for how to conduct the experiment. Include materials and quantities for each, and data that should be collected.

Answers will vary but should include multiple samples, prepared in identical ways placed in different amounts of light. Covering plates with different numbers of mesh or screens is one way to decrease the amount of light.

5. In this activity, *E. coli* was grown on a solid culture medium (agar). To grow large amounts of *E. coli* broth culture (liquid), large fermentation tanks are used. Search the Internet to find a picture of a fermentation tank that is used to grow large amounts of bacteria. Print an image of the tank, and label it with the reference (Web site URL). Propose a different environmental condition that should be varied and tested when growing *E. coli* in broth instead on agar.

Answers will vary. Conditions that could be varied and tested when growing *E. coli* in broth instead on agar include: temperature, amount of each food nutrient, the amount of aeration, or the pH of the broth (acid-base level).

6. Suppose a biotechnology company is growing cells to make a protein product for sale. Describe the possible impact on a company of growing cells in less-than-optimum conditions.

   Answer: When conditions are not optimum, cells grow more slowly and produce less protein, in this case less product. Less product means less sales.

Lab 2c, Thinking Like a Biotechnician

1. What cell structures did you observe in all of the cell samples?

   Answer: All cells have an outer boundary, the cell (plasma) membrane. Sometimes the cell wall of plant, fungi, or bacteria cells obscures the cell membrane. All cells have cytoplasm and all cells have one or more chromosome(s). In a eukaryotic cell, the chromosome(s) are in the nucleus. All cells also have ribosomes, but ribosomes are too small to be seen with a compound microscope.

2. What structures were only visible in the *Elodea* cells? What is their function? Why do the other cells not have these structures? What might happen if stain is used (accidentally) on *Elodea*?

   Answer: Chloroplasts are visible in the *Elodea* cells and in some types of algae. This is because these leaf cells conduct photosynthesis and the chloroplasts are the site of photosynthesis. Cells that do not do photosynthesis normally would not contain chloroplasts.

3. What is the purpose of using stain to observe cheek cells and onion cells, but not on *Elodea* or the protozoa? What are the advantages and disadvantages to using a stain?

   Answer: Stains increase the contrast between the structures of the sample and the background. Stains usually contain alcohol or something similar that will kill cells. Living *Elodea* cells show cytoplasmic streaming (flowing of cell contents) that stops if the cells are killed.

4. Which cells were from multicellular organisms and which cells were single-celled organisms? What evidence of this do you have from your observations?

   Answer: All the samples are from multicellular organisms except for the protozoan cells in culture and some of the species of algae.

5. If you are having trouble getting something in focus on high power, list three things you should do to correct the problem.

   Answers may vary but the following are the best answers. Make sure the lenses are clean (with lens paper). Go back to low power and make sure your sample is centered and focused at each lower magnification before turning to a higher magnification. Adjust the light down so that there is more contrast.

6. Identify any samples that were difficult to observe. Describe reasons for the difficulties. Propose changes in the procedures that might result in better wet mounts or observations.

   Answers will vary. Any samples that had too many cells make it hard to focus on any particular cell. Take fewer cells to begin with (i.e. banana, tomato, cheek cells). Make sure cells are in a single layer. Look at edges of sample for single cell layers (i.e. *Elodea*).

Lab 2d, Thinking Like a Biotechnician

1. A technician determines the length of a banana cell at both 100X and 400X. He or she determines the length at 100X is 75 µm but the length at 400X is100 µm. Which measurement is more likely to be accurate and why?

   Answer: The measurement at 400X is most accurate since it is easier to estimate the portion of the field is occupied by the image.

2. You may have noticed that the contrast (sharpness) of the image decreases as you increase the magnification of a sample. List a few steps you can take to improve the resolution (ability to distinguish points) of the images at higher magnification.

   Answers will vary. Decrease the amount of light on the image. This will usually increase the contrast and resolution. Move the part of the sample to be observed to the center of the field. The center of the field is sharper than the edges. Make sure the sample is as thin and flat as possible.

3. A 100X objective can be used on a compound microscope, bringing the total possible magnification to 1000X. This lens is called an oil immersion lens since a drop of oil is needed between the objective lens and the coverslip

to help gather more light (The oil corrects for the refractive index of air). Predict what organelles might be visible if the oil immersion lens is used to view eukaryotic cells. Also, list those organelles that you think are so small that even 1000X magnification is not high enough to visualize them.

Answers will vary. Mitochondria, small plastids, vacuoles, lysosomes (as shiny inclusions) may be visible at 1000X. Most other small organelles and structures (Golgi apparatus, endoplasmic reticulum, ribosomes) are only visible with an electron microscope.

4. To visualize very tiny organelles, a scanning electron microscope is used. Go to the Internet and find an electron micrograph (picture from an electron microscope) that shows one or more Golgi bodies. Record the magnification of the micrograph. Record the Web site reference.

Answers will vary.

Lab 2e, Thinking Like a Biotechnician

1. How might carbohydrate structural differences affect how they function in cells and organisms?

Answer: Fructose is the sweetest to most tasters. Glucose and galactose are the same exact atoms with the single variation of one H-atom and one hydroxyl group switched in space. One is granular and one is powdery. One is substantially sweeter than the other. The shape of a molecule and the atoms available for bonding determine the actions and reactions of molecules in cells. Slight differences in shape and structure could mean that a molecule is recognized or not recognized by another molecule. In general, the fewer rings the less sweet the carbohydrate tastes. In general, the more rings, the stickier and less soluble the carbohydrate is.

2. What causes humans to taste sweetness? Use the Internet to learn how the tongue tastes. Use this information to explain how the tasters could rank the sweetness of the same samples differently.

Answer: Humans have a specific pattern of taste buds, containing nerve cells, on their tongues. Sweetness is tasted at the tip of the tongue. Depending on how many taste bud nerve cells are stimulated by sweet molecules, a different sweetness might be sensed. A good diagram and explanation of the nerve cells in taste buds is given at http://www.cf.ac.uk/biosi/staff/jacob/teaching/sensory/taste.html.

Lab 2f Thinking Like a Biotechnician

1. A technician checks the pH of an *E. coli* broth culture that is producing the protein, insulin. The technician finds that the pH has dropped to 5.7 from the desired pH of 6.5. How can the pH be adjusted back to pH 6.5?

Answer: The pH of the culture can be adjusted up by adding a small amount of a base such as 10% NaOH. An instrument called a pH meter is usually used to constantly monitor the pH of cultures.

2. Several proteins will only function within a very specific pH range. Go online and find the optimum pH for the following proteins; pepsin, amylase, and trypsin.

Answers will vary but the optimum pH for pepsin is around 2.0, amylase is around 7.5 and trypsin is around 7.5.

Lab 3a Thinking Like a Biotechnician

1. A 250 µL sample is needed from a sterile vessel that is too thin to use with anything but a sterile pipet. Which pipet and pipet pump could be used to withdraw the mL equivalent to 250 µL from the vessel?

Answer: A 1 mL pipet and blue pump could be used to withdraw 0.25 mL from the sterile vessel.

2. A 1.75 mL sample is needed for an experiment. Both a 2- and a 5-mL pipet will measure this amount. Which pipet is best to use and why?

Answer: A 2-mL pipet is best to use because it has a smaller diameter giving it less error in measurement (judging the meniscus).

3. Practice pipeting dye solution samples to create the mixtures specified in the table below.

a. Measure all solutions into 13x100-mm tubes. Label each tube with the tube number, your initials, and the date.

b. Although you may help each other, pipeting the samples as independently as possible is better practice.

Tube No.	Red Dye Volume (mL)	Blue Dye Volume (mL)	Green Dye Volume (mL)	Total Volume (mL)
1	1.1	1.7	0.33	
2	1.27	0.85	2.9	
3	0.7	2.8	1.8	
4	1.6	1.9	0.66	

- Use the smallest instrument possible for each measurement.
- More than one pipet may be necessary to measure these amounts.
- Evaluation criteria: labels, final volume, and final color/mixing.

Answer: The total volume of each tube is:

Tube 1 = 3.13 mL
Tube 2 = 5.02 mL
Tube 3 = 5.3 mL
Tube 4 = 4.16 mL

Lab 3b, Thinking Like a Biotechnician

1. For most experiments, several reagents must be added to the same tube. Propose a method to keep track of the samples that have been added to a reaction tube.

   Answer: Both of the following methods could and should be used to keep track of samples added to a tube.

   Method #1 – On the reaction matrix, check-off each sample added to the tube.

   Method #2 – Unless instructions state otherwise, when adding several reagents to one tube, release each drop of reagent onto a new location on the inside wall of the tube. This will help keep track of what has been added.

2. Demonstrate the effect of micropipeting incorrectly by doing the following:

   a. Set a P-20 or P-10 to 2 μL.

   b. Purposely, misuse the P-20 or P-10 pipet, and depress the plunger to the second stop.

   c. Suck up this apparent 2-μL volume and release onto a piece of wax paper.

   d. Now, correctly collect a 2-μL volume using the P-20 or P-10.

   e. Release it onto the wax paper next to the other drop. Are the drops noticeably different in size?

   f. How much more is there in the "misused" volume? (Use the pipet to suck up the misused volume in 2-μL increments.)

   g. If a balance or scale is available, and you have been trained to use it, make these measurements on it. Determine the percentage error that would occur if you were to accidentally misuse the pipet in this fashion.

   Answer: A 2-mL pipet is best to use because it has a smaller diameter giving it less error in measurement (judging the meniscus).

3. Practice micropipeting samples to create mixtures by producing the four tubes in the table below.

   a. Measure all solutions into 1.7-mL microtubes. Label all tubes with the tube number, your initials, and the date.

   b. Although you may help each other, micropipeting as independently as possible is better practice.

Tube No.	Red Dye Volume (µL)	Blue Dye Volume (µL)	Green Dye Volume (µL)	Total Volume (mL)
A	27.2	313.0	59.3	
B	555.0	222.0	7.8	
C	133.3	19.8	235.0	
D	9.4	4.1	2.25	

- Use the smallest instrument possible for all measurements.
- Change tips every time.
- More than one pipet may be necessary to measure amounts.
- Total volumes may be checked by using a P-1000.
- Evaluation criteria: labels, final volume, and final color/mixing.

Answer: Total volume in each tube is:

Tube A = 399.5 µL
Tube B = 784.8 µL
Tube C = 388.1 µL
Tube D = 15.75 µL

Lab 3c, Thinking Like a Biotechnician

1. What is the value of a tube containing "0 mg/dL" glucose?

   Answer: The "0 mg/dL" is the negative control and shows the result (amount of color) when no sugar is in the solution. Comparing the negative control to the other test results you can judge the amount of color change due to the presence of glucose.

2. In your opinion, how precise are the test strips in measuring glucose concentration? Give evidence.

   Answer: The test strips are just estimations of glucose concentration for several reasons. One is that the "key" scale values are widely space (i.e. 250 mg/dL down to 100 mg/dL) so exact values are impossible to determine. Also, many variables can affect the results such as timing and the ability of user to distinguish colors.

3. Suggest how the glucose test strips might be used for some other application.

   Answers will vary but one is that testing any solutions for sugar content would be useful for food testing.

4. Complete the Metric Instrument and Conversion Review Sheet that follows.

Metric Instrument and Conversion Review Sheet
Convert each unit and select the appropriate instrument for its measurement.
Instrument Choices
graduated cylinder   10-mL pipet   5-mL pipet   2-mL pipet   1-mL pipet

tabletop balance   P-1000   P-200   P-100   P-20

analytical balance   P-10

1. example 75.34 mg = <u>0.07534</u> g <u>analytical balance</u>	8. example 7.34 mL = 0.00734 L <u>10-mL pipet</u>	15. example 7.534 g = <u>7534 mg</u> <u>tabletop balance</u>
2. 4.3 mL = _____ µL _____	9. 0.34 g = _____ mg _____	16. 5.034 L = _____ mL _____
3. 0.111 mL = _____ µL _____	10. 34.0 g = _____ kg _____	17. 34 mg = _____ µg _____
4. 440.3 mL = _____ L _____	11. 0.004 L = _____ mL _____	18. 15.4 mg = _____ g _____
5. 66 mg = _____ µg _____	12. 80.34 µL = _____ mL _____	19. 1308 g = _____ kg _____
6. 3.33 g = _____ µg _____	13. 4.67 µL = _____ mL _____	20. 99.1 g = _____ mg _____
7. 330.2 mL = _____ L _____	14. 0.022 g = _____ mg _____	21. 0.23 mL = _____ µL _____

4. Answers:

1. 0.07534 g, analytical balance
2. 4,300 µL, 5 mL pipet
3. 111 µL, P-200 micropipet
4. 0.4403 L, graduated cylinder
5. 66,000 µg, analytical balance
6. 3,330,000 µg, tabletop balance
7. 0.3302 L, graduated cylinder
8. 0.00734 L, 10 mL pipet
9. 340 mg, tabletop balance or analytical balance
10. 0.034 Kg, tabletop balance
11. 4 mL, 5 mL pipet
12. 0.08034 mL, P-100 micropipet
13. 0.00467 mL, P-10 micropipet
14. 22 mg, analytical balance

15. 7.534 mg, tabletop balance
16. 5,034 mL, graduated cylinder
17. 34,000 µg, analytical balance
18. 0.0154 g, analytical balance
19. 1.308 Kg, tabletop balance (if it is below the maximum weighable)
20. 99,100 mg, tabletop balance
21. 230 µL, P-1000

Lab 3d, Thinking Like a Biotechnician

Suppose another lab technician in your group is dispensing 100 µL volumes into ten 1.7 mL tubes. On inspection of the samples, several are visibly different from the others and not within the acceptable range of error.

1. Suggest one thing that the technician could do in his operation of the micropipet to improve his pipeting technique.

   Answers will vary. Some answers might include: One thing that the technician could do in his use of a micropipet is to improve his pipeting technique using the P-100 versus the P-200 or P1000 since the small instrument should give the least error. Also, pipeting at eye level and making certain that the technician is using the first and second stop correctly.

2. Suggest something that the technician could do to ensure that the micropipet is measuring correctly.

   Answers will vary but should include checking the calibration of the micropipet by dispensing known volumes on a balance.

Lab 3e, Thinking Like a Biotechnician

1. Most solutions used in a biotechnology facility are colorless. How can the concentration of a colorless solution be checked?

   Answers will vary but one method might include using an indicator solution that changes color due to the presence and concentration of a sample (i.e. Benedict's, iodine, phenol red, Biuret reagent, etc.

2. A technician needs to read the absorbance of several samples on a spectrophotometer. But, after calibrating the spectrophotometer for reading the samples, he or she finds that all of the values are over the upper limit of 2.0 au. Why are all of the absorbance readings so high? What might the technician do to be able to use the spectrophotometer to check the samples?

   Answer: Solution concentrations are probably all too high. All the light the spectrophotometer is shining on the samples is being absorbed because there are just too many molecules in every sample. Dilute all the samples, with the same amount of solvent, until they have absorbance values within the range of the spectrophotometer (0.02-2.0 a.u.).

3. Complete the Making Solutions Review Sheet No. 1.

Making Solutions Review Sheet No. 1

Convert the values as indicated. Specify the appropriate instrument with which the final measurements should be made. For items 10 through 17, show the calculation (equation and units) for the preparation of each solution. Then, draw a diagram of how to make the solution in an appropriate container.

Instrument Choices

graduated cylinder   10-mL pipet   5-mL pipet   2-mL pipet   1-mL pipet

tabletop balance   P-1000   P-200   P-100   P-20

analytical balance   P-10

1. 3.4 mL = _____ μL _____	4. 73.12 μg = _____ mg _____	7. 10.5 μL = _____ mL _____
2. 43.9 mL = _____ L _____	5. 5.39 g = _____ mg _____	8. 7.503 mL = _____ μL _____
3. 0.17 mL = _____ μL _____	6. 30.6 g = _____ mg _____	9. 33 μg = _____ mg _____

Solution To Be Prepared	Diagram of How To Prepare It
10. 25 mL of 2.5 g/mL NaCl solution	11.
12. 10 mL of 50 mg/mL CuSO$_4$ solution	13.
14. 2 L of 0.5 g/mL dextrose solution	15.
16. 100 mL of 0.005 g/mL NaOH solution	17.

3. Answers:

1. 3, 400 μL, 5 mL pipet
2. 0.0439 L, graduated cylinder (or 50 mL pipet)
3. 170 μL, P-200 micropipet
4. 0.07312 mg, analytical balance
5. 5,390 mg, tabletop balance
6. 30,600 mg, tabletop balance
7. 0.0105 mL, P-20 micropipet
8. 7,503 μL, 10 mL pipet
9. 0.033 mg, analytical balance
10. 25 mL x2.5 g/mL = 62.5 grams NaCl in solvent (dH$_2$0) up to 25 mL
11. In a 50 mL tube
12. 10 mL × 50 mg/mL = 500 mg = 0.5 grams CuSO$_4$ in solvent (dH$_2$0) up to 10 mL.
13. In a 15 mL tube
14. Convert 2 L to 2,000 mL then, 2000 mL × 0.5 g/mL = 1000 g of dextrose in solvent (dH$_2$0) up to 2 L.

15. In a 2 L flask or bottle
16. 100 mL $\times$ 0.005 g/mL = 0.5 grams of NaOH in solvent (dH$_2$0) up to 100 mL.
17. In a 125 mL flask or bottle

Lab 3f, Thinking Like a Biotechnician

1. The solutions prepared in this activity are reported as % mass/volume concentration. How would the following % mass/volume concentrations be reported in g/mL units?

    10% NaOH = _____ g/mL NaOH
    5% CuSO$_4$ = _____ g/mL CuSO$_4$
    1.25% gelatin = _____ g/mL gelatin

    Answers:

    10% NaOH = 10 g/100 mL = <u>0.1 g/mL</u> NaOH
    5% CuSO$_4$ = 5 g/100 mL = <u>0.05 g/mL</u> CuSO$_4$
    1.25% gelatin = 1.25 g/100 mL = <u>0.0125 g/mL</u> gelatin

2. Some protein solutions, such as hemoglobin in solution, are colorful. How might the color of hemoglobin impact Biuret indicator testing?

    Answers will vary but one might think that Biuret testing should be done on known hemoglobin solutions to see what color does occur at known concentrations. But it may be hard to see or measure differences in color if the hemoglobin in solution is already colorful (red-brown). Even so, if the results show a difference in color between the hemoglobin samples and a negative control, then the Biuret might be useful as a hemoglobin indicator. Additionally, if the color of tested solutions is visibly different from the Biuret indicator, the Biuret may not be needed for an application such as hemoglobin.

3. Following the protocol in Lab 3e, use the spectrophotometer to check the gelatin solutions' concentration and preparation.

    Answer: Solution concentrations should fall on or near the straight line.

4. Complete the Making Solutions Review Sheet No. 2 that follows.

Making Solutions Review Sheet No. 2

Convert the values as indicated. Specify the appropriate instrument with which the final measurements should be made. For items 10 through 17, show the calculation (equation and units) for the preparation of each solution. Then draw a diagram of how to make the solution.

Instrument Choices

graduated cylinder   10-mL pipet   5-mL pipet   2-mL pipet   1-mL pipet
tabletop balance   P-1000   P-200   P-100   P-20
analytical balance   P-10

1. 0.079 L = _____ mL _____	4. 9.22 mg = _____ g _____	7. 0.085 mL = _____ μL _____
2. 10.72 μL = _____ mL _____	5. 841 μg = _____ mg _____	8. 1.223 mL = _____ μL _____
3. 0.3 mL = _____ μL _____	6. 3.64 g = _____ mg _____	9. 0.19 g = _____ μg _____

Solution To Be Prepared	Diagram of How To Prepare It
10. 40 mL of 6.5-mg/mL $CuSO_4$ solution	11.
12. 200 mL of 8% NaCl solution	13.
14. 0.75 L of 5% dextrose solution	15.
16. 10 mL of 1.25% NaOH solution	17.

4. Answers:

1. 79 mL, graduated cylinder
2. 0.01072 mL, P-20 micropipet
3. 300 μL, P-1000 micropipet
4. 0.00922 g, analytical balance
5. 0.841 mg, analytical balance
6. 3,640 mg, tabletop balance
7. 85 μL , P-100 micropipet
8. 1,223 μL, 2 mL pipet
9. 190,000 μg, tabletop or analytical balance
10. 40 mL × 6.5 mg/mL = 260 mg = 0.260 grams $CuSO_4$ in solvent (dH_2O) up to 40 mL
11. In a 50 mL tube
12. Convert 8% to 0.08. 200 mL × 0.08 = 16 grams NaCl in solvent (dH_2O) up to 200 mL.
13. In a 250 mL flask or bottle
14. Convert 0.75 L to 750 mL. Convert 5% to 0.05. 750 mL × 0.05 = 37.5 g of dextrose in solvent (dH_2O) up to 750 mL.
15. In a 1 L flask or bottle
16. Convert 1.25% to 0.0125. 10 mL × 0.0125 = 0.125 grams of NaOH in solvent (dH_2O) up to 10 mL.
17. In a 15 mL tube

Lab 3g, Thinking Like a Biotechnician

1. Each of the tubes in this activity was made "from scratch" by measuring out a specific mass of dry chemical and mixing it with a specified volume of solvent. Suggest a method to make a 0.5 M solution from the 1M solution. Also, suggest a way to make a 0.1M solution from the 0.5M solution.

   Answer: The 0.5M solution could have been made by diluting the 1M solution. Since 0.5 M is one-half the concentration of 1M, use equal parts water and 1M solution. For example, mix 2.5 mL of the 1 M solution with 2.5 mL of water. Likewise, since the 0.1M solution is one-fifth the concentration of the 0.5 M solution, mix 1 part 0.5 M with 4 parts water.

2. Calculate the mass/volume concentration in each tube and the % mass/volume concentration in each tube and record these data in a table similar to the one below.

Molar Concentration of Each Tube	Concentration (g/mL)	Concentration (%)	Calculations
5 mL of 1 M CuSO$_4$			
5 mL of 0.5 M CuSO$_4$			
5 mL of 0.1 M CuSO$_4$			
5 mL of 0.05 M CuSO$_4$			
5 mL of 0.01 M CuSO$_4$			

Answer: Rounding the MW of the copper sulfate pentahydrate to 250 g/mol,

5 mL of 1 M CuSO$_4$ = 1.25 g/ 5 mL = 25 g/ 100 mL = 0.25 = 25%
5 mL of 0.5 M CuSO$_4$ = 0.625 g/ 5 mL = 12.5 g/ 100 mL = 0.125 = 12.5 %
5 mL of 0.1 M CuSO$_4$ = 0.125 g/ 5 mL = 2.5 g/100 mL = 0.025= 2.5 %
5 mL of 0.05 M CuSO$_4$ = 0.0625 g/5 mL = 1.25 g/100 mL = 0.0125 = 1.25 %
5 mL of 0.01 M CuSO$_4$ = 0.0125 g/ 5 mL = 0.25 g/100 mL = 0.0025= 0.25 %

3. Following the protocol presented in Lab 3e, use the spectrophotometer to check the copper sulfate solutions concentration and preparation.

Answer: Solution concentrations shoul d fall on or near the straight line.

4. Complete the Making Solutions Review Sheet No. 3 that follows.

Making Solutions Review Sheet #3

Convert the values as indicated. Specify the appropriate instrument with which the final measurements should be made. For items 7 through 16, show the calculation (equation and units) for the preparation of each solution. Then draw a diagram showing how to make the solution.

Instrument Choices

graduated cylinder   10-mL pipet   5-mL pipet   2-mL pipet   1-mL pipet
tabletop balance   P-1000   P-200   P-20
analytical balance

1. 0.42 g = _____ μg _____	3. 90.22 μg = _____ g _____	5. 0.0285 mL = _____ μL _____
2. 999 μL = _____ mL _____	4. 80.41 mL = _____ μL _____	6. 70.503 mg = _____ g _____

Solution To Be Prepared	Diagram of How To Prepare It
7. 550 mL of 9.5 mg/mL NaOH	8.
9. 150 mL of 2% $CuSO_4$	10.
11. 3 L of 0.025% dextrose	12.
13. 125 mL of 10 M NaOH	14.
15. 75 mL of 0.1 M NaCl	16.

4. Answers:

1. 420 µg, tabletop or analytical balance
2. 0.999 mL, P-1000 micropipet
3. 0.09022 g, analytical balance
4. 80,410 µL, graduated cylinder
5. 28.5 µL, P-100 micropipet
6. 0.070503 g, analytical balance
7. 550 mL $\times$ 9.5 mg/mL = 5,225 mg = 5.225 grams NaOH in solvent (dH_2O) up to 550 mL
8. In a 1 L flask or bottle.
9. Convert 2% to 0.02. 150 mL $\times$ 0.02 = 3 grams $CuSO_4$ in solvent (dH_2O) up to 150 mL
10. In a 250 mL flask or bottle.
11. Convert 3 L to 3,000 mL. Convert 0.025% to 0.00025. 3,000 mL $\times$ 0.00025 = 0.75 g of dextrose in solvent (dH_2O) up to 3 L.
12. In a 3 L flask or bottle.
13. Convert 125 mL to 0.125 L. 0.125 L $\times$ 40 g/mol $\times$ 10 mol/L = 50 grams of NaOH in solvent (dH_2O) up to 125 mL.
14. In a 125 mL flask or bottle.
15. Convert 7.5 mL to 0.075 L. 0.0075 L $\times$ 58.4 g/mol $\times$ 0.1 mol/L = 0.0438 grams of NaOH in solvent (dH_2O) up to 7.5 mL.
16. In a 15 mL tube.

Lab 3h, Thinking Like a Biotechnician

Complete the Making Solutions Review Sheet No. 4 that follows.

Making Solutions and Dilutions Review Sheet No. 4

Show the calculation (equation and units) for the preparation of each solution. Then draw a diagram of how to make the solution.

Solution To Be Prepared	Diagram of How To Prepare It
1. 50 mL of 15 mg/mL NaOH solution from 100 mg/mL NaOH	2.
3. 10 mL of 0.5 M $CuSO_4$ solution from 10 M $CuSO_4$	4.
5. 2 L of 5 mg/mL gelatin from 1 g/mL gelatin	6.
7. 950 mL of 1X $CuSO_4$ solution from 25X $CuSO_4$	8.
9. 5 L of 0.2 M dextrose solution from 5 M dextrose	10.
11. 100 mL of 2.5X NaOH from 50X NaOH	12.
13. 50 mL of 5 mM NaCl from 1M NaCl	14.

Lab 4a, Thinking Like a Biotechnician

1. A 5M NaCl solution is used in several laboratory activities. Show the calculations and a drawing to explain how to prepare 1 L of 5M NaCl solution.

   Answer: 1. To prepare one liter of 5M NaCl solution,

   1L $\times$ 1 mol/L $\times$ 58.4 g/mol = 58.4 grams of NaCl dissolve in deionized water to a total volume of 1 liter

2. EDTA solution is usually prepared as a concentrated solution and added in small volumes to existing solutions. What volume of 0.5 M EDTA should be added to a solution to make it 1 L at a concentration of 1 mM EDTA?

   Answer: To make it 1 liter at a concentration of 1 mM EDTA, convert 0.5M EDTA to 500mM and 1 L to 1000mL, then

   500mM $\times$ V_1 = 1mM $\times$ 1000 mL

   V_1 = 2 mL

   Add 2 mL of 0.5M EDTA to 998 mL of solvent (deionized water).

3. The TE buffer protocol suggests sterilizing the filter. Why sterilize the TE buffer? Propose another method to sterilize the TE buffer besides filter sterilization.

   Answer: Sterilizing removes bacteria or fungus that could grow in the TE buffer. Since the TE buffer is used as a DNA storage solution, sterilizing the buffer decreases the chance that DNA will be degraded by microorganisms or their enzymes. Sterilizing in an autoclave at 15 psi for 15-20 minutes is an alternative to filter sterilizing.

Lab 4b, Thinking Like a Biotechnician

1. In this activity, you precipitated DNA, ordered from a biological supply house, out of a relatively pure solution. Which molecules did the supply company have to remove to purify this DNA?

   Answer: To purify the DNA, all other molecules found in salmon sperm cells had to be removed from the salmon sperm DNA sample including, carbohydrates, lipids, and proteins.

2. If 100% of the DNA was recovered during spooling and transferred to the 2 mL of TE buffer in step 10, what would the approximate final concentration of DNA be in the tube?

Answer: The pre-spooling concentration was 2 mg/mL in a volume of 2 mL. That equals 4 mg of DNA in solution. If all of the DNA is recovered and put back into 2 mL of TE buffer that would result in 2 mg/mL DNA again.

3. Why is the final sample refrigerated?

   Answer: The final sample is refrigerated because cold temperatures decrease the "breakdown" activity of any enzymes, bacteria, or fungi in solution.

Lab 4c, Thinking Like a Biotechnician

1. The spooled DNA was "pure" before spooling and should still be relatively pure after spooling. If the DNA and protein test results are not as expected, what could be contaminating the samples?

   Answer: NaCl, ethanol (most likely interferant to DPA), TE buffer, contaminant bacteria or fungus, contamination from dirty equipment or hands could be contaminating the samples.

2. If a DPA test turns brownish, what may be concluded?

   Answers may vary but if a DPA test turned brownish, it may be the result of a mixture of DNA and RNA in the sample or it may be due to outdated DPA reagents.

3. If the results of testing a known DNA solution are negative, what might be the reason?

   Answers will vary but the most likely reason for a negative test result when testing a known DNA solution is that there may be too little a concentration of DNA to be detected by the testing.

Lab 4d, Thinking Like a Biotechnician

1. Why are the positive and negative controls necessary in the EtBr dot test?

   Answer: In the EtBr Dot Test, the negative control is necessary to show the amount that EtBr glows, in UV light, when no DNA is present. And it does glow a bit. Any additional glowing is due to the presence of the DNA. The positive control is needed to show a positive test with a known concentration of sample. In this case, 2 mg/mL of DNA was the starting concentration of the spooled salmon sperm DNA sample. The unknowns should have DNA but the same or less than the starting sample.

2. EtBr is a dangerous chemical. Go online and find a Materials Safety Data Sheet (MSDS) for EtBr. Copy and paste the sections that describe the following:

   > potential health effects (acute and chronic)
   > first-aid measures
   Answer: The MSDS sheets will show the hazards.

3. Suggest a method to better estimate the concentration of DNA in the unknown samples.

   Answers will vary but a better estimate of the concentration of DNA might be made by making a serial dilution of the 4 mg/mL salmon sperm DNA stock solution. By testing each with EtBr, a better scale of concentration versus glowing could be made. This would lead to better estimates of the unknowns. Additionally a spectrophotometer might be used to estimate the amount of glowing orange.

Lab 4e, Thinking Like a Biotechnician

1. After making several batches of sterile LB broth, you see pieces of dust in the broth. Is the broth suitable to use? How could the dust have entered the bottles?

   Answers will vary. It is probably OK to use broth that has sterile pieces of inert dust in it but the technician would probably be concerned about any other contaminants. The dust is probably present from not washing or drying the glassware properly.

2. Why is it not advisable to heat or sterilize media longer than necessary?

   Answer: When preparing media, longer heating times may result in excess evaporation of water from the media. This increases the concentration of solutes in the media and depending on the concentration this could be detrimental to the microorganisms growing on it.

3. Additional compounds can be added to agar before sterilization (or sometimes after). An example of this is "milk agar," in which 2% nonfat powdered milk is added to the agar base. Lactose-digesting bacteria like to grow on milk agar. How many grams of nonfat powdered milk should be added to the 125 mL of LB agar to end up with 2% milk LB agar? Show your calculations.

Answer: To determine the amount of powdered milk needed for, 2% milk agar, convert 2% to 0.02, then 0.02 g/mL × 125 mL = 2.5 g of powdered milk

4. Growing mammalian, fungal, and bacterial cells in or on sterile, prepared media is critical for their study. Each type has specific requirements for growth. Access the Web site address that follows to find information that allows you to compare and contrast the ingredients required by *E. coli* bacteria cells versus human cells in culture: http://users.rcn.com/jkimball.ma.ultranet/BiologyPages/M/Media.html

Record your analysis in your notebook. How many more ingredients are necessary for human cell culture? Explain why mammalian cells, such as human cells, have so many more required ingredients in their growth media.

Answer: Over 40 additional ingredients are listed. Bacterial cells make are simpler and lived independently. They make most of the compounds that they need. Mammalian cells are part of a larger organism with specialized cells and tissues to synthesize and process compounds. Since the mammalian cells are grown isolated from the rest of the organism they must be given compounds normally supplied by the organism.

Lab 4f, Thinking Like a Biotechnician

1. Name five things you can do to decrease the chance of contaminating a sample.

Answers will vary but should include five of the following things you can do to decrease the chance of contaminating a sample; washing hands prior to work, tying back loose hair, taking off baggy or hanging clothes, rolling sleeves above elbows, keep fingers of faces and surfaces, working in the laminar flow hood, use of disinfectant on surfaces and apparatus, autoclaving materials as appropriate.

2. When pouring plates, you notice that the agar is coming out in lumps. Why is this undesirable and what corrective measures can you take?

Lumps in agar make it difficult to streak out individual bacteria cells. As soon as it is noticed the bottle should be reheat/reliquified to make them pourable.

3. LB agar plates are needed for several days of lab work. If eight sleeves of Petri plates (20 plates/sleeve) are need, each poured with about 20 mL, what total volume of LB agar should you prepare?

Answer: For 8 sleeves of Petri plates, 3 L of agar are needed.

Lab 4g, Thinking Like a Biotechnician

1. After streaking a plate with a colony of *E. coli* cells and incubating it overnight at 37°C, a technician returns to find no colonies on the plate. List three reasons this could happen.

Answer: Answers will vary but the following three are probably the best answers for no colonies on the plate. Too hot of an inoculating loop could have "fried" the bacteria sample. The target colony may never have been picked up by the technician (the technician missed it). The incubator could have been set at a "bad" temperature.

2. You make 1 L of LB agar and pour it into five media bottles for sterilization. After autoclaving and cooling them, you notice some of the bottles have agar that is not completely solid, while other bottles do have solidified agar, as expected. What should you do? Are any of them usable? If so, which ones?

Answer: If the agar did not solidify, then the media was not prepared correctly. In adequate heating before autoclaving can result in incomplete suspension of the agar base. All bottles should be cleaned and the media remade.

3. Propose a method to check if a laminar flow hood is still working correctly (filtering out all the bacteria and fungi from the air).

Answers will vary but one idea to check to see if the laminar flow hood is working properly is to place an opened sterile agar Petri plate into the center of the LFH countertop. Leave it for 3 days. Check for any contamination.

Lab 4h, Thinking Like a Biotechnician.

1. Protease is used in this experiment to chop up protein contaminants. There are many different kinds of proteases. One protease that can be purchased at the grocery store is papain, a protease derived from papayas, which is found in meat tenderizers, such as Adolphs® meat tenderizer. How can one know that 1 mg/mL of papain is the best concentration of the protease to use? Describe a simple experiment to determine the best concentration for protease activity.

   Answers will vary. A simple experiment to determine the best concentration for protease activity should include something about making a serial dilution of the protease and testing its ability to break down a protein (maybe gelatin) at different concentrations.

2. You used 10% SDS in the experiment to explode the bacteria cells and precipitate protein contaminants. One can purchase 20% SDS commercially. How much 20% SDS would you need to have enough to make 2000 mL of 10% SDS?

   Answer: To make 2000 mL of 10%SDS,

   $20\% \times V_1 = 10\% \times 2000$ mL
   $V_1 = 1000$ mL
   Mix 1000 mL of 20% SDS with 1000 mL of dH_2O to make 2000L of 10% SDS

3. The genomic DNA that was spooled was considerably less in volume than the salmon sperm DNA spooled in a previous lab experiment. What is the reason for the difference in DNA yield?

   Answer: The salmon sperm DNA solution was prepared at 2 mg/mL, which is very concentrated. The bacteria DNA came from bursting a relatively small number of cells that have not only DNA in them but a lot of protein and other molecules.

Lab 4i, Thinking Like a Biotechnician

1. The agarose gel in this lab is prepared with 1X TAE buffer, not water. What is the reason water is not used?

   Answer: The salmon sperm DNA solution was prepared at 2 mg/mL (which is very concentrated). The bacteria DNA came from bursting a relatively small number of cells that have not only DNA in them but also a lot of protein and other molecules.

2. A 30-mL gel is recommended for most samples. What are the disadvantages of pouring a gel thicker or thinner than 30 mL?

   Answers will vary. The disadvantages of pouring a gel thicker or thinner than 30 mL is that too thick of a gel wastes agarose which is pretty expensive, it takes longer to stain a fat gel. Too thin of a gel might break or split, the wells could be too small to hold all the sample.

3. E-gels are commercially prepared agarose gels that will run tiny volumes of samples (see Figure 4.19). They require a special e-gel box set up. Go online and find companies that sell e-gels. What concentrations are available, and how many sample wells do the gels have?

   Answer: Answers will vary, but should include information similar to this found on an invitrogen.com webpage: e-gels of 0.8% to 4% are available with 12 wells each.

Lab 4j, Thinking Like a Biotechnician

1. Give plausible reasons for the following results on your gel.

   a. When stained and visualized on the UV light box, other gels have many bands and smears of DNA. Your gel has no bands, smears, or anything on it. What may have caused these results?

   Answer: In order of likelihood:

   - Putting the gel into the gel box with the wrong orientation (wells on the positive side (red) instead of the negative side would cause the samples to run the wrong way and off the gel.
   - Running the gel at too high a voltage or current could have resulted in all the samples running of the gel.

- Sample may have never been loaded.
- The EtBr stain may be old and not staining well

b. A sample that is supposed to give a straight, single band has a big smear of DNA down most of the lane. What may have caused this smearing?

Answer: Most likely the smearing is sheared DNA, the result of DNase contamination (random cutting of the DNA into a bunch of lengths). Mechanical shearing from rough pipeting is less likely but possible.

c. All the bands and smears of samples are located right next to the wells and have not moved very far. What may have caused this?

Answer: Slow movement through the gel could be because

- Too low of concentration of buffer so not much electricity moving through gel box
- Gel gates are up or gel is blocked so electricity is not flowing through the gel correctly.
- Agarose never dissolve correctly so the gel matrix does not allow easy movement of the molecules through the gel.

2. On semi-log graph paper, plot the distance the DNA standard fragments traveled from the wells (in mm) on the horizontal axis versus their size (in base pairs) on the vertical axis. Draw a "best-fit" straight line that represents how DNA fragments of different lengths move through the gel. Use this graph to estimate the sizes of the plasmid bands.

Results: graphs will appear slightly different because of different data, but each should be a line that "averages" all the data points. If any single point is a far-outlier, it might be considered invalid. Consider drawing the best-fit straight line without the most significant outlier.

Lab 5a Thinking Like a Biotechnician

1. How likely is it that one Ouchterlony test will give results that lead to the understanding of an organism's allergic response? Explain.

Answer; It is not very likely that one Ouchterlony Test will give results that lead to the understanding of an organism's allergic response since we only test a small number of antigens as possible allergens.

2. Why is the speed of agglutination or precipitation not a valuable piece of data in this experiment?

Answer: The speed of agglutination has to do with how soon the antibody and antigen come in contact, which is dependent on how quickly they diffuse through the agar. The diffusion of a molecule through the agar is dependent on its size not its attraction to an antibody or antigen.

3. Setting up an Ouchterlony test may be time consuming. Why not just mix two solutions together to see if they clump? Suggest an advantage to having the molecules diffuse through and precipitate in the agar.

Answers will vary but it may be easier to see the degree of precipitation (how allergic) when it is in the agar Petri plate versus in a tube. Other variables such as antibody-antigen concentrations for precipitation could be tested in an Ouchterlony plate.

Lab 5b, Thinking Like a Biotechnician

1. In any of the trials, did it appear that at some point, adding more of the enzyme did not increase juice yield substantially? Why might that be true?

Answer: There is a limited amount of substrate. Once all the cells have burst open because of the action of the enzymes, there is no source of additional juice.

2. Sketch what a line graph would look like if the data showed that at some point, adding more of the enzyme did not increase juice yield substantially.

Answer: The graph would show an increase in juice yield to some point and then level off.

3. Suggest a method to determine the optimum temperature for pectinase activity. Include experimental procedures.

Answers will vary but should include samples tested at different temperatures, all samples should have the same reagent (volume, mass, and concentration), all samples should be treated (except for the temperature) and measured in the same way, juice yield should be measured in some numerical fashion.

There are no *Thinking Like a Biotechnician* questions in Lab 5c.

Lab 5d, Thinking Like a Biotechnician

1. Discuss the practicality of using Biuret reagent to identify the concentration of protein solutions. Was it a reliable method? Why? Why not?

   Answer: Only moderately reliable because the Biuret's high pH denatures the protein sample and causes it to precipitate. This makes it hard to judge the color. In addition it is difficult to distinguish between the blues at different concentrations.

2. Does a negative Biuret test mean that there is no protein in a sample? Explain.

   Answer: A negative Biuret test does not necessarily mean that there is no protein in a sample? A sample may give a negative protein test with Biuret and still have a low concentration of protein, one lower than Biuret's sensitivity.

3. A serial dilution of greater range may be needed for the Biuret standards. Explain how you would create a 1:10 dilution of the albumin for Biuret testing.

   Answer: To make a 1:10 dilution of the albumin, for every milliliter, 100 μL of sample is mixed with 900 μL of solvent.

Lab 5e, Thinking Like a Biotechnician

1. Laemmli buffer contains TRIS, boric acid, and SDS. What is the function of each ingredient in this buffer?

   Answer: TRIS is the buffering salt and it conducts electricity and maintains pH. Boric Acid brings the pH of the TRIS from about pH 9 down to about 6.8, a more protein friendly pH. The SDS linearizes the protein and covers it with negative charge.

2. It takes a bit of mixing to get some proteins to go into solution, while other proteins go into solution more easily. Why?

   Answers will vary but the solubility of molecules has to do with their size, shape, charge and polarity. To dissolve, a molecule has to be surrounded by water and some molecules have groups that repel water molecules.

3. If the protein solution needs sterilization for long-term storage, why not autoclave it?

   Answer: The high temperature that occurs during autoclaving denatures proteins and may change the protein in a way that is not desirable for the application.

Lab 5f, Thinking Like a Biotechnician

1. A technician sets up and starts a PAGE. Current is flowing, and bubbling is visible at the electrodes. After 30 minutes, none of the samples have moved out of the wells. List three things the technician should check.

   Answers will vary but if sample has not moved out of the wells of a gel some things to check include; if the tape was removed from the bottom slit, if the gel is placed in the gel box in the correct orientation – not backward, that the buffer completely covered the wells, that there are no air bubbles blocking the flow of electricity at the bottom of the gel.

2. If a gel has a band significantly darker and fatter than all the other bands on the gel, suggest a few reasons for that result.

   Answers will vary. A fat band can mean a single, highly concentrated sample of a single polypeptide. It can also mean the two bands of nearly the same molecular weight have not completely separated.

3. Every amino acid has a different molecular weight because of different R groups. Using amino acid data at: http://au.expasy.org/tools/pscale/Molecularweight.html, one can determine that the average molecular weight of an amino acid is about 137 daltons. Use the average molecular weight of an amino acid and the estimated

molecular weight of the polypeptide chains in the protein you studied to determine the approximate number of amino acids in the protein.

Answers will vary based on which protein is studied and the estimates made but the number of amino acids in a protein can usually be found at the NBCI website. For example, good estimate for amylase is 61,000 daltons/137 daltons per amino acid = 445 amino acids.

Lab 5g, Thinking Like a Biotechnician

1. Do you know the concentrations of protein in the muscle extract samples loaded on the gel? How can you find out?

   Answer: No, you do not know the concentrations of the original samples but we can consider the original extraction a 1X stock. An indicator test or a spectrophotometer could be used to determine concentration.

2. Many proteins have bands of the same molecular weight. If you find a protein band that you are fairly confident is a particular protein or polypeptide, how might you confirm that the protein is actually the one you think it is?

   Answers will vary but to confirm that the protein is actually the one you think it some techniques include protein sequencing or antibody recognition (like with an ELISA or a Western Blot).

3. A lane on a gel has a huge smear in it. What is the most likely cause, and how can the problem be corrected on future gels?

   Answer: If a lane on a gel has a huge smear in it, the sample is too concentrated or the volume is overloaded. Try diluting the sample or loading less volume. Do a bigger dilution to determine an optimum concentration and volume for resolution on the gel.

Lab 6a

There are no *Thinking Like a Biotechnician* questions in Lab 6a.

Lab 6b, Thinking Like a Biotechnician

1. How can you tell if the 2% starch solution gives the best (most comparable) results for the starch assay?

   Answer: To determine a 2% starch solution gives the best (most comparable) results for the starch assay, conduct a test of the starch assay with varying concentrations of starch to determine what indicator results to expect at higher and lower concentrations of starch.

2. The aldose assay may display up to five color changes in the 2-minute reaction time. Propose an explanation for each of the colors that appear during the assay.

   Answers will vary but one explanation of the many colors seen in a Benedict's test is that the reaction turning the Benedict's Reagent orange mixes slowly with the remaining blue unreacted Benedict's. So that leads to green, yellow, orange, red-orange, in that order, with increasing amounts of glucose.

3. Drawing on your experience with sugar testing, is there any other indicator system that could be used to assay for the presence or concentration of sugar in this experiment?

   Answer: Another indicator system that might be used to assay for the presence or concentration of sugar in this experiment is the Diastix® or other glucose testing strips.

Lab 6c, Thinking Like a Biotechnician

1. Which of these assays should give the "best" results?

   Answer: The starch breakdown assay should progress for several hours and thus the iodine starch assay should show dramatic differences. Maltose and glucose production must be fairly high to show with the indicator strips or Benedict's.

2. If an assay shows a 100-mg/dL-glucose concentration, what is that value measured in percent (%) of glucose? Show the calculations.

Answer: If an assay shows an 100 mg/dL glucose concentration then 100 mg/dL × 1 dL/10 mL = 10 mg/mL = 0.01 g/mL × 100 parts = 1% glucose

3. Why would the use of a multichannel pipet give "better" results?

Answer: The use of a multi-channel pipet gives better results for each measurement and dispensing would be the same and more comparable than using a traditional pipet.

Lab 6d, Thinking Like a Biotechnician

1. If an extract gives a negative result in the antimicrobial assay, does that mean that the extract is not an antimicrobial agent?

Answer: If an extract gives a negative result in the antimicrobial assay, it does not necessarily mean that the extract is not an antimicrobial. Only one bacteria strain was tested. Theoretically, every extracted would be tested on every bacterial strain or species of interest.

2. In preparing the sample disks, some of the methanol extractions smell like alcohol. Why is that a problem?

Answer: Methanol itself is an antimicrobial agent, so if the methanol is not removed from the extract, the test would assay methanol instead of the extracted compounds.

3. Each extract may have one or more compounds in it. What should be done to begin to identify the exact compound in an extract that is causing the antimicrobial action?

Answers will vary. To determine what compound in an extract is active, a technician should research how to do organic separations and start testing separations of the extracts. Also, protein indicators can be used on extracts to see if any measurable amount of protein may be present. If it is, a PAGE gel could be run to start to characterize it. Protein separation techniques (future chapters) could be used and isolated tested.

Lab 6e, Thinking Like a Biotechnician

1. For this assay, which is better: a fast-growing bacteria colony that has a large cloudy halo around it or a slow-growing colony that has a small- to medium-size, very clear halo around it?

Answers will vary but clarity of halo is the most important factor when try to locate good amylase producers. Size of halo could be due to amount of amylase produced or could be a diffusion issue.

2. Is there a method to get any of the bacteria colonies showing the results from question No. 1 to have additional desirable characteristics?

Answer: Yes. To try to induce more amylase production from cells, mutate the bacteria (site-specific mutagenesis) and try to get them to express more desirable traits.

3. None of these bacteria will be used in our efforts to make large volumes of amylase. Give a good reason and explanation for why these bacteria are less attractive for that purpose than genetically engineered *E. coli* to produce amylase.

Answers will vary but may include that we will not use "wild" bacteria because they have not been identified and thus could be harmful strains to humans or the environment. It would take months to characterize the bacteria to the point of understanding whether it is safe or not as well as all of its growth requirements. From experience, we know that the *E. coli* strains used for genetic engineering are safe and that it grows well in broth culture (required for large-scale manufacturing).

Lab 6f, Thinking Like a Biotechnician

1. H_2O and H_2O_2 seem similar in structure and function. Compare and contrast the structure and function of these molecules.

Answer: Both H_2O and H_2O_2 are colorless liquids but the extra oxygen on hydrogen peroxide makes it a strong oxidizing agent that is toxic to cells.

2. Enzymes are protein catalysts that may be used over and over again to speed reactions. They are not used up in the reactions they catalyze. How can you test to see whether the enzymes are used in a reaction?

Answers will vary. One way to test to see if enzymes get used up in a reaction is to measure the samples before and after the enzymatic reactions.

3. Propose a method of extracting hydrogen peroxidase from liver?

    Answers will vary. One way to purify proteins from tissue samples is to grind the liver samples and extract the proteins with a solvent containing acetone or ammonium sulfate.

Lab 6g, Thinking Like a Biotechnician

1. If large smears of sample appear in some of the lanes, what might be done to improve the resolution of sample in the lanes on the gel?

    Answer: The main reason for smearing is overloading of sample (too high of a concentration). Further diluting of samples might help. Loading less volume may help. Also, making sure the samples are hot (denatured) when loading may improve resolution.

2. Discuss methods that could be used to determine whether peroxidase is present, and, if so, at what concentration or activity.

    Answers will vary. Doing an assay for peroxidase activity would confirm the presence of the enzyme. One substrate of peroxidase is hydrogen peroxide. Peroxidase should break down hydrogen peroxide releasing bubbles that could be counted or collected.

3. The samples loaded on the gel are dilutions of the extraction. How can we know the total content of protein in the sample versus the concentration of HRP in the sample?

    Answers will vary. Total protein content could be determined using indicators or spectrophotometers. By studying the number and intensity of non-HRP bands on the gel, an estimate of the ration of HRP to other proteins in the extracts can be made.

Lab 6h, Thinking Like a Biotechnician

1. If the TMB color change is still occurring even at extremely low concentrations of HRP, what might the technician do to make the assay more usable?

    Answer: If the TMB color change is too much even at low concentrations of HRP, the technician might try to dilute the TMB reagent.

2. The HRP enzyme can be linked (conjugated) to an antibody. How might that allow better visualization of the molecules of interest?

    Answers will vary but should include that when an antibody that has HRP on it finds its antigen, a TMB assay can show that the complex is present.

3. Explain how an antibody conjugated with HRP might be used in an ELISA.

    Answer: The amount of color change due to antibody binding and HRP activity can give a concentration value for antigen present. The color change can be read on a plate reader.

Lab 7a, Thinking Like a Biotechnician

1. What are the approximate wavelengths of the colors, blue-green, mustard-yellow, and red-orange?

    Answer: Blue-green light includes wavelengths near 500 nm, mustard-yellow light includes wavelengths near 585 nm, red-orange light includes wavelengths near 610 nm.

2. The lowest wavelength at which you can see color is the lowest point of the visible spectrum for you. The highest wavelength at which you can see color at is the top of the visible spectrum for you. What is your own personal visible spectrum?

    Answers will vary but the lowest value for a person's visible spectrum would be above 300 nm and the highest value would be around 700 nm.

3. Look at another technician's graphs. Are they exact duplicates of your? Why or why not?

Answer: Other graphs are probably not exactly like others because of the precision of the instruments and more importantly the retina cells of each individual see color differently

Lab 7b, Thinking Like a Biotechnician

1. Study the peaks and valleys of each absorbance spectrum. Does the red sample absorb non-red light while transmitting red wavelengths? What about the blue and green spectra? Explain

   Answer: Yes, the red sample absorbs non-red light (blue and green wavelengths in the high 400s and low 500s) while transmitting or reflecting red wavelengths in the 600s? Blue absorbs red wavelengths and transmits and reflects blue, and green spectra?

2. What factors affect the height of a peak on an absorbance spectrum? Sketch a scratch graph showing the pattern you would predict for the relative absorbance spectra for red solutions at 1X, 0.5X, and 0.25X.

   Answer: The height of a peak on an absorbance spectrum is related to the number of molecules in solution (the concentration). On a graph, all three solutions would have the same shape. Just the amplitude (height) of the graph would be different. The 0.5X should be twice as high as the 0.25X. And the 1X should be twice as concentrated as 0.5X.

3. Sketch an absorbance spectrum that would be expected if you were studying carotene, the orange pigment in carrots.

   Answer: The absorbance spectrum for carotene will look like that for the red food coloring but lambda $_{min}$ would be shifted over to about 590 nm.

Lab 7c, Thinking Like a Biotechnician

1. Certain substances, including bleach, alcohols, and oils, do not have a "pH" value; they give false readings, or no readings, with the indicator strips or pH meter. What characteristic must a solution have to give it a pH reading?

   Answer: A solution has to have an excess of H+ or OH- ions to give a pH reading. The substances listed do not ionize to release H+ or OH- ions. They are either uncharged or nonpolar solutions. Bleach is an oxidizing agent and actually removes the color from the indicator strips.

2. A fermentation tank full of bacterial cell culture needs to be monitored for changes in pH. If the pH is too high or too low, the cells could die. Propose a method to monitor and maintain the pH of the culture.

   Answer: To monitor and maintain the pH of a culture, a pH meter could be installed and set to continuously monitor the culture. If the pH starts to get too high or low acid or base could be added. All of these things need to be done under sterile conditions.

Lab 7d, Thinking Like a Biotechnician

1. Why is the improper storage a problem?

   Answer: Improper storage is a problem because proteins begin to denature or degrade at room temperature mainly because of protease activity. Filter sterilizing removes bacteria and fungi but does not remove any protease contaminating the sample. Storing at 4°C decreases protease activity.

2. How can the sample be tested to determine whether it is still usable?

   Answer: The sample concentration could be checked through spectrophotometry. The sample activity could be checked with an amylase activity assay.

Lab 7e, Thinking Like a Biotechnician

1. When preparing a buffer, why is water added in two stages? Why is water not added to the buffering salt, up to the desired final volume, all in one step?

Answer: Water is added in two stages during buffer preparation because there has to be room to add acid or base for pH adjust without going over the final volume. If the final volume gets too high the concentration of the buffering salts in the solution will be wrong.

2. Look at other results for this experiment. Do the graphs of other groups look the same as yours? Consider two groups that have conducted the TRIS buffer effic**acy** test. Both groups' graphs are the same shape, but Group 1's entire graph is 1 pH unit lower than Group 2's graph. Explain how this could happen.

   Answer: If one or the other of the pH meters is not calibrated correctly, all values will be off by the same amount resulting in a graph that is lower at each reading.

3. In March, a buffer is prepared and used. The unused portion is stored at 4°C. In August, a technician wants to use it. On inspection, the technician sees a tiny bit of fuzz in the buffer on the bottom of the bottle. Is the buffer usable? Why or why not? What do you think the fuzz is?

   Answers will vary but the fuzz in the old buffer is probably fungal growth and the buffer should not be used. Fungal contamination will change the concentration of the buffer and may have added unwanted compounds into the buffer. One other possibility, one of the buffer ingredients came out of solution (precipitated).

Lab 7f, Thinking Like a Biotechnician

1. Instead of a nice, smooth, bell-shaped curve, the absorbance spectrum for a molecule has one point that is "spiked up" to about 0.8 au above the rest of the graph. What might cause this?

   Answer: A 'spike' in an absorbance spectrum could occur if a technician forgot to calibrate the spec (re-zero or re-100% the transmission) when changing wavelength. The absorbance would be inaccurate giving an erroneous spike or depression in the graph.

2. Amylase is a colorless molecule, thus, Bradford reagent was used in this experiment to make it visible in the Spec 20 D. Name at least one disadvantage to using the Bradford reagent on a suspected amylase sample.

   Answer: One disadvantage to using Bradford Reagent is that it denatures the protein in the sample making it unusable. If there is limited supply of sample, the technician would not want to "waste" a sample in visible spectrophotometry.

3. Xanthophyll is the yellow pigment in lemons. Sketch the absorbance spectrum that would be expected for a sample of xanthophyll.

   Answer: The absorbance spectrum for xanthophylls would have Lambda $_{max}$ probably in the blue wavelengths maybe around 475-500 and Lambda $_{min}$ in the yellow wavelengths between 560 – 580 nm.

4. Propose a method to detect colorless amylase in a sample and still be able to recover it, unaltered, for future use.

   Answer: UV spec could be used to detect colorless amylase. The UV spec does not alter the protein and it is retrievable for future use.

Lab 7g, Thinking Like a Biotechnician

1. Without using the spectrophotometer, how can you estimate the concentration of amylase in the unknown samples?

   Answer: The concentration of amylase in the unknown samples be estimated by doing the following. Prepare amylase-Bradford mixtures. The amount of blueness in the unknowns can be compared to the known solutions ("eye-balling"). These give a rough estimate of the concentrations.

2. On the best-fit standard curve, all the points are lined up, except the 10-mg/mL sample. It is much lower than the rest of the line. Why might this be? Should the value be used in the standard curve?

   Answer: If the 10-mg/mL reading is not in line with the others on the graph, the sample is probably so concentrated that it is hard to get an accurate absorbance reading. The reading is lower than it should be. If this happens, the reading should not be used in the standard curve because its changes the slope of the line.

3. A set of proteins is studied in the spectrophotometer. The linear regression ($y = mx + b$) gives a slope of $m = 0.93$. An unknown sample's absorbance is measured at 0.66 au. What is the approximate concentration of the unknown sample?

Answer: b=0, so x=y/m and $\times$ = 0.71 mg/mL. The concentration of the unknown is approximately 0.71 mg/mL.

There are no *Thinking Like a Biotechnician* questions in Lab 7h.

Lab 7i, Thinking Like a Biotechnician

1. When analyzing a 1-mg/mL amylase absorbance spectrum, most of the absorbance values peak at 2 au. Why is this a problem in determining the lambda$_{max}$ of the sample? What should be done?

   Answer: It is not helpful to have most of the absorbance values peak at 2 au because the highest point on the absorbance spectrum cannot be ascertained. It can only be guessed. The sample should be diluted until all of the absorbance values fall under 2.0 au.

2. When analyzing the 1-mg/mL amylase absorbance spectrum, most of the absorbance values peak at under 0.2 au, and most are under 0.02 au. Why is this a problem in determining the lambda$_{max}$ of the sample? What should be done?

   Answer: It is not helpful to have most of the absorbance values peak at are under 0.2 au or 0.02 au because the highest point on the absorbance spectrum cannot be easily ascertained. It can only be guessed. The sample should be prepared at a higher concentration so that lambda$_{max}$ falls between 1.0 and 2.0 au.

Lab 8a, Thinking Like a Biotechnician

1. What is the purpose of the +C and -C tubes? Did they give expected results? Should there have been any other "C" tubes? If so, what would be in them?

   Answer: The + C tube shows what uncut Lambda DNA looks like and allows you to judge if the restriction digestion was complete. The –C tube reveals that the *Hin*dIII enzyme does not show up on the gel. There should have been a +EcoRI, -Lambda tube with enzyme and no Lambda to see that EcoRI is not visible on the gel.

2. A technician runs the samples of the restriction digestion, and, in one lane, there are almost twice the number of bands expected. Give a possible reason for the extra bands.

   Answers will vary but one possibility for extra bands in a lane is that there was cross contamination of enzymes and both cut the DNA. Another is that sample from one well overflowed into an adjacent well.

3. A technician needs smaller sizing standards than the ones produced from a Lambda/*Hin*dIII digestion. She wants to create a smaller sizing standard. There is another restriction enzyme, *Hae*III, in the –20°C freezer. It cuts DNA more often than *Hin*dIII (since it has a shorter, more common recognition site). A Lambda/*Hae*III digestion is performed, and the samples are run on a gel. Smaller bands are seen. How might the technician estimate the size of these pieces?

   Answers might vary but one way to estimate fragment size is to prepare a best-fit standard curve of the Lambda/HindIII pieces versus the distance they travel on the gel. Measure the distance the Lambda/HaeIII pieces travel on the gel and use the graph to estimate their sizes.

Lab 8b, Thinking Like a Biotechnician

1. What is the actual concentration of plasmid DNA in Tube H?

   Answer: The actual concentration of plasmid DNA in tube H would be 0.1 µg/µL initial concentration $\times$ 3 µL /10 µL total = 0.03 µg/µL.

2. What mass of plasmid DNA is in Tube H?

   Answer: 0.1 µg/µL initial concentration $\times$ 3 µL used = 0.3 µg of plasmid DNA in tube H.

3. A restriction map can be drawn showing the relative positions of the *Bam*HI restriction sites to the *Hin*dIII site. To do this, determine the size of the fragments cut by each enzyme, then, try to "fit" the pieces together like a jigsaw puzzle. In the past, restriction digestion mapping helped scientists determine the A, T, C, G sequence on a piece of DNA. Can you explain why?

Answer: The map will be similar but not exactly match the Figure 8.2 pAmylase diagram. This is because the sizes of the fragments from the gel are only estimates. Since the restriction enzymes only recognize certain sequences, if a band is cut on the plasmid then we know the DNA sequence at that site.

Lab 8c, Thinking Like a Biotechnician

1. Explain how a D plate could have absolutely nothing growing on it.

   Answers will vary but the easiest way to not have cell growth is "frying" the bacteria with a superheated inoculating looping. Also, if no cells got plasmid, then they would all be sensitive to the agar and there would be no growth.

2. Sometimes, nontransformed satellite colonies are seen around a main transformed colony. Are there any satellite colonies on your plates? Observe and record the satellite colonies' morphology (size, shape, and color) compared with the transformed colonies. Give reasons why the satellite company may be present and exhibit a different growth rate than the transformed cells.

   Answer: Satellite colonies are relatively small and only grow around the colony where the amp-digesting enzyme diffuses out and destroys the ampicillin in the agar.

3. Not all the cells in the original culture are transformed. What evidence do you have to support this statement? Determine the transformation efficiency of your protocol.

   Answer: Cells from the transformed broth culture can be plated out as a 1:10, 1:100, 1:1000, or 1:10,000 serial dilutions on starch/amp LB agar. The number of colonies per unit volume in the original transformed culture can be calculated by multiplying the number of colonies counted in one of the dilutions by the dilution factor. This will give the number of cells/volume plated. Divide this number into the number of transformed colonies on your D LB/amp/starch plate and multiply by 100. This gives the transformation efficiency. A ratio of 1:10,000 transformed cells (0.01%) is considered a good result. Answers will vary transformation efficiencies will vary depending on the number of colonies on the selection plate.

Lab 8d, Thinking Like a Biotechnician

1. How can a technician be confident that a culture is not contaminated with unwanted bacteria?

   Answers will vary but if a technician wants to be sure that the culture is not contaminated with unwanted bacteria one approach would be to examine several slides of the culture under a microscope. By doing a Gram Stain (Chapter 2 Labs), the technician can have greater confidence that the cell culture is composed of only *E. coli*. Additionally several biochemical and nutitional test will confirm the presence of *E. coli*.

2. How can you tell when a culture has reached the stationary phase?

   Answer: A culture has reached stationary phase if the rise in absorbance slows down or the pH might change from wastes.

3. How can you tell if a culture has sufficient aeration?

   Answer: If the cultures do not show exponential growth then they may need more aeration.

Lab 8e, Thinking Like a Biotechnician

1. What was done in this cell culture to decrease the chance of nontransformed cells growing or contaminating the culture?

   Answer: Ampicillin was added to the broth to decrease the chance that non-transformed cells might grow or contaminate the culture.

2. Propose methods to increase culture growth rates.

   Answers will vary but to increase culture growth rate one might include increasing food nutrients like glucose, increasing aeration, modifying the light, temperature or pH.

3. Propose methods to increase a culture's amylase production.

Answers will vary but what ever improves cell growth is likely to improve protein production. Also, the substrate concentration (starch) might be modified to see its impact on amylase production.

Lab 8f, Thinking Like a Biotechnician

1. If no whole or digested plasmid bands are present on the gel, does that mean that no plasmid was extracted or no transformation **occurred**?

   Answer: If no whole or digested plasmid bands are present on the gel, it doesn't necessarily mean that there was no plasmid extracted. It may mean that the concentration of plasmid DNA extracted is too low to be seen on a gel. This is probably true if a measurable reading is given by the UV spectrophotometer.

2. What other technique could be used to determine whether the miniprep samples actually do contain DNA?

   Answer: Another technique that might be used to check to see if there was DNA in the mini-prep samples is indicator testing like DPA or EtBr dot test.

3. A concentration of 0.005 µg/µL is usually required for a transformation. Did your miniprep yield enough (at least 10 µL) of a sufficient concentration (0.005 µg/µL) of plasmid for another transformation?

   Answer: Yield answers will vary depending on the results of mini-prep.

Lab 8g, Thinking Like a Biotechnician

1. In biotechnology, "time is money." If one procedure works as well as another, and costs less, that is the procedure that will be used. Which of the miniprep procedures (lysozyme or alkaline lysis) appeared to take longer to conduct? Explain.

   Answer: The alkaline lysis mini-prep takes longer to prepare and conduct but may give a better yield. Look for evidence.

2. A concentration of 0.005 µg/µL is usually required for a transformation. Did your miniprep yield enough (at least 10 µL) of a sufficient concentration (0.005 µg/µL) of plasmid for another transformation?

   Answers will depend on results of mini-prep.

3. Which miniprep procedure, lysozyme (last lab) or alkaline lysis (this lab), worked better to produce the largest yield of a relatively pure plasmid? Give evidence.

   Answers will depend on results of the mini-preps.

Lab 9a, Thinking Like a Biotechnician

1. If the assays for amylase activity do not show much activity, does that mean there is no amylase in the broth? What may be done to remedy the problem?

   Answer: No, if the assays for amylase activity do not show much activity, that's does not mean that there is no amylase in the broth. It may mean that there is a problem with the assay or that the concentration of enzyme in the broth is too low to be detected by the assay. The technician could try to concentrate the broth, 2X, 4x, or more.

2. Without using an activity assay, how could a technician confirm that amylase, and not some other carbohydrate-interacting enzyme, is in the broth?

   Answer: A technician could confirm that amylase and not some other carbohydrate-interacting enzyme is in the broth using PAGE, and looking for a protein band at approximately 61 kD.

3. What key ingredient would be needed to design an ELISA to recognize and measure the amylase in the broth?

   Answer: An antibody that recognizes amylase is needed to design an ELISA to detect amylase.

Lab 9b, Thinking Like a Biotechnician

1. How can you be certain that amylase has not diffused or leaked out of the dialysis bag during dialysis?

Answer: To be certain that amylase has not diffused or leaked out of the dialysis bag during dialysis The buffer outside the dialysis tube can be assayed for amylase and/or samples run on a PAGE gel. The protein concentration per unit volume can be determined (using the spectrophotometer) for the sample inside the dialysis tube before and after dialysis to confirm that the protein amount has not changed.

2. Before dialysis, on inspection of the broth, cloudy areas are visible. What is the most likely cause of the cloudiness and what, if anything, should be doneabout it?

Answer: The cloudiness of a sample is probably due to bacterial contamination. Streaking a sample of the broth on an agar plate can confirm if the broth is contaminated with bacteria that should have been removed during centrifugation. If it is bacteria, filter-sterilizing the broth will remove the bacteria. There may be some concerns about whether the presence of the bacteria will decrease protein concentration.

Lab 9c, Thinking Like a Biotechnician

1. A technician checks the column bed volume on a column that is supposed to be 2 mL. If the bed volume is not 2 mL, is this a problem? Why or why not?

Answer: A bed volume larger is only a problem because it takes longer to run each sample through a larger column. A smaller bed volume means that there is not as many charged beads to bind the negatively charged protein and some sample will be lost into wash fractions.

2. The column drips very slowly. Suggest a method to increase the rate of flow through the column. How can you check to ensure that this method does not compromise the separation?

Answers will vary. If a column runs too slowly, putting a gently pressure from the top of the column down on the sample will increase the flow of fluids through the resin bead. Some apparatus such as syringe (from the top) or vacuum from the bottom may be used to create the difference in pressure. If the pressure is to great, separation may not occur. Absorbance results would indicate this.

3. A scientist would like to know the charge of a certain protein at pH 7.2. How could this column be used to help determine the overall charge of the protein at pH 7.2? What problems might occur using the proposed approach and how might they be addressed?

Answer: This column may be used to help determine the overall charge of the protein, at pH 7.2 by running the column, substituting the protein of interest for either lysozyme or albumin. At the proper concentration the protein of interest will either wash through (= + charged) or bind to the column (= - charged). Concentration of the sample is an issue though. If there is too much protein in the load, protein will be in all the fractions. Some column runs with serial dilutions of the protein sample will be necessary to determine the binding capacity (if it is a – charged protein) of the column.

Lab 9d, Thinking Like a Biotechnician

The load for each column was 0.2 mL of sample. How much amylase, in milligrams, was loaded onto each of the standard columns?

Answer: The following amounts were loaded on the columns.

Stock = 10 mg/mL → 10mg/mL × 0.2 mL = 2 mg
1:2 dilution = 5 mg/mL → 5 mg/mL × 0.2 mL = 1 mg
1:4 dilution = 2.5 mg/mL → 2.5 mg/mL × 0.2 mL = 0.5 mg

2. What is the value of running a 1:2 serial dilution of the amylase standards on columns?

Answer: It is not known what the binding capacity is of amylase on the DEAE Sepharose. By running columns with different amounts of protein, we can determine how much amylase the column will hold so that it is not overloaded.

3. If the amylase does not appear to bind in any of the columns, what might the technician try next?

Answers will vary but If amylase does not appear to bind in any of the columns approaches may include trying a different pH to give the amylase more charge or a different resin, maybe a negatively charged resin.

Lab 9e, Thinking Like a Biotechnician.

1. A technician runs a gel from an ion-exchange chromatography. He or she sees six bands in the wash samples and three bands in the elution, including a band at 61 kD. Has amylase been purified from other proteins in the broth? Explain.

   Answer: Amylase has only been partially purified if there are other bands seen in the sample lane on a gel. There has been some separation the amylase from some of the proteins but if there are other bands in the lane, other proteins are present.

2. What should the technician in question No. 1 do next?

   Answers will vary but it is common to run several columns to get complete separation of proteins in a sample. The elution from the ion exchange column should be run on another, different column, that separates proteins based on another characteristic, perhaps size.

3. A PAGE gel with ion-exchange fractions is run. If the only bands visible on the gel are the standards, what might be done to the column fraction samples to try to see any protein present in them?

   Answers will vary but if the only bands visible on the gel are the standards, then the samples might need to be concentrated (they may be too dilute). Another possibility is that the samples may not have the protein of interest in them.

Lab 10a, Thinking Like a Biotechnician

1. "Monocot" and "dicot" are two terms that describe the types of seeds, flower, and leaves of a flowering plant. Monocot plants are more closely related to each other than they are to dicots, and vice versa. Among other characteristics, most of the flower parts of monocots are in threes or multiples of threes, and their leaves have parallel veins. The flower parts of dicots are in fours or fives, or multiples of fours or fives, and their leaf veins are net-like. , Identify which of the flowers you have dissected and studied are probably monocots and which are probably dicots.

   Answers will vary depending on the type of flowers dissected but of those in the Materials list, but lily and iris are monocots and *Kalanchoe*, *Fuchsia*, pea, *Azalea*, jasmine and *Campanula* are dicots.

2. A flower is yellow and has long, dark lines running from the tip of a petal to the base, near the pistil attachment. What type of pollination might this plant use?

   Answer: Insect pollination (probably bees since they "see" yellow). The lines may guide the insect toward the male and female sex organs.

3. The petals of some flowers are fused into a long tube, with the pistil and stamen deep inside it. Suggest a reason that, over time, this type of flower has evolved.

   Answers may vary. One possibility for the presence of a long floral tube is that a long tube might guarantee that a pollinator (like an insect) will stay for a while to pick up a greater amount (or deposit) of pollen. Another possibility is that only certain (best pollinating) animals with specialized structures (like long beaks) could reach down the tube for pollination purposes.

Lab 10b, Thinking Like a Biotechnician

1. Discuss the advantages and disadvantages of larger seeds versus smaller seeds; more endosperm versus less endosperm; thick seed coats versus thinner seed coats; and any other differences you observe.

   Answers will vary but some advantages of large seeds over small seeds may include that larger seeds can store more food (endosperm) but are harder to distribute, more endosperm stores more food than less endosperm, but the seed than might be over eaten by animals, thick seed coat is more protection but may make it harder for a seed to germinate than a thinner seed coat, etc.

2. Go online and find four common methods of seed distribution or dissemination other than those dissected in this lab activity. Describe these in your notebook and record the Web site of each reference you used.

   Answers will vary.

3. Dicots have two cotyledons (seed sections) and monocots have only one. Can you tell which of the seeds that you dissected are monocots and which are dicots? Does the venation (vein pattern) in the "true" leaves confirm this?

Answers will vary depending on the seeds dissected. Corn may be the only monocot. Most monocots have parallel venation and most dicots have net-veined leaves.

Lab 10c, Thinking Like a Biotechnician

1. Of what value is a shorter germination time to a particular species and to a lab researcher studying plant genetics?

Answer: A shorter germination time means that a seed does not have to make or store as much endosperm. Also, the sooner the generation time, the sooner the next generation will be growing and reproducing making genetic studies easier. The whole population will grow faster.

2. What other factors besides genetics may affect the expected germination rates? Explain how some of those factors might affect the germination rate.

Answers will vary but some might include temperature (warmer = faster, up to a point), water availability (more water = more germination, up to a point), oxygen availability (too low will delay germination and may cause molding), maturation of seed (some seeds have a certain length dormancy, or resting period), amount of seed coat (thicker seed coats are harder to break open and take more time or may take physical breakdown.

3. What would happen if a tiny seed with only a small amount of endosperm were planted too deeply in the soil?

Answer: It would use up its endosperm before the seedling could reach light to photosynthesize.

Lab 10d, Thinking Like a Biotechnician

1. Use Microsoft® Excel® to determine the standard deviation (SD) for the average stem growth of your WFPs. If you do not know how to do this, access the Help feature from the Menu bar of Excel® and search for the topic.

Answers will vary depending on the experimental results.

2. For the F2 phenotypic counts, list at least three reasons why these counts might be inaccurate.

Answers will vary but some reasons why counts might be inaccurate may include that it is hard to tell some of the phenotypes (i.e. green from yellow-green), that counters are easily distracted or may count the same plant twice or not at all. Counters might be biased and expecting certain phenotypes and looking for them.

Lab 10e, Thinking Like a Biotechnician

Answers to genetics problems.

1. Cross a homozygous-dominant, green-leafed (G) plant with a homozygous-recessive, yellow/green-leafed plant.

   Parents' genotypes: GG × gg

   Alleles possible in gametes: G   g

   Punnett Square of the Cross

Genotypes of Male/Female Gametes	g
G	Gg

   Expected Genotypic results of crossing these gametes:

   100% of offspring = Gg

   Expected Phenotype(s) of offspring:

   100% green-leafed plants are expected

   50 out of 50 offspring are expected to be green-leafed plants.

2. Cross a heterozygous, purple-stemmed plant with a homozygous-recessive one (pp).

   Parents' genotypes: Pp × pp

   Alleles possible in gametes: P or p   p

   Punnett Square of the Cross

Genotypes of Male/Female Gametes	p
P	Pp
p	pp

   Expected Genotypic results of crossing these gametes:

   1/2 of offspring = Pp
   1/2 of offspring = pp

   Expected Phenotype(s) of offspring:

   1/2 of offspring = purple-stemmed plants are expected (25 out of 50)
   1/2 of offspring = green-stemmed plants are expected (25 out of 50)

3. Cross a plant, heterozygous for both green leaf color and purple stems, with a plant that is homozygous recessive for leaf color and heterozygous for stem color.

   Parents' genotypes: GgPp × ggPp

   Alleles possible in gametes: GP, Gp, gP, or gp   gP or gp

Punnett Square of the Cross

Genotypes of Male/Female Gametes	gP	gp
GP	GgPP	GgPp
Gp	GgPp	Ggpp
gP	ggPP	ggPp
gp	ggPp	ggpp

Expected Genotypic results of crossing these gametes:

GgPP = 1/8 = 12.5%
GgPp, GgPp = 2/8 = 25%
Ggpp = 1/8 = 12.5%
ggPP = 1/8 = 12.5%
ggPp, ggPp = 2/8 = 25%
ggpp = 1/8 = 12.5%

Expected Phenotype(s) of offspring:

GgPP, GgPp = 37. 5% should be green leaf, purple-stemmed plants (18 or 19 plants*)
Ggpp = 12.5% should be green leaf, green-stemmed plants (6 or 7 plants)
ggPP, ggPp = 37.5 % should be yellow leaf, purple-stemmed plants (18 or 19 plants)
ggpp = 12.5% should be yellow leaf, green-stemmed plants (6 or 7 plants)

*You can't have part of a plant.

Lab 11a, Thinking Like a Biotechnician

1. The procedures suggest smaller leaf sizes for leaf cuttings. What is a possible disadvantage of a large leaf cutting?

   Answers will vary but one disadvantage is that larger leaves have more surface area to lose water from, and the leaves may dehydrate before any rooting occurs.

2. The media in this experiment was sterilized. Discuss the advantages and disadvantages of sterilizing the media before using it in this experiment.

   Answers may very but an advantage of sterilizing the media before use might include that if the media is sterile there is less chance of bacterial or fungal damage to the "stressed" plant samples. A disadvantage is the amount of time it takes to sterilize all the media.

3. Suggest a method of encouraging more root development in cuttings that are slow to root or that do not root.

   Answers will vary but two ideas are to, 1) aerate the vessel – increased oxygen may stimulate root growth, or 2) use a plant hormone to encourage rooting.

Lab 11b, Thinking Like a Biotechnician

1. What benefits might the runner plantlets gain by remaining attached to the parent plant?

   Answer: Some benefits the runner plantlets might have by being attached to the parent include sharing food, minerals, or hormones.

2. What disadvantage might the runner plantlets have by being attached to the parent?

   Answer: Some disadvantages the runner plantlets might have by being attached to the parent include sharing diseases (including viruses or bacterial) or insect pests.

3. Why might the size and/or age of a runner plantlet skew the results of this experiment?

   Answer: Larger plantlets may have a root system already in development and therefore are more likely to succeed independently of the parent plant.

Lab 11c, Thinking Like a Biotechnician

1. Does it appear that there is a limit to the amount of hormone that will affect the rooting process? If so, above what concentration is there no additional effect? Sketch a graph showing how such results would look.

   Answer: Typically, the more hormone the more rooting up to some maximum amount of hormone. At that point more hormone actually begins to decrease the amount of rooting. If this is the case, a graph would have a straight line of increasing rooting until some concentration where no addition roots occur and the line would level off or go down.

2. How can you tell if the concentration of hormones is too high in all of the treatments?

   Answer: If the concentration of hormones is too high in all of the treatments, there would be no rooting and the cutting would die.

3. On the graph, how would a line appear if there were no relationship between the rooting hormone concentration and rooting?

   Answer: If there is no relationship between rooting hormone concentration and rooting, a line on a graph would look one of two ways. Either it would be a flat line with all the samples producing almost the same number of roots or the line would go up and down rather erratically.

Lab 11d, Thinking Like a Biotechnician

1. Discuss the texture of the PTC media compared with that of LB agar. Propose a reason for any difference.

   Answers will vary but may include a discussion of how the explant must absorb all of its nutrients from the media by diffusion and it is easier to do so if the media is softer and the explant is slightly embedded in it.

2. If the explant shows no signs of swelling or callus after 6 weeks, what may be the reason?

   Answer: If the explant shows no signs of swelling or callus after 6 weeks, possible reasons may include overheating the media which destroys the hormones or reduces their concentration, over-sterilizing the explant which kills too much of the tissue, explant drying out, or if the explant becomes contaminated with bacteria or fungi.

3. Suggest a few other herbaceous plants that might be successfully cultured using the same media and protocol.

   Answer: A few other herbaceous plants that might be able to be cultured using the same media and protocol as African Violets may include *Fuschia*, *Geranium*, *Coleus*, *Gloxinia*.

Lab 11e, Thinking Like a Biotechnician

Answers will vary.

Lab 11f, Thinking Like a Biotechnician

Answers will vary.

Lab 11g, Thinking Like a Biotechnician

1. Write a statement that reviews, for your supervisor, the pros and cons of using each kit. Include an assessment of the price, time, equipment, ease of use, and product yield.

   Answers will vary but should include an assessment of the price, time, equipment, ease of use, and product yield of each kit.

2. Suggest a gel electrophoresis method for assessing the type and quality of DNA in each extraction.

   Answer: To assess the type and quality of DNA in each extraction, depending on the concentrations in each sample, a PAGE (TBE or TB gel) or an agarose gel (0.8%) electrophoresis could be done.

3. Explain why using DNA extractions contaminated with proteins could lead to future experimental problems.

Answer: Contaminate proteins are problematic because they could include enzymes that could degrade the sample (DNase) or interfere with other enzyme activity, as in the enzymes needed for PCR.

Lab 11h, Thinking Like a Biotechnician

1. If samples float out of wells and do not sink when loading, what may be wrong?

   Answer: If samples float out of wells, and do not sink when loading, the most likely reason is that there is still alcohol in the sample that was not removed properly during the DNA isolation.

2. The salmon sperm DNA is used as a positive standard. Are you able to use it to estimate the concentration of your spinach DNA samples? Explain why or why not.

   Answers will vary depending on the spinach samples but the amount of glowing in comparison to the salmon sperm DNA does provide some information on DNA concentration.

3. Why are contaminant proteins not visible on these DNA gels?

   Answer: Contaminant proteins are not visible on these DNA gels since they will probably not run on these gels even if they are present and certainly won't stain. Wrong gel, wrong buffer. But proteins should not be contaminating the sample, any way, because the procedures are designed to remove contaminating proteins.

Lab 11i, Thinking Like a Biotechnician

1. What happens to the absorbance reading, concentration, and purity calculation if the DNA is too concentrated, for example, at 1 mg/mL. What must be done to solve this problem?

   Answer: If a sample is too concentrated, light will not be able to get through the sample and any reading will be nonsensical. Samples that are too concentrated must be diluted with TE buffer until they have absorbance readings somewhere between 0.02 and 2.0 au. Multiplication of the calculation at that dilution times the dilution factor will give an estimate of the true concentration.

2. If a A260/A280 purity reading were calculated to be 2.8, what should the technician think?

   Answer; If a purity reading is calculated to be 2.8, then either the sample is very concentrated with DNA, or it is very contaminated with RNA or something else, or it is just too concentrated or dilute to get an accurate reading. Also, inaccurate readings result from the cuvette not having enough volume of sample.

There are no *Thinking Like a Biotechnician* questions in Lab 11j.

Lab 11k, Thinking Like a Biotechnician

1. If there is a PCR product, could any additional testing show that the DNA from the extraction actually contained the GUS gene? Explain.

   Answer: If there is a PCR product, an additional test that could be done to show that the DNA from the extraction really contained the GUS gene is DNA sequencing.

Lab 12a, Thinking Like a Biotechnician

1. Why is it necessary for the carbonated drinks to "go flat" before taking readings?

   Answer: Before taking readings of carbonated beverages, the carbonation bubbles should be allowed to escape. This is because they interfere with the light in the spec and result in inaccurate absorbance readings.

2. Why do the pigments in the colas not interfere with the absorbance readings of caffeine?

   Answer: The colored pigments in colas do not interfere with the absorbance readings of caffeine. Caffeine absorbs in the UV wavelengths. The colored pigments absorb in the visible spectrum. At the wavelength of this study, the spec is only "seeing" the caffeine.

3. Should the standard curve go through the "zero, zero" point? Why or why not?

Answer: The standard curve in this study should go through the zero, zero point. If there is no concentration of caffeine, there should be no absorbance. In fact, that is what the blank should be, the reading that gives 0,0.

There are no *Thinking Like a Biotechnician* questions in Lab 12b.

Lab 12c, Thinking Like a Biotechnician

1. Give reasons for recrystallizing the aspirin. What is being removed with each wash? How does this affect the end product? How can you test your answer?

    Answer: Each re-crystallization of the acetylsalicylic acid removes impurities. This can be tested by doing a melting point on some of the intermediate products and comparing them to the final product.

2. Propose other methods to determine the presence and purity of a synthesized acetylsalicylic acid product.

    Answer: One method to determine the presence and purity of a synthesized acetylsalicylic acid product is to use the UV spectrophotometer to do an absorbance spectrum of pure acetylsalicylic acid. From the Lambda $_{max}$, a standard curve can be done on known acetylsalicylic acid samples and the concentration of unknowns can be determined.

3. If it tested very pure, would it be safe to use your synthesized acetylsalicylic acid for medical purposes?

    Answer: No, even if it tested very pure, it would not be safe to use your synthesized acetylsalicylic acid for medical purposes. Do not ingest anything in the lab. To be approved for medical use, the product would need to be approved by the FDA.

Lab 12d, Thinking Like a Biotechnician

1. Why is the melting-point determination done in oil rather than water?

    Answer: Water boils at 100°C and will not reach the high temperatures need for the melting point determinations.

2. When the capillary tubes cool, what should be visible inside of them?

    Answer: The original crystals tested. They should melt and then re-solidify upon cooling.

3. What will happen if one test has twice as many crystals in the melting-point determination as another test?

    Answer: It will start melting at the same time (temperature) but it will take longer to melt making it harder to get an exact value for the melting point.

Lab 12e, Thinking Like a Biotechnician

1. Considering your experience with alcohol precipitation of DNA, why is the petroleum ether added to the watery salicylic acid solution?

    Answer: Petroleum ether is used in the salicylic acid protocol because it is nonpolar and drives water out of the mixture. This allows the salicylic acid to move close enough together to form crystals.

2. Why might willow leaves contain a large amounts salicylic acid?

    Answers will vary but since salicylic acid is bitter it may stop pests from eating willow leaves.

Lab 13a, Thinking Like a Biotechnician

1. In this experiment, the type of dNTP in the reaction is varied so you can see the effect on strand synthesis. Make a prediction as to what negative consequences may result if other key ingredients were varied.

    a) Primer concentration

    b) DNA polymerase concentration

    Answer:

A) If the primer concentration is lower then all of the template strands might not get template and the amount of strands produced could be less. If the primer concentration is raised the primer may bind (incompletely but enough to interfere with the reaction) with itself or other spots on the template.

B) DNA polymerase concentration is lower then it will take longer for all of the strands to be replicated. This may be OK if the incubation time can be increased, but the enzyme may degrade at longer incubation times. If the enzyme concentration is increased, nothing may happen (and it is just a waste of expensive reagent) or they may be unwanted synthesis at spots where excess primer is bound.

2. During the annealing reactions, the primer-template mixture is cooled very slowly from 65°C to 35°C. Describe what is happening in the AM tube during this period and what may happen if the AM tube is cooled too rapidly.

Answer: During the 65°C–35°C cooling period, primers find the correct sequence on the template and anneal through complementary base pairing. The slow cooling gives time for this to happen more accurately. If the cooling rate is too fast, random binding of primer and template, template and template, and primer and primer will result decreasing the amount of intended product.

3. After all of the reagents are mixed together, what is the final concentration of template DNA in each of the synthesis-reaction tubes?

Answer: The amount of DNA added to each tube 3 pmoles (2 µL × 1.5 pmol/µL). The final volume of each synthesis tube is 5.5 µL (3 µL of AM + 2.5 µL of NM). Therefore, the final concentration of DNA in each synthesis tube 3 pmoles/5.5 µL = 0.55 pmol/µL.

Lab 13b, Thinking Like a Biotechnician

1. At the end of the gel run, blue bands can be seen at the bottom of the gel. What are the blue bands? Where are the DNA synthesis fragments?

Answer: The DNA fragments are not visible in the gel even if they are present. To visualize them they must either be stained with ethidium bromide or blotted to a membrane and colorized. The blue bands are loading dye molecules, bromophenol blue and maybe a second dye, xylene cyanol. These move at the approximate speed of the invisible DNA synthesis fragments.

2. If the samples are loaded on the gel too slowly, the template and primer pieces will reanneal. What is the size of the template-primer complex compared with the template alone or any of the synthesized fragments? Why is it important to consider the template-primer complex.

Answer: There are a total of 92 bases in the template primer complex (60 bases of template and 32 bases of primer). If these erroneous complexes are made then they will show up as high molecular weight bands on the gel and blot.

3. Why does the TBE buffer have to be diluted from 5X to 1X? What consequences are expected if the buffer is not correctly diluted to 1X?

Answer: Too high of an ion concentration in the buffer will cause the current too get too high and the gel will get too hot, bands will smear and the gel box fuse might blow. Too low a concentration, and the gel box will run too slowly and it may not stay hot enough to keep the DNA fragments denatured.

Lab 13c, Thinking Like a Biotechnician

1. What may be the consequences of trapping a large air bubble between the gel and the nylon membrane during blotting?

Answer: There must be a continuous "column" of water between layers in the blot so that capillary action will draw the DNA samples from the gel to the membrane. If there is a large air bubble, it will stop the transfer of the DNA to the membrane because there will be no capillary action in that spot.

2. Speculate as to why the cross-linker speeds cross-linking.

Answers will vary but the cross-linker might speeds cross-linking by providing UV light energy, which may cause changes in charge on the polymers making them more attractive to the membrane.

Lab 13d, Thinking Like a Biotechnician

1. Each lab group is a replication of the DNA synthesis experiment. If one lab group has results different than the others, it is probably due to technician error. But, if all groups had the same unexpected results, a problem could exist in the shared materials, instruments, or procedures.

   Propose some reasons for the following:

   a. No groups had anything on their membranes except DNA loading-dye bands.
   b. All groups had sizing-standard bands visible on their membranes, but nothing else.
   c. All groups only had bands in one row higher than the 60-base standard and in one row at 32 bases.

   Answers may vary but on reason that all groups could get unexpected results in the DNA synthesis experiment include:

   A. One of the reagents in the colorization reactions was bad/expired.or the cross-linking did not work.
   B. One of the reagents in the synthesis or the procedure did not work.
   C. The samples did not get or stayed denatured and all where in template-primer complexes or primer alone.

2. If some of the six samples are shown to contain oligos, how might a technician determine the concentration of DNA remaining in the six sample tubes?

   Answer: UV spectrophotometry could be used to determine the concentration of DNA in the oligo synthesis tubes.

Lab 13e, Thinking Like a Biotechnician

1. A technician finds a long, white smear of DNA in a PCR product lane from about 500 bp down to 100 bp. What may be the cause of such a smear?

   Answer: A long smear of white on a DNA gel at about 100-500 bp could be sheared DNA or RNA contamination. DNase contamination could cause fragmentation or shearing of the PCR product. DNase contamination occurs from unclean tubes or tips including by touch. Skin cells produce a high amount of DNase. RNA contamination for the original sample would also appear as a smear form 100-500 bp.

2. What might cause many bands at random positions in all lanes, including the control?

   Answer: A lot of bands at random positions in all lanes of a DNA gel might be due to DNA contamination from other PCR or lab work. This unwanted DNA could end up in the tube (contamination) and be recognized by the primers and amplified. This would give a lot of random bands.

Lab 13f, Thinking Like a Biotechnician

1. How could the purity and concentration of the check-cell DNA sample be determined?

   Answer: Using a UV spectrophotometer, the concentration (absorbance at 260 nm) and the purity (absorbance at 260 nm / absorbance at 280 nm) can be determined.

2. Do these cheek-cell DNA sample tubes contain genomic DNA? Yes or no? Explain.

   Answer: Yes, when the cheek cells burst open the chromosomes are released. Chromosomes contain the DNA of the cell. A sample that contains all the chromosomes of the cell represents the genomic DNA.

Lab 13g, Thinking Like a Biotechnician

1. Why is the band for 415 bp so much darker than the band for 715 bp?

   Answers will vary but one explanation for the band at 415 bp being so much darker than the band at 715 bp is that it may be harder for the 715 bp piece to get amplified because it is so long that the polymerase does not make it to the end of the strand. Less amplification = less sample = less glowing. On the other hand, usually the longer the strand, the more EtBr intercalates, making longer pieces glow more and easier to see.

2. Why are there so few of one genotype compared with the others?

Answer: One reason that there are so few of one of the genotypes versus the others may be that until recently there were few interracial marriages keeping alleles (mutations) isolated. Think of certain diseases like Tay-Sachs and Sickle Cell Anemia.

Lab 14a, Thinking Like a Biotechnician

1. What is the most likely reason for all of the wells showing color (false positive results)?

   Answers will vary since there are a lot of reasons for false positives. The most likely ones though are not enough washing of unbound antibody or insufficient blocking.

2. Propose a method to decrease the number of false positive results.

   Answers will vary, but methods to decrease the number of false positive results might include increased washing, samples could be submerged in buffer and flipped up side down several times. Appropriately bound antibody should not be knocked off with this method.

3. How can the data be made more quantitative? Is there an instrument that can quantify the amount of color in each well? Describe how these readings could be taken.

   Answer: A spectrophotometer could be used to see the difference in yellow color and collect more quantitative data. The samples should be judged against a set of standards that are used to make a best-fit standard curve of protein concentration. An ELISA plate reader as a spec in it can be programmed to take the readings.

4. In your notebook, draw and label a schematic to show what is attaching to what in the ELISA plate cells during the ELISA and color development.

   Answer: In a diagram to illustrate an ELISA, an antigen should stick up from the well surface. A Y-shaped antibody should be face down and attached to the antigen. On the tail of the Y should be an "HRP" enzyme molecule, grabbing and modifying TMB.

Lab 14b, Thinking Like a Biotechnician

1. What is the most likely reason for no bands appearing anywhere on a membrane?

   Answers will vary but a few reasons for no bands appearing anywhere on a membrane include insufficient concentration of protein in the sample, incorrect membrane or membrane use, incorrect setup of the membrane transfer apparatus including dry spots or air bubbles, or incorrect visualization method.

2. What may be a reason for the unknown samples not showing actin bands, while the known samples show actin bands?

   Answers will vary but the most likely reason for the unknowns not showing actin bands is poor preparation or storage of the unknowns, including degradation form bacterial contamination.

3. In your notebook, draw a schematic diagram to show what is attaching to what on the membrane during color development.

   Answer: A schematic to show what is attaching during a Western blot, should have antigen sticking up from the membrane surface. A Y-shaped antibody should be face down, attached to the antigen. A secondary antibody with an "HRP" enzyme molecule, should be attached to the 1° antibody. The enzyme on the end of the 2° antibody should be grabbing and modifying TMB.

3

Quizzes and Tests

Included in this section are chapter concepts quizzes and unit concepts tests for the *Biotechnology* textbook. Chapter quizzes contain 20 items of matching, multiple-choice, and short answer types. A separate page with the answers follows each quiz.

Unit tests are similarly structured, although they contain from 40 to 100 items, depending on the length of the unit. The four units are

- Unit 1: Standard Laboratory Operating Procedures (Chapters 1-5)
- Unit 2: Introduction to Recombinant DNA and Protein Production (Chapters 6-9)
- Unit 3: Agricultural and Pharmaceutical Biotechnology (Chapters 10-12)
- Unit 4: Advanced Biotechnology Techniques and Diagnostics (Chapters 13-14)

Both the quizzes and the tests have been created from the item bank in the ExamView test generator that is available with the textbook.

Name _____

Course _____

Date _____

Biotechnology Chapter 01 Quiz

Matching

For the following items, match each word with the most appropriate definition below.

    a. An entire set of an organism's genetic information
    b. A testable prediction to a scientific question
    c. Values that help one decide between right and wrong
    d. The study and manipulation of living things, or their components
    e. A factor that will yield a predictable result
    f. A factor that gets manipulated during an experiment
    g. Applying moral values to decision-making on topics brought up by advances in biology, medicine, and technology
    h. A combination of DNA from different sources in one molecule
    i. Information gathered during an experiment
    j. A scientific magazine or periodical where scientists publish their experiments

_____ 1. Biotechnology

_____ 2. Data

_____ 3. Hypothesis

_____ 4. Journal

_____ 5. Recombinant DNA

_____ 6. Variable

For the following items, put in order the sequence of events that occurs during process development of a pharmaceutical product.

    a. Manufacturing
    b. Product identification
    c. Sales and marketing
    d. Testing for safety and efficacy
    e. Research and development
    f. Small-scale manufacturing

_____ 7. Third

_____ 8. Fifth

    For the following items determine which federal agency oversees the production of the following products.
    a. FDA
    b. EPA
    c. USDA

_____ 9. Contact lens solution

_____ 10. Antibiotics

Multiple Choice

Identify the letter of the choice that best completes the statement or answers the question.

_____ 11. The primary goal at a biotechnology company is to
    a. engage in "pure science."
    b. cure all the diseases of the world.
    c. publish results in scientific journals.
    d. provide a product or service that is useful to society and results in earnings.

Name _____

Course _____

Date _____

_____ 12. A product that has entered the product pipeline
   a. is ready for clinical testing to begin.
   b. is being produced on a large-scale by the manufacturing department.
   c. has been determined safe and effective.
   d. needs to be reviewed regularly with a comprehensive product development plan.

_____ 13. Biotechnology research laboratories are commonly found at all of the following facilities except:
   a. Universities
   b. Medical clinics
   c. Companies
   d. Government agencies

_____ 14. What enabled the onset of recombinant DNA technology?
   a. The ability to identify similarities and differences between individuals.
   b. The Biotechnology Industry Organization.
   c. The ability to cut and paste pieces of DNA together.
   d. The beginning of research findings getting published in scientific journals.

_____ 15. Which of the following is an example of a product easily found in nature?
   a. Antibiotic
   b. GMO
   c. Recombinant DNA
   d. All of the above

_____ 16. Which of the following is an application of agricultural biotechnology?
   a. Genetic testing and screening
   b. Vaccine therapy
   c. Transgenic crops
   d. Genetically engineered enzymes

_____ 17. Recombinant DNA is the term used for
   a. DNA that has been cut with restriction enzymes.
   b. DNA molecules composed of DNA from different sources.
   c. Molecules that have undergone DNA fingerprinting analysis.
   d. Genetic information from selectively bred organisms.

_____ 18. All of the following should be included in a legal scientific notebook except:
   a. Testable questions for experiments
   b. Experimental plans
   c. Data gathered during an experiment
   d. Personal antidotes regarding the work of colleagues

_____ 19. One of the first genetically engineered products sold was
   a. Bt corn, a variety resistant to the corn borer larvae
   b. Cipro, a strong antibiotic
   c. Human t-PA, an enzyme that dissolves blood clots
   d. GloFish, a fish that glows in UV light

_____ 20. When discussing practical applications in the conclusion of an experiment, what should be addressed?
   a. Long and short term value of that experiment
   b. Possible sources of error
   c. Analysis of the data gathered
   d. A statement that accepts or rejects the hypothesis

Biotechnology Chapter 01 Quiz

Answer Section

Matching

1. ANS: D   REF: 4
2. ANS: I   REF: 19
3. ANS: B   REF: 19
4. ANS: J   REF: 22
5. ANS: H   REF: 10
6. ANS: F   REF: 19
7. ANS: F   REF: 16
8. ANS: A   REF: 16
9. ANS: A   REF: 15-17
10. ANS: A   REF: 15-17

Multiple Choice

11. ANS: D   REF: 6
12. ANS: D   REF: 15
13. ANS: B   REF: 5
14. ANS: C   REF: 10
15. ANS: A   REF: 10
16. ANS: C   REF: 9
17. ANS: B   REF: 10
18. ANS: D   REF: 19
19. ANS: C   REF: 11
20. ANS: A   REF: 22

Name _____

Course _____

Date _____

Biotechnology Chapter 02

Matching

For the following items, match the following words with the best description (a-k).

　　a. A six-carbon sugar molecule used by cells for making energy
　　b. A process where plants and algae use light energy to make chemical energy
　　c. Information-carrying molecules within all cells
　　d. The process of breaking down food molecules to generate energy
　　e. Thousands of different types of macromolecules that have various functions within and around a cell
　　f. Molecules containing carbon, hydrogen, and oxygen in approximately a 1:2:1 ratio
　　g. Packages of DNA
　　h. The subunits of proteins, each of which contains an amino group, carboxyl group, and a functional "R" group all attached to a central carbon atom
　　i. Specialized membrane-bound structures that have specialized functions within cells
　　j. Hydrophobic molecules that have specific functions within and around cells
　　k. Large molecules composed of repeating units of smaller molecules

_____ 1. Chromosomes

_____ 2. Macromolecules

_____ 3. Organelles

_____ 4. Photosynthesis

_____ 5. Proteins

For the following items, determine whether each of the following cell types is eukaryotic or prokaryotic.

　　a. ANS:　　Eukaryotic
　　b. ANS:　　Prokaryotic

_____ 6. *E. coli*

For the following items, match the following protein functions with specific examples (a-e).

　　a. Insulin
　　b. gp120
　　c. Hemoglobin
　　d. Keratin
　　e. Amylase

_____ 7. Structure

_____ 8. Hormone

_____ 9. Transport

_____ 10. Recognition

Multiple Choice

Identify the letter of the choice that best completes the statement or answers the question.

_____ 11. What are the most common molecules in cells?
　　a. Sugars
　　b. Lipids
　　c. Proteins
　　d. Nucleic acids

_____ 12. Membrane proteins may have any of the following functions except:
  a. Transport molecules through the cell
  b. Synthesize phospholipids
  c. Identify other molecules or be recognized by other molecules
  d. Maintain cell shape

_____ 13. By the process of translation,
  a. amino acids are connected together in the order specified by the mRNA molecule.
  b. ribosomes link nucleic acids together into polypeptide chains.
  c. molecules are transported out of the cell.
  d. the DNA code is read and encoded into a messenger RNA molecule.

_____ 14. All of the following are considered benefits of recombinant insulin over therapeutic insulin derived from livestock except:
  a. Some patients have severe allergies to livestock insulin.
  b. Some livestock insulin does not perform well in humans.
  c. The price and availability of livestock insulin varies.
  d. Livestock insulin may cause cowpox.

_____ 15. What is meant by cell specialization?
  a. Different cell lines (CHO and HeLa cells, for example) are more suited to producing certain kinds of recombinant proteins.
  b. Prokaryotic cells specialize in certain tasks and can therefore grow more rapidly than eukaryotic cells.
  c. There is great cell variety in multicellular organisms in which different kinds of cells have different jobs to do.
  d. All of the above

_____ 16. Glucose is a
  a. peptide.
  b. polysaccharide.
  c. disaccharide.
  d. monosaccharide.

_____ 17. The hydrophilic ends of phospholipid molecules
  a. face each other.
  b. point away from each other.
  c. twist in a spiral.
  d. form the interior area of lipid bilayers.

_____ 18. How do carbohydrates affect DNA isolation from plant cells?
  a. They cause the DNA to degrade.
  b. They are sticky and interfere with the purification process.
  c. They are easily removed with a simple centrifugation step.
  d. They bind to the proteins and are removed during the protein precipitation step.

_____ 19. About how many different proteins are found in a typical cell?
  a. 20
  b. 200
  c. 2,000
  d. 20,000

_____ 20. All of the following influence the way a polypeptide folds into a functional protein except:
  a. The order of amino acids
  b. The amino acid R-groups
  c. The interaction between amino acids
  d. The central carbon of each amino acid

Biotechnology Chapter 02

Answer Section

Matching

1. ANS: G   REF: 44
2. ANS: K   REF: 48
3. ANS: I   REF: 40-41
4. ANS: B   REF: 42
5. ANS: E   REF: 39-40
6. ANS: B   REF: 46
7. ANS: D   REF: 52-53
8. ANS: A   REF: 52-53
9. ANS: C   REF: 46, 53
10. ANS: B   REF: 53, 55

Multiple Choice

11. ANS: C   REF: 41
12. ANS: B   REF: 44
13. ANS: A   REF: 44
14. ANS: D   REF: 58
15. ANS: C   REF: 46
16. ANS: D   REF: 50
17. ANS: B   REF: 51
18. ANS: B   REF: 49
19. ANS: C   REF: 52
20. ANS: D   REF: 52-53

Name _____

Course _____

Date _____

Biotechnology Chapter 03

Matching

For the following items, match each word with the most appropriate definition below.

    a. The proportion of solute to solvent in a solution
    b. The concentration of a solution expressed as the number of moles of solute per liter of solvent
    c. A solution that resists changes in pH
    d. What gets dissolved in a solution
    e. The number of molecules that equals the molecular weight of a substance, in grams
    f. The addition of solvent to make a mixture less concentrated
    g. The solution that dissolves added molecules
    h. Containing water

_____ 1. aqueous

_____ 2. buffer

_____ 3. concentration

_____ 4. dilution

For the following items, select which tool below would most accurately measure the following amounts.

    a. micropipet
    b. pipet
    c. graduated cylinder
    d. tabletop balance
    e. analytical balance

_____ 5. 50 μL

_____ 6. 3.5 g

_____ 7. 0.07 mg

_____ 8. 1.5 L

_____ 9. 32 g

In the following items, determine which equation (a-c) would be most useful in calculating the amount of solute needed to make each solution.

    a. Concentration × Volume = Mass
    b. Decimal Value × Volume = Mass
    c. Volume × Molarity × Molecular Weight = Mass

_____ 10. 600 μL of 0.5 m*M* protein solution

Multiple Choice

Identify the letter of the choice that best completes the statement or answers the question.

_____ 11. Which of the following can be measured using a micropipet?
    a. A gram of sodium chloride
    b. A liter of oxygen gas
    c. 10 μL of DNA solution
    d. 2.5 L of protein solution

_____ 12. Which of the following is an expression of concentration units?
    a. $\mu g/\mu L$
    b. mg/mL
    c. μM
    d. All of the above

_____ 13. How much 95% ethanol do you need to make a 600 mL solution of 70% ethanol?
    a. 1.1 L
    b. 81.4 mL
    c. 110 mL
    d. 442 mL

_____ 14. As a solution becomes more dilute
    a. the proportion of solute to solvent increases.
    b. the proportion of solvent to solute increases.
    c. the normality of the solution shifts.
    d. re-ionization begins to occur.

_____ 15. A p1000 micropipet is used to measure volumes
    a. between 100 and 1000 μL.
    b. between 1-1000 μL.
    c. over 1000 μL.
    d. between 10-1000 mL.

_____ 16. 300 mL of a 1/40 dilution of 20X TBE buffer stock solution is needed, what volume of solute is needed?
    a. 2.7 mL
    b. 7.5 mL
    c. 40 mL
    d. 150 mL

_____ 17. When measuring liquids using a graduated cylinder or pipet,
    a. the top of the meniscus should be at the graduation.
    b. the bottom of the meniscus should be at the graduation.
    c. the meniscus should be anywhere near the graduation.
    d. there is no meniscus when using these measurement tools.

_____ 18. In a biotechnology lab, tap water is best used for
    a. making buffers.
    b. washing glassware.
    c. the final rinse when washing glassware.
    d. All of the above

_____ 19. Which solution is more concentrated?
    a. 5 mg/mL
    b. 5 $\mu g/\mu L$
    c. 5 g/L
    d. They are equivalent.

_____ 20. Calculate the mass of 17 moles of HCl.
    a. 17 amu
    b. 170 amu
    c. 306 g
    d. 620 g

Biotechnology Chapter 03

Answer Section

Matching

 1. ANS: H   REF: 75
 2. ANS: C   REF: 86
 3. ANS: A   REF: 76
 4. ANS: F   REF: 85
 5. ANS: A   REF: 69
 6. ANS: D   REF: 75
 7. ANS: E   REF: 75
 8. ANS: C   REF: 68
 9. ANS: E   REF: 75
10. ANS: C   REF: 84

Multiple Choice

11. ANS: C   REF: 85-87
12. ANS: D   REF: 77
13. ANS: D   REF: 75
14. ANS: B   REF: 76
15. ANS: A   REF: 73
16. ANS: B   REF: 87
17. ANS: B   REF: 68
18. ANS: B   REF: 76
19. ANS: D   REF: 67
20. ANS: D   REF: 83, periodic table

Name _____

Course _____

Date _____

Biotechnology Chapter 04

Matching

For the following items , match each word with the most appropriate definition (a-j) below.

    a. A region on prokaryotic DNA where one or more genes and their controlling elements are located
    b. Process of correcting DNA codes that cause genetic diseases and disorders
    c. Cells that have taken up foreign DNA and start expressing it
    d. Source of nutrients, in liquid or solid form, for growing cell cultures
    e. A region of DNA that can increase expression of a gene
    f. Using electricity to separate molecules on a gel slab
    g. Two nitrogenous bases connected with hydrogen bonds
    h. A DNA molecule that is used as a host to carry foreign pieces of DNA into a cell
    i. The expressed part of genes
    j. Non-coding intervening sequence within genes

_____ 1. Enhancer

_____ 2. Exon

_____ 3. Gel electrophoresis

_____ 4. Gene therapy

For the following items, place the following steps of genetic engineering in the proper order.

    a. First
    b. Second
    c. Third
    d. Fourth

_____ 5. Transfer gene of interest into a host organism

_____ 6. Isolate gene of interest

_____ 7. Identify a molecule that can be improved/enhanced

For the following items, which gel electrophoresis system best matches the following descriptions or applications?

    a. Agarose
    b. Polyacrylamide
    c. Either

_____ 8. Used for separating proteins

_____ 9. Used to separate DNA samples

_____ 10. Separates smaller molecules such as polypeptides

Multiple Choice

Identify the letter of the choice that best completes the statement or answers the question.

_____ 11. The order of amino acids on a polypeptide chain is encoded by
    a. DNA.
    b. mRNA.
    c. rRNA.
    d. regulatory proteins.

_____ 12. Nucleotides are connected together in a DNA molecule by
    a. hydrogen bonds.
    b. antiparallel bonds.
    c. peptide bonds.
    d. phosphodiester bonds.

_____ 13. How is gene expression controlled in prokaryotic cells?
    a. Operons
    b. Ribosomes
    c. Enhancers
    d. All of the above

_____ 14. All of the following may be used to induce changes at a particular locus on a DNA molecule except:
    a. Exposure to chemicals
    b. Exposure to radiation
    c. Exposure to low temperatures
    d. Viral infection

_____ 15. How do DNA molecules vary from one species to another?
    a. The type of nitrogenous bases they contain
    b. Number of genes and non-coding regions
    c. The way nitrogenous bases pair
    d. The directionality of the strands

_____ 16. All of the following regulate gene expression in eukaryotes except:
    a. Enhancers
    b. Transcription factors
    c. Histone-DNA complexes
    d. Operators

_____ 17. All of the following are reasons to use TRIS during an electrophoresis except
    a. To stabilize the pH
    b. To conduct electricity
    c. To maintain the shape of molecules
    d. To stain molecules

_____ 18. Which stain causes DNA to glow orange when exposed to UV light?
    a. Agarose
    b. Polyacrylamide
    c. Methylene blue
    d. Ethidium bromide

_____ 19. A circular plasmid was cut with a restriction enzyme and three bands were visualized after electrophoresis. How many cuts were made in the plasmid?
    a. 1
    b. 2
    c. 3
    d. 4

_____ 20. Which agarose concentration would work best for separating very large molecules?
    a. 3%
    b. 2%
    c. 0.8%
    d. All of the choices would work well

Biotechnology Chapter 04

Answer Section

Matching

1. ANS: E   REF: 108
2. ANS: I   REF: 108
3. ANS: F   REF: 116
4. ANS: B   REF: 111
5. ANS: C   REF: 112-113
6. ANS: B   REF: 112-113
7. ANS: A   REF: 112-113
8. ANS: B   REF: 117
9. ANS: C   REF: 117
10. ANS: B   REF: 117

Multple Choice

11. ANS: B   REF: 99-100
12. ANS: D   REF: 107
13. ANS: A   REF: 104
14. ANS: C   REF: 114
15. ANS: B   REF: 102
16. ANS: D   REF: 108
17. ANS: D   REF: 118
18. ANS: D   REF: 118
19. ANS: C   REF: 119
20. ANS: C   REF: 118

Name _____

Course _____

Date _____

Biotechnology Chapter 05

Matching

For the following items, match each word with the best description (a-j).

    a. A specific region on an antigen where an antibody will bind
    b. A molecule on which an enzyme acts
    c. An enzyme that synthesizes DNA from RNA
    d. A process of making an RNA code from DNA
    e. A process in which RNA is decoded and polypeptides are formed
    f. A three letter code that indicates a particular amino acid
    g. A specific kind of antibody made by hybridomas to target a particular epitope
    h. A method of separating small DNA fragments or proteins using a vertical gel made of polyacrylamide
    i. A molecule or atom required by an enzyme in order to function
    j. An immortal tumor cell fused with a specific white blood cell that will produce monoclonal antibodies

_____ 1. Epitope

_____ 2. Hybridomas

_____ 3. PAGE

_____ 4. Translation

For the following items, match each structure with its corresponding interaction.

    a. Primary structure
    b. Secondary structure
    c. Tertiary structure
    d. Quaternary structure

_____ 5. The order of amino acids in a polypeptide chain

_____ 6. Hydrogen bonding between hydrogen, oxygen and nitrogen that result in alpha helices and beta sheets

_____ 7. Folding due to interactions between polar/nonpolar amino acids

_____ 8. Disulfide bonds between different polypeptide chains

For the following items, match each of the following PAGE procedures with the appropriate purpose.

    a. To determine the relative sizes of the samples
    b. To visualize proteins after electrophoresis
    c. To conduct electricity and establish an electric field through a gel
    d. To visualize samples when loading wells and monitor the sample migration
    e. To achieve the best separation of molecules

_____ 9. Stain gel with Coomassie® Blue

_____ 10. Add loading dye to samples

Multiple Choice

Identify the letter of the choice that best completes the statement or answers the question.

_____ 11. How can the molecular mass of a protein be determined?
    a. X-ray crystallography
    b. PAGE
    c. Mass spectrometer
    d. All of the above

Name _____

Course _____

Date _____

_____ 12. Proteins are composed of
   a. amino acids.
   b. nucleic acids.
   c. substrates.
   d. epitopes.

_____ 13. Which part of an amino acid interacts with another amino acid to fold a peptide into a protein?
   a. Amino group
   b. Carboxyl group
   c. R-group
   d. All of the above

_____ 14. Reverse transcriptase generates a lot of errors. What affect does this have on the newly synthesized HIV particles?
   a. It can cause the gp120 protein to fold in a different way.
   b. It produces new strains of HIV that existing antibodies may not recognize.
   c. The gp120 proteins may have a different amino acid sequence.
   d. All of the above

_____ 15. Monoclonal antibodies are produced by
   a. HIV.
   b. epitopes.
   c. hybridomas.
   d. mass spectrometers.

_____ 16. The region of activity on an enzyme is the
   a. cofactor domain.
   b. epitope.
   c. active site.
   d. R-group.

_____ 17. Under what conditions do posttranscriptional modifications to mRNA occur?
   a. In prokaryotic cells to remove introns
   b. In prokaryotic cells to remove exons
   c. In eukaryotic cells to remove introns
   d. In eukaryotic cells to remove exons

_____ 18. Where does translation occur in prokaryotes?
   a. In the endoplasmic reticulum
   b. At the ribosomes
   c. Outside the cell
   d. In the nucleus

_____ 19. To learn more about a protein's characteristics, a good first step is to do what?
   a. Determine the protein's charge using mass spectrometry
   b. Determine the protein's size by polyacrylamide gel electrophoresis
   c. Determine the amino acid sequence
   d. Determine the charge by affinity chromatography

_____ 20. What enzyme secures amino acids together by peptide bonds?
   a. Peptidyl transferase
   b. Taq polymerase
   c. Reverse transcriptase
   d. DNA polymerase

Biotechnology Chapter 05

Answer Section

Matching

1. ANS: A   REF: 136
2. ANS: J   REF: 136
3. ANS: H   REF: 148
4. ANS: E   REF: 140
5. ANS: A   REF: 133-135
6. ANS: B   REF: 133-135
7. ANS: C   REF: 133-135
8. ANS: D   REF: 133-135
9. ANS: B   REF: 148-149
10. ANS: D   REF: 148-149

Multple Choice

11. ANS: C   REF: 132
12. ANS: A   REF: 132
13. ANS: C   REF: 132
14. ANS: D   REF: 135
15. ANS: C   REF: 136
16. ANS: C   REF: 144
17. ANS: C   REF: 139
18. ANS: B   REF: 140
19. ANS: B   REF: 148
20. ANS: A   REF: 143

Name _____

Course _____

Date _____

Biotechnology Chapter 06

Matching

For the following items, match each assay type with the appropriate function (a-g).

　　a. A highly specific test to determine protein concentration based on a particular antigen-antibody inter-action.
　　b. Shows if a specific protein is present and conducting the expected reaction
　　c. Helps researchers measure the amount of protein present
　　d. Determines the amount and length of activity for a given protein in test organisms
　　e. Used for understanding the relationship between dosage and activity of a given pharmaceutical
　　f. A way to determine how long the pharmaceutical is effective and how it should be stored
　　g. Used to determine what are safe and unsafe levels of a given drug

_____　1. Concentration assay

_____　2. Potency assay

_____　3. Activity assay

_____　4. ELISA

_____　5. PK/PD assays

For the following items, match each word with the best definition.

　　a. The expression of a particular gene
　　b. Mammalian cells that have incorporated rDNA
　　c. The delivery method of a pharmaceutical product
　　d. A test for determining the presence or a particular characteristic of a protein of interest
　　e. Molecules that inhibit bacterial growth, produced by bacteria or fungi
　　f. the combination of alleles for a particular gene

_____　6. Genotype

_____　7. Formulation

_____　8. Assay

For the following items, determine which phase of the pharmaceutical product pipeline (a, b, or c) is responsible For the tasks below.

　　a. Research and Development
　　b. Manufacturing
　　c. Clinical trials

_____　9. Safety and efficacy studies on human subjects are monitored by the FDA.

_____　10. A potential product is identified.

Multiple Choice

Identify the letter of the choice that best completes the statement or answers the question.

_____　11. What is the function of amylase?
　　a. Degrades plant starch into maltose
　　b. Degrades disaccharides into glucose molecules
　　c. Bonds with other starch molecules to form plant cell wall
　　d. Artificial sweetener

_____　12. What genetic modification was made to Bollgard™ cotton?
　　a. The cotton plants contain a gene for producing more blossoms per plant, resulting in higher yields per plant.
　　b. The cotton plants contain a gene for producing larger balls of cotton.

Name _____

Course _____

Date _____

c. The cotton plants contain a gene for producing a neurotoxin protein that kills insects.

d. The cotton plants contain a gene for resistance to common herbicides used on cotton crops.

_____ 13. A starch test was performed on four different samples by adding iodine drops. After incubation, sample A was light brown, sample B was dark blue, sample C was light blue and sample D was medium blue. Which sample exhibited the most amylase activity?

    a. A

    b. B

    c. C

    d. D

_____ 14. What assay should be done to test for the presence and concentration of a specific goat antigen throughout research and manufacturing processes?

    a. Activity assay

    b. ELISA

    c. Potency assay

    d. Stability assay

_____ 15. A new pharmaceutical company has discovered a promising protein product that kills a rare form of lymphoma cancer cells in 92% of the 75 rats tested. What step of the CPDP does this finding address?

    a. Patent protection can be secured.

    b. The market is large enough to produce high volumes of sales.

    c. Preliminary data support the efficacy of this product.

    d. Safety of this pharmaceutical is assured.

_____ 16. New antibiotics are in big demand because

    a. new methods need to be devised for large scale production.

    b. the flu virus infects many people each year.

    c. bacteria mutate quickly and may become resistant to current antibiotics.

    d. All of the above

_____ 17. If the concentration of lactase in a protein solution needed to be determined as accurately as possible using Bradford reagent, what other instrument would a lab technician need?

    a. Thermocycler

    b. Spectrophotometer

    c. Fermenter

    d. Capillary detector

_____ 18. To detect amylase activity, iodine was added to three tubes containing protein solution from different fermenters. If the color in tube A, after a 1 minute incubation, is dark blue, the color in tube B is a light brown, and the color in tube C is a faint blue, which tube contains more active amylase?

    a. A

    b. B

    c. C

    d. This test would not measure amylase activity.

_____ 19. What organism is likely to be a natural producer of amylase?

    a. Cat

    b. Algae

    c. Fungi

    d. Dog

_____ 20. Protoplasts are useful in genetic engineering because

    a. they are easily inoculated with foreign DNA by way of a gene gun.

    b. treatment of protoplasts with cellulase or pectinase will degrade the cell wall.

    c. the rectangular cell shape is easier to accommodate in the confined tissue culture bottles.

    d. their thick, sticky cell walls provide extra rigidity and protection for foreign DNA.

Biotechnology Chapter 06

Answer Section

Matching

1. ANS: C   REF: 166
2. ANS: D   REF: 167
3. ANS: B   REF: 166
4. ANS: A   REF: 166
5. ANS: E   REF: 167
6. ANS: F   REF: 172
7. ANS: C   REF: 176
8. ANS: D   REF: 165
9. ANS: C   REF: 176
10. ANS: A   REF: 176

Multple Choice

11. ANS: A   REF: 163
12. ANS: C   REF: 174
13. ANS: A   REF: 166
14. ANS: B   REF: 166
15. ANS: C   REF: 164
16. ANS: C   REF: 171
17. ANS: B   REF: 166
18. ANS: B   REF: 166
19. ANS: C   REF: 163-164
20. ANS: A   REF: 173

Name _____

Course _____

Date _____

Biotechnology Chapter 07

Matching

For the following items, match the following words with the best description (a-j).

    a. The wavelength at which a sample absorbs the most light
    b. Light with wavelengths between 200-350 nm
    c. Amount of light that passes through a sample
    d. The light wavelengths that the human eye can see
    e. An aqueous solution that ionizes and yields H^+
    f. An aqueous solution that ionizes and yields OH^-
    g. A solution that resists changes in pH
    h. An aqueous solution with an equal number of H^+ and OH^- ions
    i. Light energy held within a sample
    j. An instrument that shines light on a sample and measures the amount of light transmitted.

_____ 1. Acid

_____ 2. Buffer

_____ 3. Transmittance

_____ 4. Visible spectrum

For the following items, determine whether UV or visible light spectrophotometry should be used.

    a. UV light spectrometry
    b. Visible light spectrometry

_____ 5. Monitoring the enzyme activity of amylase with an indicator solution

For items, place the following steps For calibrating a pH meter in the proper order, assuming the instrument is already turned on.

    a. Place electrode in pH 7 buffer standard and calibrate the meter to "7"
    b. Us pH 4 or pH 10 buffer to slope the meter if measuring a strong acid or strong base
    c. Rinse the electrode with distilled water
    d. Place the electrode in the solution to be measured

_____ 6. First

_____ 7. Second

_____ 8. Third

_____ 9. Fourth

_____ 10. Fifth

Multiple Choice

Identify the letter of the choice that best completes the statement or answers the question.

_____ 11. Which sample is the most concentrated?
    a. 34 %T
    b. 52 %T
    c. 1.40 a.u.
    d. 0.22 a.u.

Name _____

Course _____

Date _____

_____ 12. Which of the following is one of the most common tasks for entry-level technicians and research associates in biotechnology laboratories?

    a. Column chromatography

    b. Determine concentrations of samples

    c. Conduct ELISAs

    d. Buffer preparation

_____ 13. At what wavelength would a red molecule absorb the most light?

    a. 200 nm

    b. 350 nm

    c. 530 nm

    d. 700 nm

_____ 14. A sample with a peak absorbance at 640 nm is probably

    a. colorless.

    b. violet.

    c. green.

    d. red.

_____ 15. pH is a measurement of _____ a sample.

    a. the concentration of H^+ ions in

    b. the concentration of OH^- ions in

    c. light absorbed by

    d. light transmitted by

_____ 16. A pure sample of water has

    a. more H^+ ions than OH^- ions.

    b. fewer H^+ ions than OH^- ions.

    c. no H^+ or OH^- ions.

    d. An equal amount of H^+ and ions.

_____ 17. What is a neutral solution?

    a. A solution with no H^+ ions

    b. A solution with no H^+ ions

    c. A solution with equal numbers of H^+ and OH^- ions

    d. A solution with more H^+ ions than OH^- ions

_____ 18. Which of the following is a strong acid?

    a. pH 2

    b. pH 5

    c. pH 9

    d. pH 13

_____ 19. Which of the following would be a reasonable expectation for the $Lambda_{max}$ of a sample of yellow protein?

    a. 1.75 a.u. at 400 nm

    b. .023 a.u. at 420 nm

    c. 1.8 a.u. at 570 nm

    d. 0.99 a.u. at 530 nm

_____ 20. How does a buffer work?

    a. It adds H^+ ions to the solution

    b. It adds OH^- ions to the solution

    c. The buffering salts interact with the excess H^+ or OH^- ions in the solution

    d. It removes all ions from the solution

Biotechnology Chapter 07

Answer Section

Matching

  1. ANS: E   REF: 194
  2. ANS: G   REF: 198
  3. ANS: C   REF: 190
  4. ANS: D   REF: 190
  5. ANS: B   REF: 192
  6. ANS: C   REF: 197
  7. ANS: A   REF: 197
  8. ANS: C   REF: 197
  9. ANS: D   REF: 197
10. ANS: B   REF: 197

Multple Choice

11. ANS: C   REF: 192
12. ANS: D   REF: 196
13. ANS: B   REF: 192
14. ANS: B   REF: 192
15. ANS: A   REF: 195
16. ANS: D   REF: 195
17. ANS: C   REF: 195
18. ANS: A   REF: 195
19. ANS: B   REF: 200
20. ANS: C   REF: 198

Biotechnology Chapter 08

Matching

For the following items, match each scientific term with the description (a-j) that best fits.

    a. When complementary DNA strands come together

    b. Host DNA structures that accept and incorporate DNA resulting in rDNA

    c. A short, "tagged" piece of DNA complementary to the DNA of interest

    d. The liquid above a pellet after centrifugation

    e. The scaled-up process by which cells are grown under optimal conditions for maximum cell division and product formation

    f. FDA regulated manufacturing protocol

    g. The desired result of endonuclease activity for the purpose of rDNA production

    h. Cells treated with calcium chloride to increase DNA uptake

    i. Probes used specifically to initiate the polymerase chain reaction

    j. When cells grow rapidly such that in each cell cycle, the cell count doubles

_____ 1. Hybridize

_____ 2. Fermentation

_____ 3. Exponential growth

_____ 4. cGMP

_____ 5. Sticky ends

For the following items, match each technique with its corresponding host DNA organisms (a-c).

    a. bacteria

    b. mammalian cells

    c. viruses

_____ 6. transfection

For the following items, match each enzyme with its corresponding activity (a-c).

    a. cuts DNA

    b. pastes pieces of DNA together

    c. bursts cells open

_____ 7. lysozyme

For the following items, match each process with its appropriate department (a-c) in a biotech or pharmaceutical company.

    a. R&D

    b. Manufacturing

    c. Both departments

_____ 8. Assays are done to check for the presence, purity, and activity of target protein.

_____ 9. Host cell type is considered for target gene.

_____ 10. Conditions optimized and exponential growth of transformed cells occurs.

Name _____

Course _____

Date _____

Multiple Choice

Identify the letter of the choice that best completes the statement or answers the question.

_____ 11. A new _____ is an example of a product that could have been derived from genetic engineering.
   a. pharmaceutical
   b. vitamin
   c. metal
   d. centrifuge

_____ 12. Before recombinant cells are produced, what must be done?
   a. An assay must be done to confirm protein activity in transformed cells.
   b. The recombinant protein is isolated, purified, and formulated.
   c. The DNA encoding for the desired characteristic is identified, isolated, and confirmed.
   d. Fermentation must be optimized.

_____ 13. What is a form of selection used to identify transformed cells?
   a. The green fluorescent protein gene is included on the vector plasmid.
   b. Suspected transformed cells are spun in a centrifuge.
   c. An antibiotic resistance gene is added to the vector.
   d. The target gene is recombined into a plasmid with the beta-galactosidase gene.

_____ 14. A piece of DNA that results from being spliced into a vector is called
   a. a sticky end.
   b. recombinant DNA.
   c. an endonuclease.
   d. an RFLP.

_____ 15. Which of the following treatments will work to extract and isolate chromosomal DNA from bacterial cells?
   a. Add lysozyme to cells in buffered solution, treat with detergent and enzymes to remove proteins, centrifuge and then collect DNA in the supernatant
   b. Add enzyme cocktail containing lysozyme, RNase, and proteases to burst cells, then salts and detergent to remove proteins, followed by centrifugation, where supernanatant is dumped and the pellet is resuspended in buffer to collect DNA
   c. Add NaOH and SDS to burst cells, precipitate out proteins, and isolate DNA through a series of ethanol and isopropanol precipitations
   d. Centrifuge cell mixture to burst cells, collect supernatant, precipitate out proteins with TE buffer, centrifuge again and add lysozyme

_____ 16. Which restriction enzyme listed in the chart below will result in a blunt end cut?

Restriction Enzyme	Recognition Site
Alu I	AG^CT
Eco RI	G^AATTC
HindIII	A^AGCTT

   a. *Alu I*
   b. *Bam HI*
   c. *HindIII*
   d. All of the above

Name _____

Course _____

Date _____

_____ 17. How is DNA spliced?
   a. PCR
   b. Scalpel
   c. Restriction enzymes
   d. Probes

_____ 18. In a mini-prep, how is DNA extracted in the final step?
   a. alcohol precipitation
   b. potassium acetate precipitation
   c. TE buffer precipitation
   d. treatment with SDS-NaOH

_____ 19. During scale-up of cultured CHO cells, cultures in spinner flasks grow for _____ before being used to seed a larger culture.
   a. 1-2 days
   b. 3-4 days
   c. 5-7 days
   d. 2 weeks

_____ 20. During fermentation,
   a. assays are developed to monitor cell growth.
   b. recombinant DNA is produced.
   c. DNA extractions and plasmid preparations are done.
   d. big, sterile, and automated tanks are used for growing large volumes of cell culture.

Biotechnology Chapter 08

Answer Section

Matching

1. ANS: A   REF: 213
2. ANS: E   REF: 225
3. ANS: J   REF: 227
4. ANS: F   REF: 229
5. ANS: G   REF: 216
6. ANS: B   REF: 215
7. ANS: C   REF: 231
8. ANS: C   REF: 224-226
9. ANS: A   REF: 224-226
10. ANS: C   REF: 224-226

Multple Choice

11. ANS: A   REF: 209-210
12. ANS: C   REF: 210
13. ANS: B   REF: 221
14. ANS: B   REF: 216
15. ANS: A   REF: 212
16. ANS: A   REF: 216
17. ANS: C   REF: 217
18. ANS: A   REF: 230
19. ANS: B   REF: 224
20. ANS: D   REF: 224

Biotechnology Chapter 09

Matching

For the following items, match each word with the best description (a-h).

    a. Membrane filter at one end of a chromatography column
    b. Outside of a cell
    c. Inside of a cell
    d. Treatment made to look genuine, but it does not contain the product being tested
    e. Separation of molecules on or through a stationary phase
    f. A small amount of sample that is collected during column chromatography
    g. A process that uses high frequency sound waves to burst open cells
    h. The process of releasing molecules from resin during column chromatography

_____ 1. Chromatography

_____ 2. Extracellular

_____ 3. Fraction

_____ 4. Intracellular

_____ 5. Sonication

For the following items, decide which chromatography method (a-c) best fits the following descriptions.

    a. Paper chromatography
    b. Thin-layer chromatography
    c. Column chromatography

_____ 6. Resin beads are utilized which have an opposite charge of the protein of interest. A final wash with an elution buffer knocks off the protein of interest and fractions are collected.

_____ 7. Instruments that exert high pressure are attached to sophisticated computers and operated by highly trained technicians to run samples through and collect protein fractions.

For the following items, determine which phase of clinical trials (a-d) best fits each description.

    a. Phase I
    b. Phase II
    c. Phase III
    d. Phase IV

_____ 8. Several thousand patients receive treatment with the pharmaceutical. In addition to monitoring safety and efficacy, a comparison with other available treatments is also done.

_____ 9. Several hundred patients are used to study safety, dosage, and efficacy of the product.

For the following items, decide which gel filtration characteristic (a-c) should be altered to optimize the following separations.

    a. column length
    b. column width
    c. pore size

_____ 10. A large batch of proteins from the largest fermentation tank needs to be isolated

Multiple Choice

Identify the letter of the choice that best completes the statement or answers the question.

_____ 11. What is the purpose of SDS when harvesting intracellular proteins?
   a. It solubilizes extracellular proteins, making it easier to recover the intracellular ones.
   b. It is used during sonication.
   c. It degrades the cell membrane causing the cells to burst.
   d. All of the above

_____ 12. _____ proteins are easier to isolate from cell cultures.
   a. Extracellular
   b. Intracellular
   c. Transcellular
   d. Antigenic

_____ 13. What is the purpose of conducting double-blind tests during clinical trials?
   a. To minimize the chance a patient receives a placebo
   b. To prevent cross-contamination of product
   c. To help keep track of the numerous patients involved in the trial
   d. To help ensure that neither the experimenter nor the test subject can influence the results

_____ 14. All of the following might be reasons a product would not be marketable except:
   a. Patent protection may not be secured
   b. Assays 99.9% reactivity
   c. Production of the product is uneconomical
   d. FDA may not approve the product

_____ 15. Which of the following methods may be used to recover intracellular proteins?
   a. Sonication of cell culture
   b. Performing column chromatography on the growth media
   c. Dialysis of SDS with elution buffer
   d. Performing an assay to determine protein acitivity and concentration

_____ 16. In gel filtration chromatography, which molecules would be collected in the first fraction?
   a. Water-soluble molecules
   b. Hydrophobic molecules
   c. Relatively large molecules
   d. Relatively small molecules

_____ 17. About how long does the clinical testing phase typically last?
   a. Less than a year
   b. 1-2 years
   c. 2-5 years
   d. 5-10 years

_____ 18. Affinity chromatography can be very specific, but it can also pose a challenge because
   a. finding the right elution buffer for the final rinse can be troublesome.
   b. identifying an antibody to attach to the resin and interact specifically with the protein that needs to be separated can be laborious.
   c. it is hard to determine whether cations or anions should be coupled with the resin molecules.
   d. it can be difficult to select the most appropriate pore size for the resin.

_____ 19. The columns used in FPLC are
  a. very small and are used for handling micro volumes.
  b. hooked up to pumps and contain minute resin beads for separating very large molecules.
  c. connected to pumps and can withstand high pressure as samples are forced through.
  d. fed directly into a VIS spectrophotometer for determining the concentration of colorless proteins.

_____ 20. If you want to separate 75 kD and 300 kD molecules from each other by gel filtration chromatography, which pore size would yield the best result?
  a. 50 kD
  b. 100 kD
  c. 300 kD
  d. All of the above would work well.

Biotechnology Chapter 09

Answer Section

Matching

1. ANS: E   REF: 245
2. ANS: B   REF: 241
3. ANS: F   REF: 243
4. ANS: C   REF: 241
5. ANS: G   REF: 242
6. ANS: C   REF: 245-246
7. ANS: C   REF: 245-246
8. ANS: C   REF: 256
9. ANS: B   REF: 256
10. ANS: B   REF: 252

Multple Choice

11. ANS: C   REF: 241
12. ANS: A   REF: 242
13. ANS: D   REF: 256
14. ANS: B   REF: 257
15. ANS: A   REF: 242
16. ANS: C   REF: 247
17. ANS: C   REF: 255
18. ANS: B   REF: 248
19. ANS: C   REF: 247
20. ANS: B   REF: 252

Name _____

Course _____

Date _____

Biotechnology Chapter 10

Matching

For the following items, match the following words with the best description (a-j) below.

    a. Cell division process for sex cell formation

    b. Cell division process for making more body cells

    c. Propagation, from a single parent, in which the offspring are identical to the parent

    d. A single cell that is formed when an egg and sperm combine.

    e. Containing two sets of homologous chromosomes

    f. Containing one set of chromosomes

    g. In a combination of two alleles, only one is necessary to express a specific trait

    h. In a combination of two alleles, two copies are necessary to express a specific trait

    i. Sprouting of a seed into new plant

    j. Sex cells

_____ 1. Cloning

_____ 2. Diploid

_____ 3. Gametes

_____ 4. Haploid

For the following items, determine whether each of the following cells are haploid or diploid.

    a. Haploid

    b. Diploid

_____ 5. Pumpkin seed

_____ 6. Zygote

_____ 7. Pollen gathered by a bee

_____ 8. Root tip

For the following items, match each function with the corresponding plant organ (a-d).

    a. Leaf

    b. Stem

    c. Root

    d. Flower or cone

_____ 9. Reproduction

_____ 10. Food production and storage

Multiple Choice

Identify the letter of the choice that best completes the statement or answers the question.

_____ 11. If a friend took a cutting from your favorite African violet and planted it in a vermiculite and soil mixture to grow, what type of propagation would this be?

    a. Asexual

    b. Sexual

    c. Tissue culture

    d. Selective breeding

Name _____

Course _____

Date _____

_____ 12. What can be added to a plant cutting to encourage it to root?
   a. Sand
   b. Vermiculite
   c. Protocorms
   d. Hormones

_____ 13. How do woody plants increase in width?
   a. Each cell in the stem swells.
   b. Cortex cell replicates.
   c. Cells are added at the vascular cambium.
   d. The palisade layer adds new cells.

_____ 14. A mass of cells growing on plant tissue growth media that has yet to differentiate is called a
   a. callus.
   b. meristem.
   c. protocorm.
   d. radicle.

_____ 15. A flower heterozygous for pink petals produced 100 seeds from a cross with another heterozygous pink flowered plant. The seeds have been collected and planted by a research assistant and they are now flowering. Which of the following numbers would be expected for the number of blue flowering (recessive) offspring plants?
   a. 23
   b. 56
   c. 71
   d. 99

_____ 16. Which food is an example of a plant ovary?
   a. Wheat
   b. Apple
   c. Broccoli
   d. Corn

_____ 17. During a dihybrid, heterozygous cross,
   a. a single trait or characteristic is studied.
   b. parents contain identical genetic information as compared to the offspring.
   c. the resulting offspring's genotypes can be predicted.
   d. offspring have increased antibiotic resistance.

_____ 18. Cellulose molecules are
   a. essential for photosynthesis.
   b. long and fibrous.
   c. rectangular and rigid.
   d. All of the above

_____ 19. To determine if a measurement from an individual trial is "good" data, all of the following would be useful except:
   a. The mean value of all the trials
   b. The conditions of the experimental setting
   c. The standard deviation of the values
   d. The 10% Error Rule

_____ 20. When propagating plants by tissue culture, what type of tissue is used?
   a. Epidermis
   b. Cortex
   c. Meristem
   d. Ovule

Biotechnology Chapter 10

Answer Section

Matching

1. ANS: C   REF: 270
2. ANS: E   REF: 279
3. ANS: J   REF: 269
4. ANS: F   REF: 279
5. ANS: B   REF: 279
6. ANS: B   REF: 279
7. ANS: A   REF: 279
8. ANS: B   REF: 279
9. ANS: D   REF: 273-274
10. ANS: A   REF: 273-274

Multple Choice

11. ANS: A   REF: 270
12. ANS: D   REF: 271
13. ANS: B   REF: 277
14. ANS: A   REF: 271
15. ANS: A   REF: 283
16. ANS: B   REF: 273
17. ANS: C   REF: 283
18. ANS: B   REF: 274
19. ANS: B   REF: 284-285
20. ANS: C   REF: 274

Name _____

Course _____

Date _____

Biotechnology Chapter 11

Matching

For the following items, match each of the following words with the best description (a-j).

    a. Breeding between closely related organisms
    b. Water-based plant growing technique
    c. Used as a vector for plant transformations
    d. Plants transformed with foreign DNA
    e. Using pollen from one plant to pollinate a flower on another plant
    f. Type of plant hormone that causes cells to divide
    g. Type of plant hormone that directs cell elongation
    h. Small pieces of plants used for plant tissue culture
    i. Producing plants for ornamental purposes
    j. A protein product grown in plants for human medicinal purposes.

_____ 1. Auxin

_____ 2. Explants

_____ 3. Inbreeding

_____ 4. Transgenic plants

For the following items, decide which hormone (a-f) should be manipulated to develop plants with the listed traits.

    a. Abscisic acid (ABA)
    b. Auxin
    c. Cytokinin
    d. Ethylene
    e. Gibberellin
    f. Phytochrome

_____ 5. Tall variety of sunflowers

_____ 6. Fruit that ripens slowly

_____ 7. Faster development of callus during plant tissue culture

For the following items, cotton plants were transformed using the pBI121 plasmid containing the NPT II and GUS genes. State whether the resulting plantlets have been properly transformed or not.

    a. Transformed
    b. Not transformed

_____ 8. Kanamycin added to the growth media and there is no growth.

_____ 9. X-Gluc added to the growth media and the cells look blue.

_____ 10. X-Gluc added to the growth media and plants are a vibrant green.

Multiple Choice

Identify the letter of the choice that best completes the statement or answers the question.

_____ 11. The most challenging method of asexual plant propagation is
    a. by plant tissue culture.
    b. using stem cuttings.
    c. using runners.
    d. using meristematic tissue.

Name _____

Course _____

Date _____

_____ 12. After a plant is transformed with human DNA, it must be _____ and then planted in the field.
    a. hydroponically grown
    b. sterilized
    c. cloned
    d. selectively bred

_____ 13. Countries or regions with poor soil quality can grow plants
    a. by tissue culture.
    b. that contain Bt transgenes.
    c. hydroponically.
    d. All of the above

_____ 14. Sterile explants are grown in sterilized media that contain a mixture of
    a. lipids.
    b. hormones.
    c. DNA.
    d. All of the above

_____ 15. In nature, the Ti plasmid
    a. makes crops resistant to pesticides.
    b. induces tumors in plants.
    c. produces an insecticidal protein that benefits crops.
    d. infects Agrobacteria which hinders plant transformations.

_____ 16. The concentration of genomic DNA can be checked by
    a. gel electrophoresis.
    b. ELISA.
    c. UV Spectrophotometry.
    d. All of the above

_____ 17. The first sign of a successful plant tissue culture is
    a. evidence of the media getting metabolized.
    b. the formation of root tips.
    c. the swelling of the explant.
    d. runner formation.

_____ 18. Plant cell walls can be ruptured
    a. using a cell lysis solution.
    b. using a protein-degrading buffer.
    c. by alcohol extraction.
    d. by freezing with liquid nitrogen.

_____ 19. If transformed bacteria containing the Ti plasmid are incubated with growth media and
    _____, transgenic plants will develop.
    a. GFP
    b. *Arabidopsis*
    c. plant tissue
    d. phytochrome

_____ 20. The enzyme encoded by the GUS gene breaks down
    a. X-Gal and forms a blue product.
    b. X-Gluc and forms a blue product.
    c. GFP and forms a green product.
    d. GFP and results in a colorless product.

Biotechnology Chapter 11

Answer Section

Matching

1. ANS: G   REF: 303
2. ANS: H   REF: 303
3. ANS: A   REF: 307
4. ANS: D   REF: 313
5. ANS: E   REF: 303
6. ANS: D   REF: 303
7. ANS: C   REF: 303
8. ANS: B   REF: 314
9. ANS: A   REF: 314
10. ANS: B   REF: 314

Multple Choice

11. ANS: A   REF: 300
12. ANS: C   REF: 309-310
13. ANS: C   REF: 308
14. ANS: B   REF: 304
15. ANS: B   REF: 312-313
16. ANS: C   REF: 311
17. ANS: C   REF: 304
18. ANS: D   REF: 311
19. ANS: C   REF: 313
20. ANS: B   REF: 314

Name _____

Course _____

Date _____

Biotechnology Chapter 12

Matching

For the following items, match each of the following words with the best description (a-j).

a. Compounds that act to treat, prevent, or alleviate symptoms of disease
b. A treatment that causes the body to produce many antibodies in response to the injected antigen
c. Research, development, and manufacturing of substances that prevent, treat, or alleviate diseases or their symptoms
d. Understanding the nature, origins, transmission, evolution, and hosts of a disease
e. Process of combining chemical components to produce new or varied organic compounds
f. Short chains of up to 50 amino acids
g. Chemicals that alter the affect of proteins or other molecules on disease-causing mechanisms
h. Long-term protection from cellular invaders
i. Short chains of up to 50 nucleotides
j. Assemblies of DNA, RNA, or proteins for screening

_____ 1. Combinatorial chemistry

_____ 2. Medical biotechnology

_____ 3. Oligonucleotides

_____ 4. Pathogenesis

For the following items, determine which process (a-c) would be the best choice For production of the following therapeutics?

a. Genetic Engineering
b. Isolate from nature
c. Combinatorial chemistry

_____ 5. Modifications must be made by to this compound to reduce toxicity

_____ 6. Aspirin, buffered to a neutral pH

For the following items, determine whether each statement is true (a) or false (b).

a. True
b. False

_____ 7. A compound in the foxglove plant is known to have an effect on heart rate.

_____ 8. The only source of commercial aspirin is willow tree bark and leaves.

_____ 9. A microarray can be used to purify antibodies from a cell culture.

_____ 10. The gp120 molecule is being used in HIV vaccine research.

Multiple Choice

Identify the letter of the choice that best completes the statement or answers the question.

_____ 11. How are peptides synthesized?
a. Using peptide synthesizers
b. By affinity chromatography
c. In an automated process utilizing HPLC
d. Linking together nucleic acids, one at a time

_____ 12. What is the most successful pharmaceutical to date?
   a. Viagra
   b. Acetaminophen
   c. Aspirin
   d. Insulin

_____ 13. Which of the following is a reason that compound libraries need to be screened?
   a. To verify the molecular structure of each compound.
   b. To determine the pH each compound.
   c. To determine the molecular weight of the compounds.
   d. To determine the wavelength of each compound.

_____ 14. Antibodies are made up of _____ peptide chains.
   a. 2
   b. 4
   c. 13
   d. 20

_____ 15. A "blocker" drug acts by
   a. causing an immune response facilitated by memory cells.
   b. binding to a recognition molecule on a host cell.
   c. eliminating the antigen that causes the disease symptoms.
   d. binding to an antigen during affinity chromatography.

_____ 16. A protein chip was used to screen blocker compounds against the gp120 receptor. The chip reader detected fluorescence in several trials of compound X. What does this mean?
   a. Compound X may be a good target for drug development to combat HIV.
   b. An error resulted during several of the trials so compound X should be re-screened.
   c. Compound X is contaminated and the trials must be re-conducted.
   d. It is time to upgrade to a high throughput screener.

_____ 17. In order to develop a potential drug target for a specific disease, what information should scientists research?
   a. The socioeconomics of each patient.
   b. The average temperature of the pathogen's native environment.
   c. The pathogen's interaction with the host
   d. The pathogen's scientific name.

_____ 18. A mass spectrometer graph shows three peaks. What does this indicate?
   a. The compound is at a concentration of 3 M
   b. There are three different molecules in this compound
   c. The compound has gone through 2 degradations
   d. There are three fluorescing potentially active drug targets

_____ 19. If a company needs primers to target a specific gene of interest and does not have the ability to synthesize them, what would be a good way to obtain them?
   a. Assemble an in-house oligo factory
   b. Manufacture them by affinity chromatography
   c. Order them from an oligonucleotide synthesis company
   d. Contract out to another company that has a peptide synthesizer

_____ 20. How can molecular modeling software help a researcher design potential drug targets?
   a. The computer can track the cost of testing potential drugs.
   b. The models explain how a patient absorbs the drug.
   c. Interactions between the target molecule and a potential drug can be "tested" virtually.
   d. The software can be programmed to track all of the researchers experiments.

Biotechnology Chapter 12

Answer Section

Matching

1. ANS: E   REF: 328
2. ANS: C   REF: 325
3. ANS: I   REF: 333
4. ANS: D   REF: 327
5. ANS: C   REF: 328-332
6. ANS: C   REF: 328-332
7. ANS: A   REF: 327
8. ANS: B   REF: 328
9. ANS: B   REF: 331
10. ANS: A   REF: 332

Multple Choice

11. ANS: A   REF: 332
12. ANS: C   REF: 328
13. ANS: A   REF: 330
14. ANS: B   REF: 334
15. ANS: B   REF: 326
16. ANS: A   REF: 331
17. ANS: C   REF: 327
18. ANS: B   REF: 331
19. ANS: C   REF: 333
20. ANS: C   REF: 331

Name _____

Course _____

Date _____

Biotechnology Chapter 13

Matching

For the following items, match each word with the most appropriate definition (a-j) below.

    a. A strand of DNA from which new DNA is synthesized
    b. Unique DNA banding pattern used for identity purposes
    c. Separation of DNA strands by breaking hydrogen bonds
    d. The application of biology, chemistry, physics, math, and sociology to solve legal problems
    e. Determining the best conditions and concentrations for a reaction
    f. Replication of DNA many times
    g. Source of As, Cs, Gs, and Ts during DNA replication
    h. An area on the genome where there is great variability from individual to individual
    i. Two chromosomes containing the same genes in the same order
    j. Hybridization of an oligonucleotide with its complement on the template

_____ 1. Amplification

_____ 2. DNA fingerprinting

_____ 3. Forensics

_____ 4. Primer annealing

_____ 5. VNTR

For the following items, match the following enzymes with their functions in DNA replication (a-f) below.

    a. Adds RNA nucleotides to template to act as a primer
    b. Unwind and untwist DNA to initiate replication
    c. Connects replicated strands together, terminating the replication process
    d. Relieves the tension in double helix to untwist the strands
    e. Edits out RNA nucleotides
    f. Adds DNA nucleotides to end of RNA primer and fills in gaps once RNA nucleotides have been removed

_____ 6. Topoisomerase

_____ 7. RNA primase

For the following items, place the following steps (a-d) of a Southern Blot in chronological order.

    a. Step 1
    b. Step 2
    c. Step 3
    d. Step 4

_____ 8. Treat with labeled probes for visualization

_____ 9. Electrophorese fragments on agarose or acrylamide gel

_____ 10. Cross linking with UV light

Name _____

Course _____

Date _____

Multiple Choice

Identify the letter of the choice that best completes the statement or answers the question.

_____ 11. How does DNA stick to a nylon membrane or nitrocellulose paper during a Southern Blot?
    a. DNA has a negative charge and the membrane or paper has a positive charge.
    b. Hydrophobic interaction is used to transfer the sample to the membrane or paper.
    c. A nucleometer is used to bind the DNA to the membrane or paper.
    d. DNA is attracted to the membrane or paper by the attraction of its sugar groups.

_____ 12. If a VNTR repeat unit is 17 bases long and an allele with 22 repeats that has been amplified by PCR is 495 bases long, how long would an allele be if it has 32 repeats?
    a. 495 bp
    b. 527 bp
    c. 544 bp
    d. 665 bp

_____ 13. How many chromosomes do onion cells contain?
    a. 1
    b. 8
    c. 16
    d. 46

_____ 14. How does a blood sample need to be prepared before PCR?
    a. Isolate and extract DNA from the white blood cells
    b. Isolate and extract DNA from the red blood cells
    c. Remove the DNA from the hemoglobin cells
    d. Ensure chromosomes are in metaphase stage of cell cycle

_____ 15. What does it mean if an individual contains only one band after D1S80 amplification?
    a. The PCR reaction needs to be optimized
    b. The individual is homozygous at that locus
    c. The MgCl2 concentration needs to be adjusted
    d. Bad primer design

_____ 16. A unique DNA fingerprint can be established for suspects in a crime by
    a. amplifying one VNTR locus.
    b. amplifying several different VNTR loci.
    c. using a microarray panel of RNA.
    d. regulated gene expression.

_____ 17. When trying to locate the insulin gene, which probe would be best?
    a. A probe that has specificity with a few places on the genome
    b. A probe that is about 10 bases long
    c. A probe with several Cs at the end to anchor it down.
    d. A probe with a fluorescent tag and complimentary to part of the insulin gene

_____ 18. A DNA microarray read by a chip reader has every spot illuminating bright green. What does this mean?
    a. All these genes represented on the microarray are being expressed.
    b. The whole plate is full of potential drug targets.
    c. All the spots on the plate hybridized with their corresponding probes.
    d. None of the spots on the plate hybridized with probes.

_____ 19. Which of the following primers is well designed?
a. CTATCCGGCCCCGGAAAATTTTT
b. TATCCGATCATGCGGGTAGAT
c. TACCTAGGA
d. CGAGCCCGGATTCCGGACCGCGC

_____ 20. What is regulated gene expression?
a. A process by which microarrays detect which cells are producing which proteins
b. The cells ability to turn "on" and "off" genes at particular times
c. A VNTR amplification protocol
d. A method for blotting DNA fragments onto a positively charged membrane

Biotechnology Chapter 13

Answer Section

Matching

1. ANS: F   REF: 349
2. ANS: B   REF: 349
3. ANS: D   REF: 360
4. ANS: J   REF: 355
5. ANS: H   REF: 359
6. ANS: D   REF: 345-346
7. ANS: A   REF: 345-346
8. ANS: D   REF: 350
9. ANS: A   REF: 350
10. ANS: C   REF: 350

Multple Choice

11. ANS: A   REF: 350
12. ANS: D   REF: 359
13. ANS: C   REF: 344
14. ANS: A   REF: 359
15. ANS: B   REF: 359
16. ANS: B   REF: 359
17. ANS: D   REF: 350
18. ANS: D   REF: 351
19. ANS: B   REF: 350
20. ANS: B   REF: 345

Name _____

Course _____

Date _____

Biotechnology Chapter 14

Matching

For the following items, match the following words with the best description (a-j).

a. Determination of the position of atoms on a molecule using X-rays
b. The study of an organism's entire genetic information
c. The massive undertaking to decode the entire human DNA sequence
d. Study of how, when, and what forms of proteins are active
e. A combination of computer programs and mathematical models to analyze sequence data
f. Using genetic and protein codes to improve medications
g. A technique for determining the order of nucleotides in a DNA fragment
h. A field where monitoring and correcting the health of species, populations, communities, and ecosystems is done using genomic and proteomic information
i. A nucleotide that is missing an oxygen atom on carbon number 3 of the sugar molecule
j. An instrument that measures the masses of atoms or molecules

_____ 1. Environmental biotechnology

_____ 2. Protein crystallography

_____ 3. Proteomics

_____ 4. Human Genome Project

For the following items, order the following steps For conducting an ELISA to screen For individuals exposed to HIV. (You may need to use an item more than once.)

a. Wash plates with PBS buffer to remove excess molecules
b. Collect blood samples
c. Add acid to turn the blue precipitate yellow (more stable)
d. Add TMB substrate to the wells. A blue precipitate should appear at the location of any antigen-antibody binding.
e. Lyse cells to release proteins
f. Add enzyme-tagged anti-HIV antibodies
g. Add cell lysates to 96-well plate (proteins will stick to the plastic, including virus antigens)
h. Wash plates with blocking solution that contains 5% milk to reduce non-specific binding

_____ 5. Fourth

_____ 6. Fifth

_____ 7. Sixth

_____ 8. Seventh

_____ 9. Eighth

_____ 10. Ninth

Multiple Choice

Identify the letter of the choice that best completes the statement or answers the question.

_____ 11. What happens when a deoxynucleotide gets added to a DNA molecule during a DNA sequencing reaction?
a. The molecule stops fluorescing
b. Synthesis proceeds as normal
c. The primer degrades
d. The chain terminates

_____ 12. All of the following are potential benefits of personalized medicine except:
   a. Reduced side effects
   b. Reduced risk of allergic reactions
   c. Increased drug effectiveness
   d. Lower costs

_____ 13. What improvements have been made with bioremediation?
   a. Oils spills have been cleaned
   b. Toxic metals have been removed from foods.
   c. Dry cleaning solvents have been substituted with salt-based cleaners
   d. Plant photosynthesis has been increased by 70% worldwide.

_____ 14. When setting up a sequencing reaction, what amount of ddNTPs is needed?
   a. Fewer ddNTPs than dNTPs
   b. More ddNTPs than dNTPs
   c. Equal amounts of ddNTPs and dNTPs
   d. None

_____ 15. What tool is available for comparing a specific DNA sequence with all other known similar sequences?
   a. BLAST
   b. X-ray crystallography
   c. Shot-gun cloning
   d. Northern Blot

_____ 16. All of the following are involved in a typical Western Blot visualization except:
   a. Primary antibody
   b. Secondary antibody
   c. Substrate
   d. Colloid suspensions

_____ 17. What will help ensure that protein molecules will form clear, clean crystals?
   a. Flash freezing technique
   b. Quick salting-out process
   c. Slow salting-out process
   d. Slow thawing process

_____ 18. What disease is being treated by pharmacogenetics now?
   a. Food poisoning
   b. Certain cancers
   c. Huntington's Chorea
   d. All of the above

_____ 19. How does an ELISA work in home pregnancy tests?
   a. It detects the HCGH hormone from urine using an anti-HCGH antibody.
   b. It detects the anti-HCGH antibody using the hormone HCGH.
   c. It detects HGH from the fetus using the anti-HGH antibody.
   d. It detects the HGH antibody from the mother's urine using an anti-HGH hormone.

_____ 20. A lab technician suspects that a band on a PAGE gel, at 61kD, is amylase. Which method can she use to confirm that it is amylase?
   a. Eastern Blot
   b. Northern Blot
   c. Southern Blot
   d. Western Blot

Biotechnology Chapter 14

Answer Section

Matching

1. ANS: H   REF: 387
2. ANS: A   REF: 378
3. ANS: D   REF: 377
4. ANS: C   REF: 372
5. ANS: A   REF: 381
6. ANS: H   REF: 381
7. ANS: A   REF: 381
8. ANS: F   REF: 381
9. ANS: A   REF: 381
10. ANS: D   REF: 381

Multple Choice

11. ANS: B   REF: 371
12. ANS: D   REF: 386
13. ANS: A   REF: 387
14. ANS: A   REF: 371
15. ANS: A   REF: 371
16. ANS: D   REF: 383
17. ANS: C   REF: 379
18. ANS: B   REF: 386
19. ANS: A   REF: 382
20. ANS: D   REF: 382

Name _____

Course _____

Date _____

Biotechnology Unit 1 (Chapters 1–5)

Matching

For the following items, match each word with the most appropriate definition below.

  a. An entire set of an organism's genetic information
  b. A testable prediction to a scientific question
  c. Values that help one decide between right and wrong
  d. The study and manipulation of living things, or their components
  e. A factor that will yield a predictable result
  f. A factor that gets manipulated during an experiment
  g. Applying moral values to decision-making on topics brought up by advances in biology, medicine, and technology
  h. A combination of DNA from different sources in one molecule
  i. Information gathered during an experiment
  j. A scientific magazine or periodical where scientists publish their experiments

_____ 1. Bioethics

_____ 2. Variable

For the following items, put in order the sequence of events that occurs during process development of a pharmaceutical product.

  a. Manufacturing
  b. Product identification
  c. Sales and marketing
  d. Testing for safety and efficacy
  e. Research and development
  f. Small-scale manufacturing

_____ 3. First

_____ 4. Fifth

_____ 5. Sixth

For the following items determine which federal agency oversees the production of the following products.

  a. FDA
  b. EPA
  c. USDA

_____ 6. Antibiotics

Name _____

Course _____

Date _____

For the following items, match the following words with the best description (a-k).

    a. A six-carbon sugar molecule used by cells for making energy
    b. A process where plants and algae use light energy to make chemical energy
    c. Information-carrying molecules within all cells
    d. The process of breaking down food molecules to generate energy
    e. Thousands of different types of macromolecules that have various functions within and around a cell
    f. Molecules containing carbon, hydrogen, and oxygen in approximately a 1:2:1 ratio
    g. Packages of DNA
    h. The subunits of proteins, each of which contains an amino group, carboxyl group, and a functional "R" group all attached to a central carbon atom
    i. Specialized membrane-bound structures that have specialized functions within cells
    j. Hydrophobic molecules that have specific functions within and around cells
    k. Large molecules composed of repeating units of smaller molecules

_____ 7. Glucose

_____ 8. Lipids

_____ 9. Nucleic acids

_____ 10. Organelles

_____ 11. Proteins

_____ 12. Respiration

For the following items, determine whether each of the following cell types is eukaryotic or prokaryotic.

    a. Eukaryotic
    b. Prokaryotic

_____ 13. Red algae

_____ 14. E. coli

For the following items, match the following protein functions with specific examples (a-e).

    a. Insulin
    b. gp120
    c. Hemoglobin
    d. Keratin
    e. Amylase

_____ 15. Hormone

_____ 16. Transport

For the following items, match each word with the most appropriate definition below.

    a. The proportion of solute to solvent in a solution
    b. The concentration of a solution expressed as the number of moles of solute per liter of solvent
    c. A solution that resists changes in pH
    d. What gets dissolved in a solution
    e. The number of molecules that equals the molecular weight of a substance, in grams
    f. The addition of solvent to make a mixture less concentrated
    g. The solution that dissolves added molecules
    h. Containing water

_____ 17. aqueous

_____ 18. buffer

_____ 19. concentration

____ 20. dilution

____ 21. molarity

____ 22. solute

For the following items, select which tool below would most accurately measure the following amounts.

    a. micropipet
    b. pipet
    c. graduated cylinder
    d. tabletop balance
    e. analytical balance

____ 23. 3.5 g

____ 24. 4 mL

In the following items, determine which equation (a-c) would be most useful in calculating the amount of solute needed to make each solution.

    a. Concentration _ Volume = Mass
    b. Decimal Value _ Volume = Mass
    c. Volume _ Molarity _ Molecular Weight = Mass

____ 25. 1 L of 3 M NaOH

____ 26. 600 μL of 0.5 mM protein solution

For the following items , match each word with the most appropriate definition (a-j) below.

    a. A region on prokaryotic DNA where one or more genes and their controlling elements are located
    b. Process of correcting DNA codes that cause genetic diseases and disorders
    c. Cells that have taken up foreign DNA and start expressing it
    d. Source of nutrients, in liquid or solid form, for growing cell cultures
    e. A region of DNA that can increase expression of a gene
    f. Using electricity to separate molecules on a gel slab
    g. Two nitrogenous bases connected with hydrogen bonds
    h. A DNA molecule that is used as a host to carry foreign pieces of DNA into a cell
    i. The expressed part of genes
    j. Non-coding intervening sequence within genes

____ 27. Enhancer

____ 28. Gel electrophoresis

____ 29. Gene therapy

____ 30. Operon

____ 31. Transformed

For the following items, place the following steps of genetic engineering in the proper order.

    a. First
    b. Second
    c. Third
    d. Fourth

____ 32. Transfer gene of interest into a host organism

____ 33. Harvest desired product from cell culture

____ 34. Isolate gene of interest

For the following items, which gel electrophoresis system best matches the following descriptions or applications?

    a. Agarose
    b. Polyacrylamide
    c. Either

_____ 35. Used for separating proteins

_____ 36. Used in vertical gel boxes

_____ 37. Used in horizontal gel boxes

_____ 38. Separates larger molecules such as restriction digest fragments

For the following items, match each word with the best description (a-j).

    a. A specific region on an antigen where an antibody will bind
    b. A molecule on which an enzyme acts
    c. An enzyme that synthesizes DNA from RNA
    d. A process of making an RNA code from DNA
    e. A process in which RNA is decoded and polypeptides are formed
    f. A three letter code that indicates a particular amino acid
    g. A specific kind of antibody made by hybridomas to target a particular epitope
    h. A method of separating small DNA fragments or proteins using a vertical gel made of polyacrylamide
    i. A molecule or atom required by an enzyme in order to function
    j. An immortal tumor cell fused with a specific white blood cell that will produce monoclonal antibodies

_____ 39. Cofactor

_____ 40. Epitope

_____ 41. Hybridomas

_____ 42. Monoclonal antibody

_____ 43. Reverse transcriptase

_____ 44. Translation

For the following items, match each structure with its corresponding interaction.

    a. Primary structure
    b. Secondary structure
    c. Tertiary structure
    d. Quaternary structure

_____ 45. Polypeptide folding due to interactions between charged R groups

_____ 46. Folding due to interactions between polar/nonpolar amino acids

For the following items, match each of the following PAGE procedures with the appropriate purpose.

    a. To determine the relative sizes of the samples
    b. To visualize proteins after electrophoresis
    c. To conduct electricity and establish an electric field through a gel
    d. To visualize samples when loading wells and monitor the sample migration
    e. To achieve the best separation of molecules

_____ 47. Stain gel with Coomassie(r) Blue

_____ 48. Add loading dye to samples

_____ 49. Select the most appropriate gel concentration

_____ 50. Completely submerge gel in electrophoresis buffer

Name _____

Course _____

Date _____

Multiple Choice

Identify the letter of the choice that best completes the statement or answers the question.

_____ 51. What procedure was used to help identify appropriate mating partners for the endangered whooping cranes in North America?
   a. Fermentation
   b. Clinical testing
   c. Cloning
   d. DNA fingerprinting

_____ 52. What government agency oversees the clinical testing process for new pharmaceuticals?
   a. Center for Disease Control and Prevention (CDC)
   b. National Institutes of Health (NIH)
   c. Food and Drug Administration (FDA)
   d. Environmental Protection Agency (EPA)

_____ 53. Biotechnology research laboratories are commonly found at all of the following facilities except:
   a. Universities
   b. Medical clinics
   c. Companies
   d. Government agencies

_____ 54. Once data gathered by researchers is published in scientific journals, other researchers use it in all of the following ways, except:
   a. Scientists who focus on applied science can use these findings to develop new products.
   b. Other research scientists can get ideas for further research.
   c. Other scientists in the same field can learn more about a problem they have been studying.
   d. Other researchers add their own findings and reprint the research.

_____ 55. DNA fingerprinting is a method used by forensic scientists to
   a. identify a person based on their unique DNA code.
   b. find similarities between individuals.
   c. identify "black market" items such as poached animals.
   d. All of the above

_____ 56. Which of the following is an example of a product easily found in nature?
   a. Antibiotic
   b. GMO
   c. Recombinant DNA
   d. All of the above

_____ 57. A company that produces recombinant insulin by fermentation of E. coli cells is looking for a new product for its pipeline. Which of the following choices would make the most sense?
   a. Engineering of ear tissue
   b. Transgenic papaya
   c. Reagent production
   d. Production of recombinant human growth hormone

_____ 58. Where do scientists at government university laboratories get a majority of their funding?
   a. Reinvested profits from product sales
   b. Grants from industry, foundations, or the government
   c. Venture capitalists
   d Their own salaries

Name _____

Course _____

Date _____

_____ 59. All of the following are methods that scientists use to share the results of their experiments, except:
    a. Posting their results on blogs
    b. Publishing their findings in online scientific journals
    c. Presenting information at an annual scientific conference
    d Publishing their findings in printed scientific journals

_____ 60. Which of the following is an application of agricultural biotechnology?
    a. Genetic testing and screening
    b. Vaccine therapy
    c. Transgenic crops
    d Genetically engineered enzymes

_____ 61. Which of the following is an application of medical or pharmaceutical biotechnology?
    a. Recombinant insulin
    b. DNA sequencing
    c. Identification of endangered species
    d Disease resistant cotton

_____ 62. Recombinant DNA is the term used for
    a. DNA that has been cut with restriction enzymes.
    b. DNA molecules composed of DNA from different sources.
    c. Molecules that have undergone DNA fingerprinting analysis.
    d Genetic information from selectively bred organisms.

_____ 63. All of the following should be included in a legal scientific notebook except:
    a. Testable questions for experiments
    b. Experimental plans
    c. Data gathered during an experiment
    d Personal antidotes regarding the work of colleagues

_____ 64. One of the first genetically engineered products sold was
    a. Bt corn, a variety resistant to the corn borer larvae
    b. Cipro, a strong antibiotic
    c. Human t-PA, an enzyme that dissolves blood clots
    d GloFish, a fish that glows in UV light

_____ 65. Cells that undergo anaerobic respiration produce _____ per molecule of glucose.
    a. more ATP
    b. less ATP
    c. no ATP
    d the same amount of ATP as cells that undergo aerobic respiration

_____ 66. All of the following are considered benefits of recombinant insulin over therapeutic insulin derived from livestock except:
    a. Some patients have severe allergies to livestock insulin.
    b. Some livestock insulin does not perform well in humans.
    c. The price and availability of livestock insulin varies.
    d Livestock insulin may cause cowpox.

_____ 67. Which cells need to have the most mitochondria?
    a. e. coli
    b. Epithelial cells
    c. Muscle cells
    d Liver cells

_____ 68. Polysaccharides are useful for
    a. transporting molecules throughout the cell.
    b. recognition of receptor proteins on other cells.
    c. providing structure and energy storage within cells.
    d   All of the above

_____ 69. Lipids are composed mostly of what atoms?
    a. Oxygen and nitrogen
    b. Hydrogen, oxygen, and nitrogen
    c. Carbon and hydrogen
    d   Carbon, hydrogen, and oxygen

_____ 70. Phospholipids are found in all of the following except:
    a. chromosomes.
    b. the endoplasmic reticulum.
    c. organelle membranes.
    d   cell membranes.

_____ 71. How do carbohydrates affect DNA isolation from plant cells?
    a. They cause the DNA to degrade.
    b. They are sticky and interfere with the purification process.
    c. They are easily removed with a simple centrifugation step.
    d   They bind to the proteins and are removed during the protein precipitation step.

_____ 72. Which of the following can be measured using a micropipet?
    a. A gram of sodium chloride
    b. A liter of oxygen gas
    c. 10 μL of DNA solution
    d   2.5 L of protein solution

_____ 73. Which of the following is an expression of concentration units?
    a. μg/μL
    b. mg/mL
    c. μM
    d   All of the above

_____ 74. How much protein do you need to add to a 250 μL reaction that requires a concentration of 8 mg/mL?
    a. 0.2 ng
    b. 2.0 ng
    c. 0.2 mg
    d   2.0 mg

_____ 75. 3.3 liters is equivalent to
    a. 3300 mL
    b. 330 mL
    c. 33 mL
    d   0.03 mL

_____ 76. A P1000 micropipet is used to measure volumes
    a. between 100 and 1000 μL.
    b. between 1-1000 μL.
    c. over 1000 μL.
    d   between 10-1000 mL.

Name _____

Course _____

Date _____

_____ 77. How much 50X TAE buffer would you need to make a 2 liter solution of 1X TAE buffer?
   a. 40 mL
   b. 100 mL
   c. 200 mL
   d 1 L

_____ 78. 300 mL of a 1/40 dilution of 20X TBE buffer stock solution is needed, what volume of solute is needed?
   a. 2.7 mL
   b. 7.5 mL
   c. 40 mL
   d 150 mL

_____ 79. When measuring liquids using a graduated cylinder or pipet,
   a. the top of the meniscus should be at the graduation.
   b. the bottom of the meniscus should be at the graduation.
   c. the meniscus should be anywhere near the graduation.
   d there is no meniscus when using these measurement tools.

_____ 80. In a biotechnology lab, tap water is best used for
   a. making buffers.
   b. washing glassware.
   c. the final rinse when washing glassware.
   d All of the above

_____ 81. Which solution is more concentrated?
   a. 5 mg/mL
   b. 5 µg/µL
   c. 5 g/L
   d They are equivalent.

_____ 82. Calculate the mass of 17 moles of HCl.
   a. 17 amu
   b. 170 amu
   c. 306 g
   d 620 g

_____ 83. Calculate the mass of 0.3 moles of NaOH.
   a. 8.4 g
   b. 12 g
   c. 3.6 amu
   d 28 amu

_____ 84. How often will cells divide under ideal growing conditions?
   a. Every 20 minutes
   b. Every 45 minutes
   c. Every 2 hours
   d Every 12 hours

_____ 85. How do DNA molecules vary from one species to another?
   a. The type of nitrogenous bases they contain
   b. Number of genes and non-coding regions
   c. The way nitrogenous bases pair
   d The directionality of the strands

____ 86. What is a possible outcome of site-specific mutagenesis?
  a. Additions or deletions to DNA
  b. Improved protein function
  c. Cell death
  d All of the above

____ 87. A typical E. coli genome contains about _____ genes.
  a. 2
  b. 5-10
  c. 2000
  d 4000

____ 88. R plasmids are useful for both bacteria and scientists because they contain
  a. ribosomal RNA genes.
  b. one or more antibiotic resistance genes.
  c. recombinant DNA products.
  d All of the above

____ 89. A circular plasmid was cut with a restriction enzyme and three bands were visualized after electrophoresis. How many cuts were made in the plasmid?
  a. 1
  b. 2
  c. 3
  d 4

____ 90. A linear piece of DNA was cut with a restriction enzyme and four bands were visualized after electrophoresis. How many cuts were made?
  a. 1
  b. 2
  c. 3
  d 4

____ 91. What is agar?
  a. Solid media on which bacteria grow
  b. Liquid media for bacterial growth
  c. Region on a bacterial operon
  d Matrix used for vertical gel electrophoresis

____ 92. How is the packaging of DNA different in eukaryotes and prokaryotes?
  a. Eukaryotes have more chromosomes and each is linear
  b. Eukaryotes have more chromosomes and each is circular
  c. Eukaryotes have some carbohydrate molecules attached to their chromosomes.
  d Eukaryotes have less chromosomes than prokaryotes.

____ 93. How can the molecular mass of a protein be determined?
  a. X-ray crystallography
  b. PAGE
  c. Mass spectrometer
  d All of the above

____ 94. What part of an amino acid differs from one to the other?
  a. Amino group
  b. Carboxyl group
  c. R-group
  d All of the above

_____ 95. Which part of an amino acid interacts with another amino acid to fold a peptide into a protein?
a. Amino group
b. Carboxyl group
c. R-group
d All of the above

_____ 96. How can colorless proteins be monitored during electrophoresis?
a. Coomassie(r) blue stain
b. Silver stain
c. PAGE loading dye
d Ethidium bromide

_____ 97. The region of activity on an enzyme is the
a. cofactor domain.
b. epitope.
c. active site.
d R-group.

_____ 98. A single protein was denatured and electrophoresed. After visualization, four bands were noticed. Two were small and two were large. What can you infer from these results?
a. Four polypeptides made up that protein
b. The protein could be an enzyme
c. The larger peptides traveled faster than the smaller ones
d All of the above

_____ 99. Which of the following is a codon?
a. ATA
b. UAU
c. Tyrosine
d All of the above

_____ 100. What is the purpose of SDS during electrophoresis?
a. Stain the proteins for visualization
b. Use as a loading dye
c. Denature the proteins and give them a negative charge
d Conduct electricity

Biotechnology Unit 1

Answer Section

Matching

1. ANS: G   REF: 27
2. ANS: F   REF: 19
3. ANS: B   REF: 16
4. ANS: A   REF: 16
5. ANS: C   REF: 16
6. ANS: A   REF: 15-17
7. ANS: A   REF: 44, 49
8. ANS: J   REF: 41, 50
9. ANS: C   REF: 41
10. ANS: I   REF: 40-41
11. ANS: E   REF: 39-40
12. ANS: D   REF: 39
13. ANS: A   REF: 46
14. ANS: B   REF: 46
15. ANS: A   REF: 52-53
16. ANS: C   REF: 46, 53
17. ANS: H   REF: 75
18. ANS: C   REF: 86
19. ANS: A   REF: 76
20. ANS: F   REF: 85
21. ANS: B   REF: 77
22. ANS: D   REF: 75
23. ANS: D   REF: 75
24. ANS: C   REF: 68
25. ANS: C   REF: 84
26. ANS: C   REF: 84
27. ANS: E   REF: 108
28. ANS: F   REF: 116
29. ANS: B   REF: 111
30. ANS: A   REF: 104
31. ANS: C   REF: 104
32. ANS: C   REF: 112-113

33. ANS: D   REF: 112-113
34. ANS: B   REF: 112-113
35. ANS: B   REF: 117
36. ANS: B   REF: 117
37. ANS: A   REF: 117
38. ANS: A   REF: 117
39. ANS: I   REF: 144
40. ANS: A   REF: 136
41. ANS: J   REF: 136
42. ANS: G   REF: 136
43. ANS: C   REF: 135
44. ANS: E   REF: 140
45. ANS: C   REF: 133-135
46. ANS: C   REF: 133-135
47. ANS: B   REF: 148-149
48. ANS: D   REF: 148-149
49. ANS: E   REF: 148-149
50. ANS: C   REF: 148-149

Multple Choice

51. ANS: D   REF: 8
52. ANS: C   REF: 15
53. ANS: B   REF: 5
54. ANS: D   REF: 7
55. ANS: A   REF: 8
56. ANS: A   REF: 10
57. ANS: D   REF: 11, 14
58. ANS: B   REF: 7
59. ANS: A   REF: 22
60. ANS: C   REF: 9
61. ANS: A   REF: 3, 9
62. ANS: B   REF: 10
63. ANS: D   REF: 19
64. ANS: C   REF: 11
65. ANS: B   REF: 46
66. ANS: D   REF: 58
67. ANS: C   REF: 45

68. ANS: C   REF: 49
69. ANS: C   REF: 50
70. ANS: A   REF: 51
71. ANS: B   REF: 49
72. ANS: C   REF: 85-87
73. ANS: D   REF: 77
74. ANS: D   REF: 78
75. ANS: A   REF: 67
76. ANS: A   REF: 73
77. ANS: A   REF: 87
78. ANS: B   REF: 87
79. ANS: B   REF: 68
80. ANS: B   REF: 76
81. ANS: D   REF: 67
82. ANS: D   REF: 83, periodic table
83. ANS: B   REF: 83, periodic table
84. ANS: A   REF: 106
85. ANS: B   REF: 102
86. ANS: D   REF: 114
87. ANS: C   REF: 103
88. ANS: B   REF: 103
89. ANS: C   REF: 119
90. ANS: C   REF: 119
91. ANS: A   REF: 105
92. ANS: A   REF: 103
93. ANS: C   REF: 132
94. ANS: C   REF: 132
95. ANS: C   REF: 132
96. ANS: C   REF: 149
97. ANS: C   REF: 144
98. ANS: A   REF: 149
99. ANS: B   REF: 141
100. ANS: C   REF: 149

Biotechnology Unit 02 (Chapters 6–9)

Matching

For the following items, match each assay type with the appropriate function (a-g).

   a. A highly specific test to determine protein concentration based on a particular antigen-antibody inter-action.
   b. Shows if a specific protein is present and conducting the expected reaction
   c. Helps researchers measure the amount of protein present
   d. Determines the amount and length of activity for a given protein in test organisms
   e. Used for understanding the relationship between dosage and activity of a given pharmaceutical
   f. A way to determine how long the pharmaceutical is effective and how it should be stored
   g. Used to determine what are safe and unsafe levels of a given drug

_____ 1. Potency assay

_____ 2. Stability assay

_____ 3. Activity assay

_____ 4. ELISA

_____ 5. PK/PD assays

For the following items, match each word with the best definition.

   a. The expression of a particular gene
   b. Mammalian cells that have incorporated rDNA
   c. The delivery method of a pharmaceutical product
   d. A test for determining the presence or a particular characteristic of a protein of interest
   e. Molecules that inhibit bacterial growth, produced by bacteria or fungi
   f. the combination of alleles for a particular gene

_____ 6. Phenotype

_____ 7. Genotype

_____ 8. Assay

For the following items, determine which phase of the pharmaceutical product pipeline (a, b, or c) is responsible For the tasks below.

   a. Research and Development
   b. Manufacturing
   c. Clinical trials

_____ 9. Purification process for recombinant protein is determined.

_____ 10. Toxicity and efficacy studies are performed on mice.

_____ 11. Safety and efficacy studies on human subjects are monitored by the FDA.

_____ 12. Large volume production of the drug occurs.

_____ 13. Host cells get transformed and gene regulation is studied.

For the following items, match the following words with the best description (a-j).

   a. The wavelength at which a sample absorbs the most light
   b. Light with wavelengths between 200-350 nm
   c. Amount of light that passes through a sample
   d. The light wavelengths that the human eye can see

Name _____

Course _____

Date _____

    e. An aqueous solution that ionizes and yields H^+
    f. An aqueous solution that ionizes and yields OH^-
    g. A solution that resists changes in pH
    h. An aqueous solution with an equal number of H^+ and OH^- ions
    i. Light energy held within a sample
    j. An instrument that shines light on a sample and measures the amount of light transmitted

_____ 14. Absorbance

_____ 15. Base

_____ 16. Spectrophotometer

_____ 17. UV light

For the following items, determine whether UV or visible light spectrophotometry should be used.

    a. UV light spectrometry
    b. Visible light spectrometry

_____ 18. Monitoring the enzyme activity of amylase with an indicator solution

For items, place the following steps For calibrating a pH meter in the proper order, assuming the instrument is already turned on.

    a. Place electrode in pH 7 buffer standard and calibrate the meter to "7"
    b. Us pH 4 or pH 10 buffer to slope the meter if measuring a strong acid or strong base
    c. Rinse the electrode with distilled water
    d. Place the electrode in the solution to be measured

_____ 19. First

_____ 20. Second

_____ 21. Fourth

For the following items, match each scientific term with the description (a-j) that best fits.

    a. When complementary DNA strands come together
    b. Host DNA structures that accept and incorporate DNA resulting in rDNA
    c. A short, "tagged" piece of DNA complementary to the DNA of interest
    d. The liquid above a pellet after centrifugation
    e. The scaled-up process by which cells are grown under optimal conditions for maximum cell division and product formation
    f. FDA regulated manufacturing protocol
    g. The desired result of endonuclease activity for the purpose of rDNA production
    h. Cells treated with calcium chloride to increase DNA uptake
    i. Probes used specifically to initiate the polymerase chain reaction
    j. When cells grow rapidly such that in each cell cycle, the cell count doubles

_____ 22. Probe

_____ 23. Fermentation

_____ 24. Vector

_____ 25. Supernatant

For the following items, match each technique with its corresponding host DNA organisms (a-c).

    a. bacteria
    b. mammalian cells
    c. viruses

Name _____

Course _____

Date _____

_____ 26. transduction

_____ 27. transformation

For the following items, match each enzyme with its corresponding activity (a-c).

      a. cuts DNA
      b. pastes pieces of DNA together
      c. bursts cells open

_____ 28. DNA ligase

For the following items, match each process with its appropriate department (a-c) in a biotech or pharmaceutical company.

      a. R&D
      b. Manufacturing
      c. Both departments

_____ 29. Host cell type is considered for target gene.

For the following items, match each word with the best description (a-h).

      a. Membrane filter at one end of a chromatography column
      b. Outside of a cell
      c. Inside of a cell
      d. Treatment made to look genuine, but it does not contain the product being tested
      e. Separation of molecules on or through a stationary phase
      f. A small amount of sample that is collected during column chromatography
      g. A process that uses high frequency sound waves to burst open cells
      h. The process of releasing molecules from resin during column chromatography

_____ 30. Chromatography

_____ 31. Elution

_____ 32. Extracellular

_____ 33. Intracellular

_____ 34. Placebo

_____ 35. Sonication

For the following items, decide which chromatography method (a-c) best fits the following descriptions.

      a. Paper chromatography
      b. Thin-layer chromatography
      c. Column chromatography

_____ 36. Resin beads are utilized which have an opposite charge of the protein of interest. A final wash with an elution buffer knocks off the protein of interest and fractions are collected.

_____ 37. A solvent is used to separate out proteins, deposited on a filter paper, based on their size and solubility.

_____ 38. A glass plate lined with silicia gel is used while a buffer carrying the soluble molecules creeps along the plate, depositing molecules based on their size and solubility in the buffer.

For the following items, determine which phase of clinical trials (a-d) best fits each description.

      a. Phase I
      b. Phase II
      c. Phase III
      d. Phase IV

_____ 39. Large and diverse populations are used to better understand the safety and efficacy of the new drug.

For the following items, decide which gel filtration characteristic (a-c) should be altered to optimize the following separations.

    a. column length
    b. column width
    c. pore size

_____ 40. Proteins of similar size need to be separated

Multiple Choice

Identify the letter of the choice that best completes the statement or answers the question.

_____ 41. What is amylase?
    a. An enzyme
    b. A sugar
    c. A polysaccharide
    d. A starch

_____ 42. What extra effort might be taken to extract DNA or proteins from plant cells?
    a. Addition of vitamin solution to increase cell activity
    b. Treatment with enzymes to degrade the cellulose in the cell walls
    c. Mixing sample with iron sulfate to increase molarity
    d. Incubation of sample at 4°C with glass beads

_____ 43. Two different antimicrobials, A and B, are soaked into paper disks and placed on a Petri dish with bacteria spread on the top. After 24 hours of incubation, the plates are examined. The zone of inhibition around antimicrobial A is completely clear and measures 2.4 cm in diameter. The zone of inhibition around antimicrobial B is mostly clear and measures 3.2 cm in diameter. Which antimicrobial is more effective at inhibiting bacterial growth?
    a. A
    b. B
    c. A and B are equally effective
    d. Neither A nor B are effective

_____ 44. What assay should be done to test for the presence and concentration of a specific goat antigen throughout research and manufacturing processes?
    a. Activity assay
    b. ELISA
    c. Potency assay
    d. Stability assay

_____ 45. Herbal therapies have been used in some cultures for hundreds of years, however caution must be taken when using herbal remedies for all the following reasons except:
    a. Herbal products are not subject to FDA approval.
    b. Adverse effects may occur if the wrong concentration is taken.
    c. Herbal remedies often taste better than other medicines.
    d. Certain combinations of herbal therapies may be harmful.

_____ 46. A new pharmaceutical company has discovered a promising protein product that kills a rare form of lymphoma cancer cells in 92% of the 75 rats tested. What step of the CPDP does this finding address?
    a. Patent protection can be secured
    b. The market is large enough to produce high volumes of sales.
    c. Preliminary data support the efficacy of this product.
    d. Safety of this pharmaceutical is assured

_____ 47. What assay could a scientist use to determine that a potential drug has a short shelf life?
  a. Activity
  b. ELISA
  c. Pharmacodynamic assay
  d. Stability assay

_____ 48. If the concentration of lactase in a protein solution needed to be determined as accurately as possible using Bradford reagent, what other instrument would a lab technician need?
  a. Thermocycler
  b. Spectrophotometer
  c. Fermenter
  d. Capillary detector

_____ 49. A plant cell that has been treated with cellulase and pectinase
  a. is called a tissue culture.
  b. is left with only a plasma membrane separating the cell from its environment.
  c. is ready for breeding.
  d. gains strength.

_____ 50. Protoplasts are useful in genetic engineering because
  a. they are easily inoculated with foreign DNA by way of a gene gun.
  b. treatment of protoplasts with cellulase or pectinase will degrade the cell wall.
  c. the rectangular cell shape is easier to accommodate in the confined tissue culture bottles.
  d. their thick, sticky cell walls provide extra rigidity and protection for foreign DNA.

_____ 51. Recombinant DNA
  a. is used to produce hundreds of other DNA products
  b. can be found in fungus cells.
  c. is produced by pasting together DNA from two sources.
  d. is larger than a typical chromosome.

_____ 52. Plant cell walls contain _____ for rigidity.
  a. protoplasts and enzymes
  b. cellulase and pectinase
  c. cellulose and pectin
  d. All of the above

_____ 53. What range of wavelength is used by UV spectrophotometers?
  a. up to 200 nm
  b. 200-350 nm
  c. 350-700 nm
  d. 700 nm-950 nm

_____ 54. What range of wavelength is used by visible light spectrophotometers?
  a. up to 200 nm
  b. 200-350 nm
  c. 350-700 nm
  d. 700 nm-950 nm

_____ 55. What is the relationship between absorbance and transmittance of light through a sample in a spectrophotometer?
  a. An increase in transmittance usually results in an increase in absorbance
  b. A decrease in transmittance usually results in a decrease in absorbance
  c. A decrease in transmittance usually results in an increase in absorbance
  d. Transmittance and absorbance should remain equal.

____ 56. Which sample is the most concentrated?
a. 34 %T
b. 52 %T
c. 1.40 a.u.
d. 0.22 a.u.

____ 57. How should the concentration of a colorless sample be determined?
a. Using a UV spectrophotometer
b. Using a VIS spectrophotometer
c. Either a UV or VIS spectrophotometer
d. Using an indicator solution and pH paper

____ 58. At what wavelength would a red molecule absorb the most light?
a. 200 nm
b. 350 nm
c. 530 nm
d. 700 nm

____ 59. A sample with a peak absorbance at 640 nm is probably
a. colorless.
b. violet.
c. green.
d. red

____ 60. pH is a measurement of _____ a sample.
a. the concentration of ions in
b. the concentration of ions in
c. light absorbed by
d. light transmitted by

____ 61. How should the concentration of a red sample, such as hemoglobin, be determined?
a. Using UV spectrophotometry
b. Using VIS spectrophotometry
c. Either UV or VIS spectrophotometry
d. With pH paper

____ 62. A pure sample of water has
a. more ions than ions.
b. fewer ions than ions.
c. no or ions.
d. An equal amount of and ions.

____ 63. Which of the following is a strong acid?
a. pH 2
b. pH 5
c. pH 9
d. pH 13

____ 64. Which of the following is a weak base?
a. pH 2
b. pH 5
c. pH 9
d. pH 13

Name _____

Course _____

Date _____

_____ 65. Which of the following would be a reasonable expectation for the of a sample of yellow protein?
   a. 1.75 a.u. at 400 nm
   b. .023 a.u. at 420 nm
   c. 1.8 a.u. at 570 nm
   d. 0.99 a.u. at 530 nm

_____ 66. What treatment encourages cells to incorporate rDNA plasmids during a bacterial transformation?
   a. Heat shock in warm water bath followed by ice bath
   b. Plating on nutrient agar with antibiotic
   c. Achieving exponential cell growth
   d. Assaying for recombinant proteins

_____ 67. Rennin was used in cheese making, but due to its inconsistent availability, was
   a. replaced by its genetically engineered equivalent, Chymosin.
   b. hybridized with another protease.
   c. lysed and precipitated out of solution.
   d. All of the above

_____ 68. What happens during the stationary phase of cell growth?
   a. Cell growth and division slows down because broth nutrients have been used up.
   b. Anaerobic fermentation begins as oxygen is used up.
   c. Transfected cells begin to die off, causing the broth to appear cloudy.
   d. Extracellular fluid is released into the growth media.

_____ 69. What is the purpose of adding cations (Ca^5 or Mg^{2+}) to host cells before a transformation?
   a. Increases transformation efficiency
   b. Allows for selection of transformed cells
   c. Gets rid of sticky ends
   d. All of the above

_____ 70. Which restriction enzyme listed in the chart below will result in a blunt end cut?

Restriction Enzyme	Recognition Site
Alu I	AG^CT
Eco RI	G^AATTC
HindIII	A^AGCTT

   a. *Alu I*
   b. *Bam HI*
   c. *HindIII*
   d. All of the above

_____ 71. Cutting DNA into fragments and then figuring out their order is called
   a. restriction fragment length polymorphism (RFLP).
   b. restriction enzyme mapping.
   c. restriction digest.
   d. rDNA probing.

Name _____

Course _____

Date _____

____ 72. During scale-up of cultured CHO cells, cultures in spinner flasks grow for _____ before being used to seed a larger culture.
    a. 1-2 days
    b. 3-4 days
    c. 5-7 days
    d. 2 weeks

____ 73. Thin layer chromatography is useful for separating
    a. large molecules like hydrophobic proteins.
    b. small molecules like amino acids.
    c. ninhydrin compounds.
    d. proteases.

_____74. About how long does the clinical testing phase typically last?
    a. Less than a year
    b. 1-2 years
    c. 2-5 years
    d. 5-10 years

____ 75. If a positively charged molecule is to be separated by ion exchange chromatography, what sort of resin should be used?
    a. negatively charged beads
    b. positively charged beads
    c. neutral beads
    d. frit

Short Answer

76. A start-up biotech company has discovered a new bacterium that decomposes waste at a rapid rate. Could the product meet a critical need? Would large-scale production be justified? Explain your answer.

77. Explain the importance of buffers and identify four uses of buffers in biotechnology.

78. What are the basic parts of any spectrophotometer and what are their functions?

Restriction Enzyme	Recognition Site
Alu I	AG^CT
Eco RI	G^AATTC
HindIII	A^AGCTT

5' ATAAGCTTCTCCGGATCCTAACGGATCCAAGCTTA 3'
3' TATTCGAAGAGGCCTAGGATTGCCTAGGTTCGAAT 5'

79. What are the three common methods to select for transformed cells? Describe each mechanism.

80. A new pharmaceutical that reduces blood pressure has just been released. List three possible reasons the earnings may not turn out quite as high as expected?

Biotechnology Unit 02

Answer Section

Matching

1. ANS: D   REF: 167
2. ANS: F   REF: 167
3. ANS: B   REF: 166
4. ANS: A   REF: 166
5. ANS: E   REF: 167
6. ANS: A   REF: 172
7. ANS: F   REF: 172
8. ANS: D   REF: 165
9. ANS: A   REF: 176
10. ANS: A   REF: 176
11. ANS: C   REF: 176
12. ANS: B   REF: 176
13. ANS: A   REF: 176
14. ANS: I   REF: 190
15. ANS: F   REF: 194
16. ANS: J   REF: 190
17. ANS: B   REF: 190
18. ANS: B   REF: 192
19. ANS: C   REF: 197
20. ANS: A   REF: 197
21. ANS: D   REF: 197
22. ANS: C   REF: 213
23. ANS: E   REF: 225
24. ANS: B   REF: 210
25. ANS: D   REF: 212
26. ANS: C   REF: 215
27. ANS: A   REF: 215
28. ANS: B   REF: 217
29. ANS: A   REF: 224-226
30. ANS: E   REF: 245
31. ANS: H   REF: 247
32. ANS: B   REF: 241
33. ANS: C   REF: 241
34. ANS: D   REF: 256
35. ANS: G   REF: 242
36. ANS: C   REF: 245-246
37. ANS: A   REF: 245-246
38. ANS: B   REF: 245-246
39. ANS: D   REF: 256
40. ANS: A   REF: 252

Multple Choice

41. ANS: A   REF: 162
42. ANS: B   REF: 173
43. ANS: A   REF: 171
44. ANS: B   REF: 166
45. ANS: C   REF: 168-170
46. ANS: C   REF: 164
47. ANS: D   REF: 167
48. ANS: B   REF: 166
49. ANS: B   REF: 173
50. ANS: A   REF: 173
51. ANS: C   REF: 175-176
52. ANS: C   REF: 173
53. ANS: B   REF: 190
54. ANS: C   REF: 190
55. ANS: C   REF: 192
56. ANS: C   REF: 192
57. ANS: A   REF: 190
58. ANS: B   REF: 192
59. ANS: B   REF: 192
60. ANS: A   REF: 195
61. ANS: B   REF: 200
62. ANS: D   REF: 195
63. ANS: A   REF: 195
64. ANS: C   REF: 195
65. ANS: B   REF: 200
66. ANS: A   REF: 220
67. ANS: A   REF: 211
68. ANS: A   REF: 228
69. ANS: A   REF: 220
70. ANS: A   REF: 216
71. ANS: B   REF: 219
72. ANS: B   REF: 224
73. ANS: B   REF: 245-246
74. ANS: C   REF: 255
75. ANS: A   REF: 253

Name _____

Course _____

Date _____

SHORT ANSWER

76. ANS:

Waste is a concern on this earth, particularly in more developed countries. A bacterium that could decompose waste could be very helpful in reducing the amount of waste that accumulates and therefore would meet a critical need. Furthermore, large-scale production of bacteria is easily done by fermentation processes.

REF: 164

77. ANS:

DNA and proteins are sensitive to changes in pH. Proteins have optimal pHs for maximum activity. Buffers maintain the pH of a solution. Uses of buffers include: 1) Used to maintain the pH of DNA or protein solutions; 2) Added to growth media to resist changes in pH; 3) Used for column chromatography; 4) Used to conduct electricity during polyacrylamide or agarose gel electrophoresis.

REF: 199

78. ANS:

Tungsten lamp for white light and/or deuterium lamp for UV light; Prism or grating to change the wavelength of light being emitted; Calibration buttons or knob to control set the wavelength; Sample holder is dark so no light gets reflected, the sample also gets place here; Display to see the settings and/or read the %T or absorbance

REF: 190

79. ANS:

CATEGORY1–Using antibiotic resistance—The rDNA vector would contain an antibiotic resistance gene. When plating the cell suspension after transformation, only the cells that took in the rDNA with the antibiotic resistance gene (and the gene of interest) will grow.

CATEGORY2–GFP—The rDNA vector would contain the Green Fluorescent Protein (GFP) gene as well as the gene of interest. When cells are plated, transformed cells will fluoresce under UV light.

CATEGORY3–β-gal—The target gene would be cloned into the middle of the beta-galactosidase gene that results in a blue color when x-gal is present. After transformation, the cell suspension would be spread on plates that have the x-gal substrate. The resulting colonies would be white if they contain the gene of interest that disrupted the beta-galactosidase gene. Cells that do not contain a disrupted b-gal gene would be blue.

REF: 221

80. ANS:

Patent protection may be in jeopardy, product may be priced too high, marketing team may be doing a poor job, there are other therapies for reducing blood pressure that are more effective or have fewer side effects, FDA may have approved a similar drug around the same time.

REF: 257

Name _____

Course _____

Date _____

Biotechnology Unit 3 (Chapters 10--12)

Matching

For the following items, match the following words with the best description (a-j) below.

    a. Cell division process for sex cell formation
    b. Cell division process for making more body cells
    c. Propagation, from a single parent, in which the offspring are identical to the parent
    d. A single cell that is formed when an egg and sperm combine.
    e. Containing two sets of homologous chromosomes
    f. Containing one set of chromosomes
    g. In a combination of two alleles, only one is necessary to express a specific trait
    h. In a combination of two alleles, two copies are necessary to express a specific trait
    i. Sprouting of a seed into new plant
    j. Sex cells

_____ 1. Cloning

_____ 2. Diploid

_____ 3. Dominant

_____ 4. Germination

_____ 5. Meiosis

_____ 6. Zygote

For the following items, determine whether each of the following cells are haploid or diploid.

    a. Haploid
    b. Diploid

_____ 7. Pollen gathered by a bee

_____ 8. Root tip

For the following items, match each function with the corresponding plant organ (a-d).

    a. Leaf
    b. Stem
    c. Root
    d. Flower or cone

_____ 9. Food storage and anchorage

_____ 10. Water and food transport

For the following items, match each of the following words with the best description (a-j).

    a. Breeding between closely related organisms
    b. Water-based plant growing technique
    c. Used as a vector for plant transformations
    d. Plants transformed with foreign DNA
    e. Using pollen from one plant to pollinate a flower on another plant
    f. Type of plant hormone that causes cells to divide
    g. Type of plant hormone that directs cell elongation
    h. Small pieces of plants used for plant tissue culture
    i. Producing plants for ornamental purposes
    j. A protein product grown in plants for human medicinal purposes.

_____ 11. Explants

_____ 12. Plant-based pharmaceutical

_____ 13. Ti plasmid

_____ 14. Transgenic plants

For the following items, decide which hormone (a-f) should be manipulated to develop plants with the listed traits.

      a. Abscisic acid (ABA)
      b. Auxin
      c. Cytokinin
      d. Ethylene
      e. Gibberellin
      f. Phytochrome

_____ 15. Rose with long lasting blooms

_____ 16. Tall variety of sunflowers

_____ 17. Faster growing roots

_____ 18. Faster development of callus during plant tissue culture

For the following items, cotton plants were transformed using the pBI121 plasmid containing the NPT II and GUS genes. State whether the resulting plantlets have been properly transformed or not.

      a. Transformed
      b. Not transformed

_____ 19. Kanamycin added to the growth media and there is no growth.

_____ 20. Kanamycin added to the growth media and a callus forms.

_____ 21. X-Gluc added to the growth media and the cells look blue.

For the following items, match each of the following words with the best description (a-j).

      a. Compounds that act to treat, prevent, or alleviate symptoms of disease
      b. A treatment that causes the body to produce many antibodies in response to the injected antigen
      c. Research, development, and manufacturing of substances that prevent, treat, or alleviate diseases or their symptoms
      d. Understanding the nature, origins, transmission, evolution, and hosts of a disease
      e. Process of combining chemical components to produce new or varied organic compounds
      f. Short chains of up to 50 amino acids
      g. Chemicals that alter the affect of proteins or other molecules on disease-causing mechanisms
      h. Long-term protection from cellular invaders
      i. Short chains of up to 50 nucleotides
      j. Assemblies of DNA, RNA, or proteins for screening

_____ 22. Microarrays

_____ 23. Combinatorial chemistry

_____ 24. Oligonucleotides

_____ 25. Pathogenesis

_____ 26. Vaccine

For the following items, determine which process (a-c) would be the best choice For production of the following therapeutics?

    a. Genetic Engineering

    b. Isolate from nature

    c. Combinatorial chemistry

_____ 27. Modifications must be made by to this compound to reduce toxicity

_____ 28. A compound found in chamomile flowers soothes upset stomachs

_____ 29. Aspirin, buffered to a neutral pH

For the following items, determine whether each statement is true (a) or false (b).

    a. True

    b. False

_____ 30. A microarray can be used to purify antibodies from a cell culture.

Multiple Choice

Identify the letter of the choice that best completes the statement or answers the question.

_____ 31. During mitosis, the number of chromosomes in the resulting daughter cells _____ as compared to the original mother cell.

    a. remains the same

    b. doubles

    c. decreases by half

    d. increases by half

_____ 32. Woody plants have increased cell division at the _____ to become strong and hard.

    a. vascular cambium

    b. xylem

    c. apical meristem

    d. epidermis

_____ 33. What can be used as cuttings during plant propagation?

    a. Stems

    b. Seeds

    c. Fruits

    d. Flowers

_____ 34. New gene combinations are produced during meiosis as a result of

    a. gene shuffling and cross-over.

    b. phenotypic restructuring.

    c. asexual reproduction.

    d. species isolation.

_____ 35. Genes that control the production of _____ trigger cell specialization during seed germination.

    a. calluses

    b. radicles

    c. hormones

    d. All of the above

_____ 36. A pair of alleles for a particular trait is called

    a. a genotpye.

    b. a phenotype.

    c. haploid

    d. diploid

_____ 37. What percent of the offspring will have wrinkled seeds? [Use the following cross: A plant that is homozygous recessive for wrinkled seeds is crossed with a plant that is heterozygous dominant for smooth seeds.]
   a. 25%
   b. 50%
   c. 75%
   d. 100%

_____ 38. Which food is an example of a plant ovary?
   a. Wheat
   b. Apple
   c. Broccoli
   d. Corn

_____ 39. Which food is an example of a plant seed?
   a. Pinto bean
   b. Cauliflower
   c. Potato
   d. All of the above

_____ 40. The part of a new plant that ruptures the seed coat during germination is called the
   a. cotyledon.
   b. chloroplast.
   c. radicle.
   d. shoot.

_____ 41. The most challenging method of asexual plant propagation is
   a. by plant tissue culture.
   b. using stem cuttings.
   c. using runners.
   d. using meristematic tissue.

_____ 42. All of the following are true about meristematic cells except:
   a. They are responsible for triggering flowering.
   b. They are responsible for vertical growth of a plant.
   c. They are responsible for lateral growth of a plant.
   d. They are needed for plant propagation

_____ 43. Countries or regions with poor soil quality can grow plants
   a. by tissue culture.
   b. that contain Bt transgenes.
   c. hydroponically.
   d. All of the above

_____ 44. Which propagation method would probably yield the best results?
   a. Stem cutting, trimmed at both top and bottom, leaving 2 nodes, cleared of leaves
   b. Young branch, cleared of leaves, containing 1 node
   c. Stem cutting, cleared of leaves, containing 2 nodes and shoot tip intact
   d. Leaf cutting

_____ 45. Currently, plant-made pharmaceuticals are
   a. being tested in clinical trials.
   b. are being marketed to doctors.
   c. available by prescription only.
   d. proving more effective than pharmaceuticals produced by fermentation.

Name _____

Course _____

Date _____

_____ 46. What transgene do Bt corn, Bt soybeans, and Bt potatoes share?
    a. A gene from *Bacillus thuringiensis* for faster growth
    b. A gene from *Bacillus thuringiensis* for an insecticide
    c. A gene from *Bacillus thuringiensis* for resistance to topical insecticides
    d. A gene from *Bacillus thuringiensis* for higher nutrient content

_____ 47. Hydroponically grown plants are grown in
    a. cell culture media.
    b. water-based media.
    c. high mineral soil.
    d. calcium rich soil.

_____ 48. The first sign of a successful plant tissue culture is
    a. evidence of the media getting metabolized
    b. the formation of root tips.
    c. the swelling of the explant.
    d. runner formation.

_____ 49. Cells are burst open to retrieve DNA
    a. using a cell lysis solution.
    b. using a protein-degrading buffer.
    c. by alcohol extraction.
    d. by heating them with liquid nitrogen.

_____ 50. Plant cell walls can be ruptured
    a. using a cell lysis solution.
    b. using a protein-degrading buffer.
    c. by alcohol extraction.
    d. by freezing with liquid nitrogen.

_____ 51. What serves as a vector for plant transformations?
    a. Ti plasmid
    b. *Arabidopsis thaliana*
    c. *Agrobacterium tumefaciens*
    d. *Bacillus thuringiensis*

_____ 52. If transformed bacteria containing the Ti plasmid are incubated with growth media and _____, transgenic plants will develop.
    a. GFP
    b. *Arabidopsis*
    c. plant tissue
    d. phytochrome

_____ 53. The enzyme encoded by the GUS gene breaks down
    a. X-Gal and forms a blue product.
    b. X-Gluc and forms a blue product.
    c. GFP and forms a green product.
    d. GFP and results in a colorless product.

_____ 54. New drugs are discovered in all of the following ways except:
    a. They can be harvested from sources in nature.
    b. They can be created by applying column chromatography.
    c. Protein products can be genetically engineered
    d. New molecules can be created by organic synthesis and screened

Name _____

Course _____

Date _____

_____ 55. Before insulin was genetically engineered for diabetes patients, how was therapeutic insulin produced?
   a. It was isolated and purified from cow, pig, and sheep pancreases.
   b. It was produced by combinatorial chemistry.
   c. Insulin was extracted from willow tree bark and leaves.
   d. Insulin was extracted from the pancreases of deceased humans.

Short Answer

56. A dihybrid cross between a heterozygous tall and homozygous dominant hairy plant and a homozygous short with a heterozygous hairy plant was done. Determine the chance, using a Punnett Square, for each of the possible genotypes.

57. Use a Punnett Square to determine how many yellow and how many white flowered plants you would expect to see in the offspring. [Use the following breeding data: Fifty crosses were done between a heterozygous yellow flowered plant and homozygous white flowered plant.]

58. In the previous question, suppose the resulting offspring were 19 yellow and 31 white flowered plants. Use Chi Square analysis to determine if you should reject this data.

59. List the five places meristematic tissue is found in plants and describe its function.

60. An experiment was performed to test the effect Indoleacetic acid (IAA) had on soybean seedlings. Plant A was tall and had short branches, while Plant B was about as tall and had many long branches. Which plant was treated with the most IAA and what affect did it have on soybean plant growth?

Biotechnology Unit 3

Answer Section

Matching

1. ANS: C REF: 270
2. ANS: E REF: 279
3. ANS: G REF: 280
4. ANS: I REF: 276
5. ANS: A REF: 269
6. ANS: D REF: 268
7. ANS: A REF: 279
8. ANS: B REF: 279
9. ANS: C REF: 273-274
10. ANS: B REF: 273-274
11. ANS: H REF: 303
12. ANS: J REF: 309
13. ANS: C REF: 312
14. ANS: D REF: 313
15. ANS: F REF: 303
16. ANS: E REF: 303
17. ANS: B REF: 303
18. ANS: C REF: 303
19. ANS: B REF: 314
20. ANS: A REF: 314
21. ANS: A REF: 314
22. ANS: J REF: 330
23. ANS: E REF: 328
24. ANS: I REF: 333
25. ANS: D REF: 327
26. ANS: B REF: 335
27. ANS: C REF: 328-332
28. ANS: B REF: 328-332
29. ANS: C REF: 328-332
30. ANS: B REF: 331

Multple Choice

31. ANS: A REF: 276
32. ANS: A REF: 277
33. ANS: A REF: 271
34. ANS: A REF: 270
35. ANS: C REF: 277
36. ANS: A REF: 280
37. ANS: B REF: 283
38. ANS: B REF: 273
39. ANS: A REF: 273
40. ANS: C REF: 277
41. ANS: A REF: 300
42. ANS: A REF: 301
43. ANS: C REF: 308
44. ANS: C REF: 301
45. ANS: A REF: 309
46. ANS: B REF: 308
47. ANS: B REF: 308
48. ANS: C REF: 304
49. ANS: A REF: 310
50. ANS: D REF: 311
51. ANS: A REF: 312
52. ANS: C REF: 313
53. ANS: B REF: 314
54. ANS: B REF: 327
55. ANS: A REF: 327

SHORT ANSWER

56. ANS:

Tt HH × tt Hh

Gametes	tH	th
TH	TtHH	TtHh
tH	ttHH	ttHh

Probability of:
TtHH = 25%
TtHh = 25%
TtHH = 25%
TtHh = 25%
REF: 283

57. ANS:

Yy × yy

Gametes	Y	y
Y	Yy	yy

Expect 25 yellow plants and 25 white plants

REF: 282-283

58. ANS:

Expected = E = 25 yellow, Observed = O = 19 yellow

degrees of freedom = N-1= 2-1=1

X^2 = 2.88 at 1 df falls between (P) 0.05 and 0.10

The data is accepted as no different than expected

REF: 286-289

59. ANS:

Root tips, shoot tips, branch tips, stem perimeter (vascular cambium), root perimeter (vascular cambium). These are all the growing areas of plants. Meristematic tissue contains cells that will eventually differentiate into specialized plant cells.

REF: 301

60. ANS:

IAA controls lateral branch growth (low concentration = more lateral branch growth). Plant A, which had few branches received a higher concentration of IAA.

Name _____

Course _____

Date _____

Biotechnology Unit 04 (Chapters 13–14)

Matching

For the following items, match each word with the most appropriate definition (a-j) below.

    a. A strand of DNA from which new DNA is synthesized
    b. Unique DNA banding pattern used for identity purposes
    c. Separation of DNA strands by breaking hydrogen bonds
    d. The application of biology, chemistry, physics, math, and sociology to solve legal problems
    e. Determining the best conditions and concentrations for a reaction
    f. Replication of DNA many times
    g. Source of As, Cs, Gs, and Ts during DNA replication
    h. An area on the genome where there is great variability from individual to individual
    i. Two chromosomes containing the same genes in the same order
    j. Hybridization of an oligonucleotide with its complement on the template

_____ 1. Amplification

_____ 2. Homologous pairs

_____ 3. Primer annealing

_____ 4. Template

_____ 5. VNTR

For the following items, match the following enzymes with their functions in DNA replication (a-f) below.

    a. Adds RNA nucleotides to template to act as a primer
    b. Unwind and untwist DNA to initiate replication
    c. Connects replicated strands together, terminating the replication process
    d. Relieves the tension in double helix to untwist the strands
    e. Edits out RNA nucleotides
    f. Adds DNA nucleotides to end of RNA primer and fills in gaps once RNA nucleotides have been removed

_____ 6. Topoisomerase

_____ 7. RNA primase

_____ 8. DNA polymerase

For the following items, place the following steps (a-d) of a Southern Blot in chronological order.

    a. Step 1
    b. Step 2
    c. Step 3
    d. Step 4

_____ 9. Treat with labeled probes for visualization

_____ 10. Blot samples onto membrane or paper

For the following items, match the following words with the best description (a-j).

    a. Determination of the position of atoms on a molecule using X-rays
    b. The study of an organism's entire genetic information
    c. The massive undertaking to decode the entire human DNA sequence
    d. Study of how, when, and what forms of proteins are active
    e. A combination of computer programs and mathematical models to analyze sequence data

    f. Using genetic and protein codes to improve medications

    g. A technique for determining the order of nucleotides in a DNA fragment

    h. A field where monitoring and correcting the health of species, populations, communities, and ecosystems is done using genomic and proteomic information

    i. A nucleotide that is missing an oxygen atom on carbon number 3 of the sugar molecule

    j. In instrument that measures the masses of atoms or molecules

_____ 11. Bioinformatics

_____ 12. Genomics

_____ 13. Proteomics

_____ 14. Human Genome Project

For the following items, order the following steps For conducting an ELISA to screen For individuals exposed to HIV. (You may need to use an item more than once.)

    a. Wash plates with PBS buffer to remove excess molecules

    b. Collect blood samples

    c. Add acid to turn the blue precipitate yellow (more stable)

    d. Add TMB substrate to the wells. A blue precipitate should appear at the location of any antigen-antibody binding.

    e. Lyse cells to release proteins

    f. Add enzyme-tagged anti-HIV antibodies

    g. Add cell lysates to 96-well plate (proteins will stick to the plastic, including virus antigens)

    h. Wash plates with blocking solution that contains 5% milk to reduce non-specific binding

_____ 15. First

_____ 16. Second

_____ 17. Fourth

_____ 18. Fifth

_____ 19. Seventh

_____ 20. Tenth

Multiple Choice

Identify the letter of the choice that best completes the statement or answers the question.

_____ 21. How does DNA stick to a nylon membrane or nitrocellulose paper during a Southern Blot?

    a. DNA has a negative charge and the membrane or paper has a positive charge.

    b. Hydrophobic interaction is used to transfer the sample to the membrane or paper.

    c. A nucleometer is used to bind the DNA to the membrane or paper.

    d. DNA is attracted to the membrane or paper by the attraction of its sugar groups.

_____ 22. Microarrays are useful for all the following reasons except:

    a. indicating which genes are being expressed in cells.

    b. indicating which proteins are being made.

    c. identifying potential resistant prions.

    d. identifying potential drug/therapeutic targets.

Name _____

Course _____

Date _____

_____ 23. If you want to design primers to amplify a VNTR on chromosome 3, to what part of the target DNA should the primers be complimentary?
  a. The sequence of the repeat units for both template strands
  b. A highly variable region outside the target region for both template strands
  c. A highly conserved region outside the target region for both template strands
  d. One primer should be oriented for 5' → 3' synthesis and the other should be oriented for 5' → 3' synthesis

_____ 24. How many chromosomes do onion cells contain?
  a. 1 b. 8 c. 16 d. 46

_____ 25. How is DNA visualized on a Southern Blot?
  a. using a radioactive or chemilluminescent marker
  b. using ethidium bromide.
  c. using Biuret Reagent and UV spectrophotometry
  d. using a fluorometer and an HPLC unit.

_____ 26. What does it mean if an individual contains only one band after D1S80 amplification?
  a. The PCR reaction needs to be optimized
  b. The individual is homozygous at that locus
  c. The MgCl2 concentration needs to be adjusted
  d. Bad primer design

_____ 27. When replicating DNA in the lab, what is used to indicate the starting place for synthesis?
  a. Template
  b. Primer
  c. dNTPs
  d. DNA polymerase

_____ 28. How many chromosomes does *E. coli* contain?
  a. 1
  b. 8
  c. 16
  d. 46

_____ 29. When trying to locate the insulin gene, which probe would be best?
  a. A probe that has specificity with a few places on the genome
  b. A probe that is about 10 bases long
  c. A probe with several Cs at the end to anchor it down.
  d. A probe with a fluorescent tag and complimentary to part of the insulin gene

_____ 30. What is attached to DNA microarrays used for screening?
  a. Probes with fluorescent tags
  b. Protein segments complimentary to the probes
  c. DNA or RNA that has the potential to be complimentary to the probes
  d. Fluorescent and radioactive probes

_____ 31. A DNA microarray read by a chip reader has every spot illuminating bright green. What does this mean?
  a. All these genes represented on the microarray are being expressed
  b. The whole plate is full of potential drug targets.
  c. All the spots on the plate hybridized with their corresponding probes.
  d. None of the spots on the plate hybridized with probes.

_____ 32. When using PCR for identity purposes,
  a. highly conserved regions of the genome should be targeted
  b. highly variable regions of the genome should be targeted
  c. any area on the genome would work well.
  d. it is important to first cross-link the DNA.

Name _____

Course _____

Date _____

____ 33. Which of the following primers is well designed?
  a. CTATCCGGCCCCGGAAAATTTTT
  b. TATCCGATCATGCGGGTAGAT
  c. TACCTAGGA
  d. CGAGCCCGGATTCCGGACCGCGC

____ 34. What is regulated gene expression?
  a. A process by which microarrays detect which cells are producing which proteins
  b. The cells ability to turn "on" and "off" genes at particular times
  c. A VNTR amplification protocol
  d. A method for blotting DNA fragments onto a positively charged membrane

____ 35. About how many genes have genome scientists predicted the human genome contains?
  a. 30,000
  b. 50,000
  c. 75,000
  d. 120,000

____ 36. Which of the following is not true about studying evolutionary relationships?
  a. The appearance of organisms reveal their evolutionary relationship.
  b. Genome sequences can be compared to see how closely related specific organisms are.
  c. Mutations can be analyzed to see what changes led to speciation.
  d. Genomic data can be analyzed to follow migration patterns of certain species and their response to ecological pressures.

____ 37. How can interference RNA help treat diseases like Huntington's Chorea?
  a. It can correct the DNA sequence that gets disrupted
  b. It can block the over-expression of the Huntington's allele.
  c. It can bind to the protein and block its activity.
  d. It can locate the defective protein being synthesized

____ 38. What disease is being treated by pharmacogenetics now?
  a. Food poisoning
  b. Certain cancers
  c. Huntington's Chorea
  d. All of the above

Short Answer

39. Describe two uses for oligonucleotides.

40. List the five necessary components (and their functions) for DNA synthesis in a test tube.

Biotechnology Unit 04

Answer Section

Matching

1. ANS: F   REF: 349
2. ANS: I   REF: 344
3. ANS: J   REF: 355
4. ANS: A   REF: 347
5. ANS: H   REF: 359
6. ANS: D   REF: 345-346
7. ANS: A   REF: 345-346
8. ANS: F   REF: 345-346
9. ANS: D   REF: 350
10. ANS: B   REF: 350
11. ANS: E   REF: 374
12. ANS: B   REF: 374
13. ANS: D   REF: 377
14. ANS: C   REF: 372
15. ANS: B   REF: 381
16. ANS: E   REF: 381
17. ANS: A   REF: 381
18. ANS: H   REF: 381
19. ANS: F   REF: 381
20. ANS: C   REF: 381

Multple Choice

21. ANS: A   REF: 350
22. ANS: C   REF: 351
23. ANS: C   REF: 359
24. ANS: C   REF: 344
25. ANS: A   REF: 350
26. ANS: B   REF: 359
27. ANS: B   REF: 346
28. ANS: A   REF: 344
29. ANS: D   REF: 350
30. ANS: C   REF: 351
31. ANS: D   REF: 351
32. ANS: B   REF: 359
33. ANS: B   REF: 350
34. ANS: B   REF: 345
35. ANS: A   REF: 375
36. ANS: A   REF: 375
37. ANS: B   REF: 376
38. ANS: B   REF: 386

SHORT ANSWER

39. ANS:
    Primer to initiate replication during PCR or DNA sequencing; Probes for identifying complimentary DNA sequences on microarrays or Southern Blots
    REF: 346

40. ANS:
    COMPONENT 1: DNA template—what will get copied
    COMPONENT 2: Primer—short piece of DNA that is complimentary to the initiation point of replication
    COMPONENT 3: Nucleotides (dATPs, dCTPs, dGTPs, dTTPs, also referred to as dNTPs)— added on to the end of the primer to make a compliment DNA strand to the template
    COMPONENT 4: DNA polymerase—the enzyme that does the work of adding dNTPs to the end of the primer
    COMPONENT 5: Reaction buffer—used to keep the pH at a level that suits the DNA polymerase
    REF: 347-348

Part

4

Additional Resources
for Students

Laboratory Manual Glossary

A

absorbance the amount of light absorbed by a sample (the amount of light that does not pass through or reflect off a sample)

absorbance unit (au) a unit of light absorbance determined by the decrease in the amount of light in a light beam

acetylsalicylic acid aspirin

acid a solution that has a pH less than 7

agarose a carbohydrate from seaweed that is widely used as a medium for horizontal gel electrophoresis

agglutination clumping together, as in the binding and clumping of antigens with their corresponding antibodies

Agrobacterium tumefaciens (A. tumefaciens) a bacterium that transfers the Ti plasmid to certain plant species, resulting in a plant disease called crown gall; used in plant genetic engineering

aldehyde a chemical compound with a C=O group at the end of a carbon chain

allergen an antigen that causes an inflammatory response (redness, swelling, itchiness) or allergic reaction

ampicillin an antibiotic that prevents bacterial cell division by inhibiting cell wall synthesis

amylase an enzyme that functions to break down the polysaccharide amylase (plant starch) to the disaccharide maltose

anion exchange a form of ion-exchange chromatography in which negatively charged ions (anions) are removed by a positively charged resin

antibiotic molecular agent derived from fungi and/or bacteria that impedes the growth and survival of some other microorganisms

antibody protein developed by the immune system that recognizes specific molecules (antigens)

antigen foreign protein or molecule that is the target of binding by antibodies

antimicrobial a substance that kills or slows the growth of one or more microorganisms

antiseptic antimicrobial solution, such as alcohol or iodine, that is used to clean surfaces

Arabidopsis thaliana (A. thaliana) an herbaceous plant, related to radishes, that serves as a model organism for many plant genetic engineering studies

asexual plant propagation a process by which identical offspring are produced by a single parent; methods include taking cuttings of leaves and stems, and plant tissue culture, etc.

assay a test

autoclave an instrument that creates high temperature and high pressure to sterilize equipment and media

auxin a plant hormone produced primarily in shoot tips that regulates cell elongation and leaf development

B

bacteria single-celled organisms characterized by a rather simple structure with no membrane-bound organelles

balance an instrument that measures mass

base a solution that has a pH greater than 7

best-fit straight-line standard curve a graphical plot of data, as an average straight line, to show the linear relationship of data points

beta-D-glucuronidase (GUS) an enzyme that cleaves X-gluc (a white carbohydrate) causing a color change to a blue product

bioinformatics the use of computers and databases to analyze and relate large amounts of biological data

blank in using a spectrophotometer, a sample that includes everything except the molecule of interest; used to calibrate a spectrophotometer to measure the molecule of interest in a mixture

broth culture the growth of cells in a liquid medium

buffers a solution that acts to resist a change in pH when the hydrogen ion concentration is changed

C

carbohydrates one of the four classes of macromolecules; organic compounds consisting of carbon, hydrogen, and oxygen, generally in a 1:2:1 ratio

cation exchange a form of ion-exchange chromatography in which positively charged ions (cations) are removed by a negatively charged resin

centrifuge a rotating instrument that uses centrifugal force to separate substances of varying densities

chelating agent a compound that binds specific ions or molecules and removes them from solution

chromatography separation of molecules by size, charge, solubility, or affinity through an immobile phase or matrix

chromogenic agents compounds that exhibit color or color change due to some reaction or process

clone cell or organism that is genetically identical to another

colony a group of cells produced by a series of cell divisions originating from a single parent cell

column chromatography a separation technique in which a sample is passed through a column packed with a resin (beads); the resin beads are selected based on their ability to separate molecules based on size, shape, charge, or chemical nature

combinatorial chemistry the synthesis of larger organic molecules from smaller ones

competent describing the ability of a cell to take up DNA

complete flowers flowers that contain all four parts (sepals, petals, stamen, and pistil)

contrast (sharpness) the ability to distinguish the difference between two images, colors, or shades of color

cross-linking chemical linking of molecules; as in DNA cross-linking to nylon membranes

cross-pollinated flowers that produce pollen that fertilize the ovules of other plants of the same species

cuttings plant propagation using portions of stems, leaves, or roots that are encouraged to produce the remaining plant parts to create a whole plant

 D

denature to unwind

dialysis in biotech, the process by which solutions are exchanged by diffusion through a semi-permeable membrane

DNA sequencing pertaining to all the techniques that lead to determining the order of nucleotides (A, G, C, T) in a DNA fragment

DNA synthesis the production of DNA polymers from nucleotide monomers

 E

embryo a plant or animal in its initial stage of development

endosperm the nutritive triploid cell filling of seeds

enzyme a protein that functions to speed up chemical reactions

enzyme-linked immunospecific assay (ELISA) a technique that measures the amount of protein or antibody in a solution

eukaryote a cell that contains membrane-bound organelles

exponential growth the growth rate that bacteria maintain when they double in population size every cell cycle

 F

fermentation a process by which, in an oxygen-deprived environment, a cell converts sugar into lactic acid or ethanol to create energy

field of vision the area that is viewed for study

fluorometer an instrument that measures the amount or type of light emitted

fractionation separation into layers or groups

 G

genetic engineering directed alteration of the genetic code of an organism usually involving the addition, removal, or modification of genes

genetically modified organism (GMO) an organism produced by genetic engineering that contains DNA from another organism and produces new proteins encoded on the acquired DNA

genomic DNA (gDNA) the chromosomal DNA of a cell

genotype the genetic makeup of an organism; the particular form of a gene present for a specific trait

gentamycin an antibiotic that kills bacteria by inhibiting cell wall synthesis

germination the initial growth phase of a plant; also called sprouting

 H

harvesting extracting protein from a cell culture

high-performance liquid chromatography (HPLC) a type of column chromatography that uses metal columns that can withstand high pressures; used mainly for identification or quantification of a molecule

***Hind*III restriction enzyme** an enzyme isolated from the bacterium, *Haemophilus influenzae,* that cuts a DNA sequence wherever the sequence ""AAGCTT"" is found

horseradish peroxidase (HRP) a peroxidase produced by the cells of a horseradish plant

hydroponics the practice of growing plants in a soilless, water-based medium

hypocotyl the part of an embryonic stem directly below the epicotyl (which is below the cotyledons); in dicots, the bent hypocotyl pushes up through the soil

 I

immunoglobulin E (IgE) a type of antibody that specifically recognizes allergenic antigens and initiates an inflammatory response

immunoglobulin G (IgG) the most common antibody circulating in the blood and tissues; also called gamma globulin

indicators chemicals that change color when other compounds are present

ion-exchange chromatography a separation technique that separates molecules based on their overall charge at a given pH

 K

kanamycin an antibiotic that kills bacteria by inhibiting protein synthesis; some plant cells are sensitive to kanamycin

ketone a chemical compound with a C=O group at the middle of a carbon chain

kilodalton (kD) 1000 daltons, the unit used to report the size of a protein

 L

lambda bacteriophage a virus that infects *E. coli* cells

lambda phage DNA the genetic material of the lambda virus

lambda/*Hind*III sizing standards lambda DNA that has been cut with the restriction enzyme *Hind*III to produce pieces of known length; used to determine the size of other DNA fragments on a gel

Luria Bertani (LB) agar a mixture of protein, nutrients, and agar specifically formulated for *E. coli* growth

magnification the amount to which an object's image is enlarged

Material Safety Data Sheet (MSDS) information on the properties, safe handling, and emergency procedures for use of a compound

melting point the temperature at which a solid becomes a liquid

microarray a small glass slide or silicon chip with thousands of samples on it that can be used to assess the presence of a DNA sequence related to the expression of certain proteins

microcentrifuge a centrifuge that separates components in small volumes (usually microliter amounts) of sample

microliter (μl) a unit measure for volume; equivalent to one thousandth of a milliliter (or one millionth of a liter, 0.000001 liter), about the size of the tiniest teardrop

micrometer (μm) one millionth of a meter, 0.000001 meter; also called a "micron"

micron (μm) one millionth of a meter, 0.000001 meter; also called a "micrometer"

micropipet an instrument used to measure very tiny volumes, usually less than a milliliter

model organism a species that is commonly used in experimental studies to discover or understand basic and underlying biological processes, representative of a larger group of organisms

molarity a measure of concentration that represents the number of moles of a solute in a liter of solution (or some fraction of that unit)

mole the mass, in grams, of 6×10^{23} atoms or molecules of a given substance; one mole is equivalent to the molecular weight of a given substance, reported as grams

nanometer (nm) 10^9 meters; the standard unit used for measuring light

negative control a group of data lacking what is being tested so as to give expected results

negative results the results of a test that show no change or a result that indicates no reaction

neomycin phosphotransferase (NPT II) gene a gene that codes for the production of the enzyme, neomoycin phosphotransferase, which gives a cell resistance to the antibiotic kanamycin

NMR Nuclear Magnetic Resonance; a technique used to determine the three-dimensional structure of a molecule in solution by measuring the position of atoms using magnetic properties

node the spot on a stem where buds, leaves, or branches attached

oil immersion lens a high power, microscope objective lens that is uses a drop of a special type of oil to increase the ability to gather light and visualize an object

oligonucleotides segments of nucleic acid that are 50 nucleotides or less in length

optical density (OD) the absorbance of a sample at a given wavelength

Ouchterlony test a test, conducted in agar, that shows the presence of an antibody to an antigen

pDNA short for plasmid DNA

peptide bond the C-N bond between two amino acids

peroxidase an enzyme that decomposes hydrogen peroxide to water and oxygen gas

petals modified leaves that are often an attractant to pollinators

pH hydrogen ion concentration, or a measure of the acidity

phenotype the characteristics observed from the expression of the genes, or genotype

pipet pump a pipetting aide that controls the uptake and dispensing of a volume of liquid in a pipet

pistil the female portion of a flower; produces ovules

plant breeding sexual reproduction of plants

plant growth regulators another name for plant hormones

plant hormone signaling molecule that, in certain concentrations, regulates growth and development, often by altering the expression of genes that trigger certain cell specialization and organ formation

plant tissue culture (PTC) the process of growing small pieces of plants into small plantlets in or on sterile plant tissue culture media; plant tissue culture media have all of the required nutrients, chemicals, and hormones to promote cell division and specialization

plate culture the growth of cells, on a solid medium, in Petri dishes

polyacrylamide gel electrophoresis (PAGE) a process in which proteins and small DNA molecules are separated by electrophoresis on vertical gels made of the synthetic polymer polyacrylamide

polymerase an enzyme that connects monomer units, such as nucleotides, into polymers, such as nucleic acids; as in DNA polymerase

polymerase chain reaction (PCR) a technique that involves copying short pieces of DNA and then making millions of copies in a short time

precipitation the separation of a solute from a solution by centrifugation

primer a short piece of DNA or RNA (15-35 bases) that is complementary to a section of template strand and acts as an attachment and starting point for the synthesis strand during DNA replication

probe a DNA or RNA molecule that is complementary to the DNA sequence being investigated, often bound to some kind of "reporter" molecule, used when looking for a gene or nucleic acid sequence; a fluorescently labeled DNA or RNA sequence (oligonucleotide) that is used for gene identification

prokaryote a cell that lacks membrane-bound organelles

proteases enzymes that cleave proteins, such as casein, into smaller fragments that will also fall out of solution

protein (x-ray) crystallography a technique that uses x-ray wave diffraction patterns to visualize the positions of atoms in a protein molecule to reveal its three-dimensional structure

protein purification isolation of a protein from other proteins and molecules in a mixture

protein sequencing method used to determine the order of amino acids in a polypeptide

Punnett Square a chart that shows the possible gene combinations that could result when crossing specific genotypes

purification the process of eliminating impurities from a sample; in protein purification, it is the separation of other proteins from the desired protein

R

radicle an embryonic root-tip

rapid-cycling *Brassica rapa (B.rapa)* seeds a variety of *Brassica* developed to have a short generation time

Rbr an abbreviation for *Brassica rapa*

recombinant DNA (rDNA) DNA created by combining DNA from two or more sources

resin the separation matrix, often beads, through which a column chromatography is run

resolution the ability to clearly see two points

resolving power a measure of the ability to clearly distinguish points in a sample

rotor the rotating part of a centrifuge where sample tubes are placed

runner long, vine-like stem that grows along the soil surface

S

salicylic acid a white, crystalline precursor compound of aspirin

satellite colonies non-transformed cells that grow within a halo of influence by a transformed colony

scale-up the process of increasing the size or volume of the production of a particular product

selection medium agar or broth with ingredients added that allows the growth of specific transformed cells only

self-pollinators flowers that produce pollen that fertilize the ovules in the same plant

sepals modified leaves that protect the developing flower bud

serial dilution a series of dilutions of samples with the same ratio of sample to diluent solvent

serological pipets long, narrow, graduated instruments used for measuring and dispensing milliliter volumes

Southern blot a process in which DNA fragments on a gel are transferred to a positively charged membrane (a blot) to be probed by labeled RNA or cDNA fragments

spectrophotometer an instrument that measures the amount of light that passes through (is transmitted through) a sample

stamen the male portion of a flower; produces pollen

standard solution a solution used in a standard test

standard test a test of a known compound to determine the appearance of a positive or negative test result

stationary phase the latter period of a culture in which growth is limited due to the depletion of nutrients

sterile technique a collection of methods for preventing the introduction of unwanted microorganisms into a sample

stock solution a concentrated form of a reagent that is often diluted to form a "working soloution"

supernatant the (usually) clear liquid left behind after a precipitate has been spun down to the bottom of a vessel by centrifugation

T

Taq polymerase a DNA synthesis enzyme that can withstand the high temperatures used in PCR

TE buffer a buffer used for storing DNA; contains TRIS and EDTA

tetramethylbenzidine (TMB) a compound oxidized from clear to blue when peroxidase transfers an electron to it from hydrogen peroxide

thermal cycler an instrument used to complete PCR reactions; automatically cycles through different temperatures

Ti plasmid a plasmid found in *Agrobacterium tumefaciens* that is used to carry genes into plants, with the goal that the recipient plants will gain new phenotypes

TMB *see* tetramethylbenzidine

transformant a cell or organism that has been genetically engineered and demonstrates expression of the newly-acquired genes

transformation efficiency a measure of how well cells are transformed to a new phenotype

transformation the uptake and expression of foreign DNA by a cell

transmittance the passing of light through a sample

U

UV spectrophotometer a spectrophotometer containing a deuterium lamp that is used to measure the absorbance of UV light by a sample

V

vector a piece of DNA that carries one or more genes into a cell, usually circular as in plasmid vectors

visible light spectrum the range of wavelengths of light that humans can see, from approximately 350 to 700 nm; also called white light

Western blot a process in which a gel with protein is transferred to a positively charged membrane (a blot) to be probed with antibodies

Wisconsin Fast Plants (WFP) the common name for *Brassica rapa*

working solution the solution that is used; the working solution is often designated a concentration value of 1X

Safety in the Laboratory

This section presents a general discussion of safety, safety hazards, and the appropriate response to accidents. Specific safety hazards in laboratory activities are highlighted in each lab protocol in the lab manual. Many more detailed discussions of laboratory safety, and biological laboratory safety in particular, are found in the following documents:

Online Publications

- The *Oklahoma State University Laboratory Safety Manual* at www.pp.okstate.edu/ehs/HAZMAT/ LABMAN/toc_b.htm
- *Biological Safety Policy* from the University of Pennsylvania Office of Environmental Health and Radiation Safety at www.ehrs.upenn.edu/programs/bio/default.html
- *Knowing How to Practice Safe Science* (a laboratory safety training program), Office of Laboratory Safety, Howard Hughes Medical Institute and Yale University Center for Advanced Instructional Media, at http://info.med.yale.edu/caim/hhmi/public/

Print Publications

- *Working with DNA & Bacteria in Pre-College Science Classrooms*, Toby Horn, PhD; check on availability at www.NABT.org
- *Science Safety Standards*, Texas Education Agency, 2000

General Safety Precautions

Some common accidents and emergencies in a laboratory setting include:

- Small to moderate size cuts or lacerations due to broken or damaged equipment
- Small or moderate size fires due to combustion or explosion and the burns from exposure to the flames
- Chemical exposure and burns resulting from chemical exposure
- Electrical shocks from misuse of or faulty equipment
- Poisoning due to ingestion of chemicals or biological agents

Many of these incidents are preventable using common sense safety practices such as the following:

1. Know the location of all potential safety hazards and emergency equipment. Know where a First Aid kit, fire extinguishers, fire blankets, fire alarms, safety showers, and eye washes can be found. Know who to call, the location of a phone, and how to call out for help in case of an emergency.
2. Do not eat, drink, or smoke in the laboratory. Do not store food in laboratory refrigerators or freezers. Do not use laboratory utensils or instruments for cooking or eating. Do not touch the mouth or put things in the mouth. To remove contaminants, wash hands frequently with liquid soaps.
3. Wear proper attire in the laboratory. Safety glasses are required for all lab work involving chemicals, heating, or flame. Gloves should be worn when chemicals or biological hazards are in use. Open-toed or open-backed shoes should not be worn in the lab. Loose, bulky, or baggy clothing, as well as hats or dangling earrings that may catch on equipment should be removed prior to working in the lab. Laboratory coats provide extra protection from fire and chemical spills. Hair that hangs below the chin should be cinched or tied back.
4. Keep flammable items (liquids, chemicals, fabric, paper) several feet away from Bunsen burners.
5. Store all items out of the walkways and aisles so that there is clear passage in case of an emergency.

Even when all safety precautions are heeded, sometimes accidents happen. In fact, that's why they are called accidents. It is the responsibility of all individuals to minimize the risks in order to create the safest working environment. All students and instructors should learn how to respond in the event of an accident or emergency.

Preventing Accidents

To prevent accidents, every individual should do the following:

- Act in an appropriate manner. Do not run, and do not push or shove anyone. No throwing or tossing of items is allowed.
- Be aware of the surroundings. Look for safety hazards such as liquid spills, flames, or electrical apparatuses. Check equipment for damage that might cause faulty operation before using. Locate all safety and emergency equipment before starting a laboratory activity.

- Read all laboratory procedures thoroughly, including safety precautions, before starting a laboratory investigation. Check for any instructions that appear unsafe. If there is a concern about a procedure, do not conduct it until the safety can be confirmed. If an activity is deemed safe, follow all steps in the procedures as written and in the order written.

- Determine the proper disposal of any product of a reaction before beginning an activity. Some chemicals may not be dumped down a sink's drain. Determine which chemicals fall into this category. Biohazards must be clearly bagged and marked and then disposed of properly (after accepted sterilization methods – see below).

- Use disinfectants to sterilize work surfaces. All disinfectants do not have the same effectiveness. Commercial Lysol® or Amphyl® are preferred for most bacterial work applications. If you are using a 10% bleach solution, it must be prepared regularly since it breaks down over time and in the presence of light.

- Sterilize cultures that are contaminated with bacteria or fungi by placing them in a biohazard bag and sterilizing in an autoclave for at least 15-20 minutes at 15-20 psi (121°C). Cultures can be sterilized by soaking in 10% bleach for at least 60 minutes. Use disinfectants, flame, or an autoclave to sterilize instruments.

- Students should not directly use ethidium bromide or handle ethidium bromide-stained gels. Instead, teachers should do all staining with ethidium bromide and should share photos of stained gels with students. Staining methods, such as the use of InstaStain® ethidium bromide cards, will work in most gel staining applications, and they decrease the amount of ethidium bromide that is used. Methylene blue or other "safer" staining methods may be used in some, but not all, applications.

What To Do in the Case of an Accident

Most accidents in a biotechnology laboratory will be minor and require only simple first aid. In the event of more serious accidents, call 911 and seek assistance from experts. When an accident occurs, students should notify the instructor immediately.

Minor Accidents

Only small cuts or exposures to small amounts of chemical on the skin should be considered minor accidents:

- Small cuts: The instructor should put on gloves to prevent blood transmission. Wash the affected area thoroughly and apply a sterile gauze pad and pressure in order to stop the bleeding. Then replace the used pad with a sterile bandage when the bleeding stops.

- Exposure to a small amount of chemical on the skin: Rinse the affected area with large volumes of tap water for a minimum of 15 minutes

Serious Accidents

All other incidents that cause injury should be considered serious and as such it is important to act quickly and call for help.

- Chemical exposure to eyes or to large areas of the skin or if any item enters the eye: Use the safety shower or eyewash. Rinse with water for a minimum of 15 minutes. Call 911 or the school authorities.

- Ingestion of chemical or biological hazardous material: Contact school officials immediately. If a chemical was ingested, locate the MSDS sheet for the substance. Contact the Poison Control Center in your area.

- Serious electrical shock: Separate the student from the electrical source and call for assistance immediately. Check for breathing and administer CPR if necessary.

Review of Metrics and Metric Measurement

Whenever possible, scientists like to collect experimental results in numerical form. Unlike words, numbers are easy to compare and contrast. In the late 1700s, scientists realized that there needed to be a standard, easy-to-use system to make numerical measurements and conversions. In response, they devised the metric system, which is based on the number 10. Now, metric measurement is the system used in every scientific application.

It is easy to understand why the metric system was rapidly adopted since it is so much easier to use than the standard, English (Imperial) system. Consider, for example, if you want to measure the distance a snake crawls in a day. Using the English system, you might measure with a yardstick and determine that the distance is 39 yards, 2 feet, and 4 inches. Now convert that value to just yards, just feet, or just inches. It would require computations and complicated fractions and decimals. By the way, the answer in inches is 1432 inches. Do you know why?

Measuring Length

Since the metric system is based on the number 10, and all metric units are greater or less than others by powers of 10, making conversions is simple. The standard metric unit of length measurement is the meter. Common units of metric length measurement are greater or less than a meter by 10, 100, or 1000 times. The metric units of length that are commonly used in biotechnology include:

Unit of Measurement	Abbreviation	Unit Equivalents	Example of Use
meter	m	0.001 km, 100 cm, 1000 mm	Measuring body height
centimeter	cm	0.01 m, 10 mm	Measuring root growth
millimeter	mm	0.001 m, 0.1 cm, 1000 μm	Measuring seed lengths
micrometer	μm	0.001 mm	Measuring cell size

By looking at the number of decimal places in the unit equivalents, you can see that the difference between these length units is 10×, 100×, or 1000×, or one decimal place, two decimal places, or three decimal places, respectively. This makes it easy to convert between units.

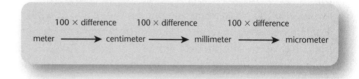

For example, 1 mm is 0.001 m. So, to convert between millimeters and meters, just remember that a millimeter is 1/10 x 1/10 x 1/10, which is 1/1000 of a meter (3 decimal places or 3 powers of 10 or 1000x smaller than a meter). Then, move the decimal point to the right three places. The direction the decimal is moved depends on which way you are converting: bigger to smaller units or smaller to bigger units. This is called the B← →S Rule.

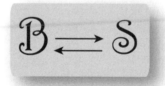

Use the B← →S Rule to know which way to move the decimal. The arrows in the B← →S Rule show how to move the decimal point in the value to be converted: to the right (multiplying) if converting from big units to small units, or to the left (dividing) if converting from small units to larger ones.

For example, let us say a measurement of 1.25 m of tubing is required, but the ruler to be used measures only in centimeters. You must convert from meters to centimeters. Since meters are bigger than centimeters, and there are 100 cm in a meter, move the decimal to the right two places (for the 2 zeroes in 100). Thus, 1.25 m = 125.0 cm.

Now consider the example problem again. You want to measure the distance a snake crawls in a day. Using the metric system, you measure with a meter stick and determine the distance to be 36.3728 m. By moving the decimal point to the right 2 and 3 places, respectively, you determine the distance to be 3637.28 cm and 36,372.8 mm. How fast and easy is that? No calculator needed!

Measuring Weight or Mass

Mass and weight are used interchangeably, although they are not really the same. Mass is a measurement of the amount of matter (stuff) something contains. It is measured on a balance, in grams. The mass of an object does not change no matter where in the universe you go. On the other hand, weight does change depending on location. This is because weight is determined by the pull of gravity. Therefore, something weighs more on Jupiter than on Earth and it would be lighter still on the moon. Although mass and weight are not the same thing, the terms are sometimes used interchangeably. Be aware, though, that when weighing a substance in a lab, a balance or scale is reporting mass, because the instrument has been calibrated in grams.

In a biotechnology lab, weight (mass) is measured on a scale, in grams or in smaller or larger metric mass equivalents of a gram. The metric units of mass that are commonly used in biotechnology include:

Unit of Measurement	Abbreviation	Unit Equivalents	Example of Use
kilogram	kg	1000 g	Measuring body weight
gram	g	0.001 kg, 100 mg	Measuring a piece of meat
milligram	mg	0.001 m, 0.1 cm, 1000 μm	Measuring most chemicals
microgram	μg	0.001 mm	Measuring most medicines

Again, use the B← →S Rule to convert between units. For example, if you need 375 mg of a chemical and the scale measures in grams, move the decimal three places to the right to get 375 mg = 0.375 g.

Measuring Volumes

Volume is defined as the amount of space something occupies. Liquid volumes are measured in a graduated cylinder, pipet, or micropipet. The metric unit of volume is the liter (L). Smaller volumes are measured in milliliters (mL). There are 1000 mL in a liter. Milliliters are also called cubic centimeters (cc). This is because a cubic centimeter of water occupies 1 mL of space. The metric units of volume that are commonly used in biotechnology include:

Unit of Measurement	Abbreviation	Unit Equivalents	Example of Use
liter	L	1000 mL	Measuring gasoline
milliliter	mL	0.001 L, 1000 μL	Measuring most drinks
microliter	μL	0.001 mL,	Measuring most enzymes

Again, use the B← →S Rule to convert between volume units. For example, if you need 2.33 mL of a chemical and the micropipets measure in microliters (μL), move the decimal point three places to the right to get 2.33 mL = 2330 μL.

A Few Other Guidelines

1. Always include the unit of measurement. If you record a seed length as 3.75, it is not clear if that is 3.75 mm or 3.75 cm. Every time you record a measurement, make certain you indicate a unit of measurement. A number without a unit is just that, a number. With reporting measurements, a number without units can lead to confusion.

2. Report numbers that show the precision of a measurement. When reporting a measurement, the last digit is considered an approximation. If a scale measures to three decimal places, the third decimal place is an approximation. For example, a seed weighs 0.125 g. We have confidence in the 0.12 g, but the 0.005 g is an approximation. The 0.12 are significant figures because we have confidence in the value. By convention, when reporting values and calculations, consider the measuring instrument and report numbers in significant figures plus one extra digit.

Measurement, units, and the instruments that are used to make measurements are discussed in depth when they are first presented in the text and the lab manual.

Constructing Data Tables Using Microsoft® Excel

This tutorial was inspired by one developed by Tina Doss and Melissa Hero, Biology teachers, Belmont, CA. The following instructions will help you set up a table for collecting data in the Chapter 1 Cheese Production Lab. These steps provide an example of how to set up a data table in all types of scientific applications.

1. Open up the Excel program by double-clicking its icon on the computer desktop.

2. When a new spreadsheet chart appears, name it by pulling down the File menu and clicking Save. Save the spreadsheet as **ave.time.curds.dt.yourname**.

3. An Excel spreadsheet has rows (across) and columns (up and down). The columns are identified by letters (A, B, C, D…) and the rows are identified by numbers (1, 2, 3, 4…).

4. The columns and rows make a grid of cells. A cell is identified by a letter and a number. For example, the top left cell is A1. Click A1 and note how it is identified in the location box above the chart. Put a title to your data table in A1.

5. A1 is already selected because you clicked on it in the previous step. Position the cursor in the Format box, which is the white box to the right of the = sign. Now type the following title into this Format box, "The Average Cheese Curdling Time for Different Curdling Agents." Notice how the title is displayed in "A1." It may not look great yet (not bold or aligned right for example), but it is there.

6. Go to the File menu again and click Save. It is good to save regularly in case there is a power failure or another catastrophe.

7. Now, set up the data table with labels in each column. Scientists always set up data table a certain way. They place the independent variable (the one that is being manipulated in the experiment) in the left column. In this experiment the curdling agents are what is being tested and manipulated, so they are the independent variable. Type "Curdling Agents" into cell A2 to label the independent variable column.

8. Now that the independent variable has been identified and labeled, all the other columns are reserved for data collected during the experiment. The data are considered dependent variables, since they change based on which independent variable is being studied. In this experiment, the average curdling time is the data to be reported. Type "Average Curdling Time (min)" in cell B2.

9. Notice how the cells may not be large enough to contain your labels. You can increase the width of the column by highlighting the column and pulling the right side of it to the right. Click the letter A at the top of the left column. This should highlight the entire column. Position your cursor over the right margin of the A label. You should see a double-ended arrow. Drag the arrow to the right until the label "Curdling Agents" fills the A2 cell. Do the same to column B so that "Average Curdling Time (min)" fills the B2 cell.

10. Now enter the four curdling agents into cells A3-A6. Type "none" (negative control) into cell A3. Type "buttermilk" into cell A4. Type "rennin" into cell A5. Type "chymosin" into cell A6. Don't forget to save your work.

11. Now enter the average data for each curdling agent from the class data table constructed in step 10 of the Lab 1a Procedures. Click B and go to the Formatting Palette and choose Alignment/Center. This makes the data easier to read.

12. Place a grid around the data table rows and columns by highlighting cells A2-B6. Then go to the Borders icon right above the Format box. Pull down the Borders menu and select the icon showing all sides and middles bordered.

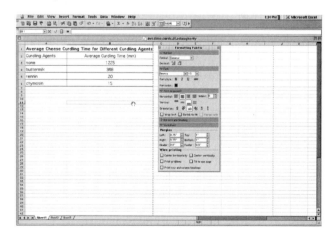

13. Make your data table look professional by increasing the font size of the title and by making both the title and column labels **bold** print.

14. Print a copy of each data table you construct. Paste the table(s) into your notebook.

Constructing Graphs Using Microsoft® Excel

This tutorial is inspired by one developed by Tina Doss and Melissa Hero, Biology teachers, Belmont, CA. The following instructions will help you set up a graph for charting data in the Chapter 1a Cheese Production Lab. These steps provide an example of how to set up a graph for all types of scientific applications.

1. Once a data table has been constructed in Excel, a graph of the data can be drawn using the Chart Wizard. The Wizard is the icon on the Standard Formatting toolbar that looks a tiny column/bar graph. (If your Standard Formatting toolbar is not visible, go to the View menu, click Toolbars, and then click Standard.) Don't open Chart Wizard until you are told to in a later step.

2. When setting up a graph, place the independent variable on the horizontal axis and the dependent variable on the vertical axis. You have to direct Excel to do it a certain way. Go to the data table and select (highlight) cells A3-B6. Make sure you do not select A2 and B2. These are labels and are not included when telling Chart Wizard what to compare.

3. With cells A3-B6 selected, double-click the Chart Wizard icon. Chart Wizard has 4 steps for basic graph design. When you open up Chart Wizard, you will be in step 1.

4. In step 1, you need to pick a chart type. Pick a simple column graph by clicking Column and then click the top left graph icon. Click Next to move to step 2 of the Chart Wizard.

5. In step 2, the program displays the column graph. Make sure "rows" is selected. This tells Chart Wizard that the independent variable goes on the horizontal and the dependent goes on the vertical.

If the graph doesn't look correct, check the data you have selected to compare on your data table. At this step you can also name the series, but don't do that now. Just click on Next.

6. In step 3 you can take care of several details now or come back to them later. The Wizard will first ask you to title the graph and axes. Do this by typing "The Average Cheese Curdling Time for Different Curdling Agents" in the chart title. Type "Curdling Agents" in the x-axis spot and "Average Curdling Time (min)" in the y-axis spot. Later you can return and eliminate the legend, change the label alignment and the scale of the graph, and change font size and style. Click Next to go to step 4.

7. In step 4, click "as object on page" to get both the data table and graph to be on the same page. Change the size of the graph and move it so it all fits with the data table. Use the Print Preview feature to view the chart before you print it.

8. At anytime you can change your graph within Chart Wizard. Click on the white background on the top left corner of the graph. This selects the entire graph. Once the graph is selected, click the Chart Wizard icon again and it will return you to step 1. You can change most qualities of the graph now.

9. Adjust the size of the graph, as necessary. If the axes' labels changed size or alignment, double-click either the x-axis or y-axis to see a menu of choices for adjusting the axis font. Your final graph should look like the one shown below. Print a copy of the graph and paste it into your notebook.

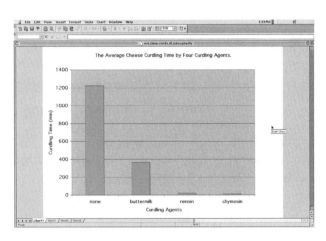

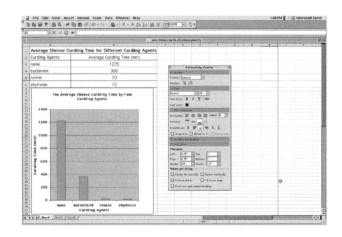

Writing Effective Conclusions

As stated in the text, a good approach for writing an experimental conclusion is to use the "REE, PE, PA" method. For REE (*results* with *evidence* and *explanation*), give the answer to the purpose question (results) with numerical data, if possible, as evidence. For most experiments, averaged data are the best numerical answer to a purpose question. Then, explain whether the data support or refute the hypothesis and why. Give specific examples.

For PE (*possible errors*), identify the sources of experimental design errors that would lead to fallacious (false or misleading) data, and explain the possible implications from making such errors. Two possible experimental errors in the bleaching experiment are errors in timing and solution preparation. Errors in either technique would provide data that might lead to incorrect assumptions. Once potential errors in experimentation are identified, give recommendations to improve the experiment to minimize these sources of errors. The goal is to design experiments that have the most reproducible and reliable data.

For PA (*practical applications*), discuss the meaning or value of the experimental results in the short term and in the long term. How are the findings valuable to the scientist, the company, or the scientific community? What recommendations can be made about using the data or for planning future experimentation? Often, the next experiment is only a slight modification or refinement of the previous one.

The final version of a conclusion should be a thorough analysis of the experiment and results reflecting on the uses of the new information. The final version should be proofread, or witnessed, by a colleague who understands enough about the experiment to analyze the data, but who was not involved in conducting the experiment.

The conclusion rubric that follows allows you to evaluate the effectiveness of conclusion drafts. Sections that do not demonstrate the characteristics of the 3-points column can be rewritten.

Conclusion Rubric

	3 points	2 points	1 points	0 points
Results	Conclusion begins with a clear, concise discussion of the purpose of the experiment or study.	The purpose of the experiment or study is mentioned but not at the beginning of the discussion.	The purpose of the experiment or study is mentioned but is not clear, concise, and accurate.	There is no mention of the purpose or the subject of the study.
	All of the important results are stated as an answer or as answers to the purpose question.	Most but not all of the important results are stated as an answer or as answers to the purpose question.	Some but not most of the important results are stated as an answer or as answers to the purpose question.	The results of the experiment or study are not stated.
Evidence	The results statement includes (numerical) evidence (including averages) when appropriate.	The results statement includes (numerical) evidence but uses individual instead of average data.	The results statement includes evidence that is not numerical when numerical data should be included.	No evidence is given for the statements given as results of the experiment.
Explanations	A clear and concise explanation of how the data supports or refutes expectations or hypotheses is given.	Some explanation of how the data supports or refutes expectations or hypotheses is given.	Some explanation of results is given but no mention of how the data supports or refutes expectations or hypotheses is given.	No explanation of whether the data supports or refutes expectations or hypotheses is given.
Possible Errors	At least two examples of procedural errors that could lead to fallacious data are identified and explained. The possible effects of these errors are explained.	Only one example of a procedural error that could lead to fallacious data is identified and explained. The possible effect of this error is explained.	Examples of procedural errors are identified but the possible effect of these errors is not explained.	No examples of procedural errors that could lead to fallacious data are identified and explained.

Continued

Conclusion Rubric—continued

Practical Applications	A clear, concise explanation or example of how the knowledge gained from the experiment can be applied to research or manufacturing is given.	An explanation or example of how the knowledge gained from the experiment can be applied to research or manufacturing is given but it is not a significant one.	An unclear or confusing explanation or example of how the knowledge gained from the experiment can be applied to research or manufacturing is given.	No explanation or example of how the knowledge gained from the experiment can be applied to research or manufacturing is given.
	A proposal for a follow-up experiment is given. Enough explanation is given to make it clear how the follow-up experiment should be done.	A proposal for a follow-up experiment is given. Not enough explanation is given to make it clear how the follow-up experiment should be done.	A proposal for a follow-up experiment is given but it is faulty or not applicable to furthering research in the area.	A proposal for a follow-up experiment is not given.
Other Considerations	No spelling or grammatical errors.	Two or less spelling or grammatical errors.	Three to four spelling or grammatical errors.	More than four spelling or grammatical errors.
	All sections of the conclusion are necessary for an effect analysis of the experiment.	Some sections of the conclusion are not necessary for an effect analysis of the experiment.	Many sections of the conclusion have little or no connection to the experiment being analyzed.	Essentially all sections of the conclusion have little or no connection to the experiment being analyzed.
	Conclusion is typed and in a font that is easy to read.	Conclusion is typed but is in a font that is not easy to read.	Conclusion is not typed.	Conclusion is not typed and is not easy to read.

Using the Internet to Access Biotechnology Information

The Internet is a worldwide network of computers that are linked to each other. It is used to retrieve information and also to share information. Research scientists who wanted to share scientific data between their research "sites" originally established the Internet. It has been called a "Super Highway" to suggest the process of information traveling between computers in two directions. Now, virtually everyone in business or industry must be skilled in searching for information in many areas of the Internet. Using the Internet for research purposes is a basic skill needed by everyone in the field of biotechnology.

The appearance of the Internet has changed substantially since its inception. In the early years the Internet was just text with no pictures or graphics. Now, virtually every form of audio or visual data can be transmitted over the Internet through the World Wide Web (WWW).

This Internet Web site has graphic (picture) links to other sites as well as text (underlined words) links to other sites. The links help the user navigate to other Web sites such as the companies shown.

In the recent past, the Internet has expanded from a scientific instrument to one used for many purposes, some appropriate for the workplace and some that are not. In this course, the Internet will only be used for legitimate biotechnology research purposes. Below are the rules for Internet use in this course.

Basic Rules for Internet Use

1. You must receive computer and Internet training before using the computers.
2. You may not use chat rooms.
3. You may not download to the hard drive without the instructor's approval.
4. You may only use the Internet computers for educational research.
5. You must report any inappropriate Internet use to the instructor.

Tutorial: Using the Internet to Access Information about Biotechnology Companies

Use the tutorial below to learn how to access scientific information on the Internet. Unless your instructor directs you otherwise, record answers to questions or tasks in your lab notebook.

Procedures: Part 1
There are three main ways to access information on the Internet:

1. **Have an address for a site you are interested in using and begin a search there.**
   To access a site this way, type the Internet address into the URL (location) box and press the Enter key. Try this for the following site.
   http://www.gene.com
   a. What company's Home page have you reached? Notice how you can click on other graphics or textual (underlined) "links."
   b. Click on the "Careers" link. Find the area called "College Programs." What three things can you learn more about in this area?
   c. On the right side of the "Careers" page, click on the "Job Postings" link. Choose one of the links to explore more information about employment opportunities and job searching at Genentech. Describe how you might review a job posting at Genentech's site.

d. By clicking on the "Back" button you can return to Web pages you have visited. Return to the Genentech Home page now. Click on the "Products" link. Find the description of the product, Pulmozyme®. What is the function of Pulmozyme®?

2. **Use a Search Engine.**

Search engines are sites that allow you to search for individual Web pages or databases for topics. A search engine looks for "keywords" or phrases within a Web page or database title. There are several well known search engines. Some are of more or less value depending on what you are searching for.

Some frequently used search engines include Google, Yahoo, AltaVista, Lycos, and Ask Jeeves. You can access these by entering their Web addresses. To access the Lycos search engine, type http://www.lycos.com and press the Enter key.

a. List two links that are available to you once you have reached the Lycos Home page.

b. Find a "Search" box at the top of the page. There are several ways to do a search, but the easiest is to just type in some keyword of interest. Depending on the keyword you use, the search may result in many appropriate finds. Sometimes a search engine finds so much information that a lot may be unimportant or a duplicate of other finds. If you were interested in finding companies that work on or use DNA, you'd have many keywords or phrases to use in your search. Go to www.google.com, type DNA into the Search box and press Enter. What are the first two "hits," or sites, listed?

c. There are many ways to limit a search. Usually each search engine will have information next to the Search box explaining these procedures. Type "DNA fingerprinting" into the Search box and press Enter.

d. List the first two hits.

3. **Use a Searchable database.**

A searchable database is a collection of Web pages that have been collected, published, or posted by an interested group. There are searchable databases on virtually every topic. Well known databases include the Smithsonian's Art Collection, the National Institutes of Health Medical Library, and Medline.

Medline is of particular interest to biotechnologists, especially those who are working on topics of medical or pharmaceutical interest. Medline has traditionally charged a fee for use of the database service. The general public can access much of Medline by searching through the National Clearinghouse for Biotechnology Information (NCBI) Web site.

a. To access the Medline database, enter through the PubMed portal at the NCBI Web site. Type the following address into the URL box: www.ncbi.nih.gov/entrez/query.fcgi?db=PubMed. Then press Enter.

b. PubMed is a service of the National Library of Medicine that includes more than 15 million full text articles and other related resources from Medline and other life science journals (periodicals). When you get to the PubMed Home page, do a search for HIV. Describe the results of your search.

Procedures: Part 2

On the Internet, find the Home page of a biotechnology company that is farther than 20 miles from your classroom. Complete the following:

a. List the name and the Home page address of the company.

b. List the products it makes or is currently developing.

c. Describe the steps you used to locate this company on the Internet. Did you use search engines or databases?